,3 B3.71

BASIC PSYCHIATRY

BASIC PSYCHIATRY

BY EDWARD A. STRECKER

Professor of Psychiatry and Chairman of the Department of
Psychiatry, School of Medicine, University of Pennsylvania

Consultant and Chief of Service, Institute of the Pennsylvania Hospital,
Philadelphia

Consultant in Psychiatry to the Surgeon General of the Army; Con-
sultant in Psychiatry to the Surgeon General of the Navy; Consultant,
Philadelphia Naval Hospital; Senior Consultant in Psychiatry, Veterans
Administration; Consultant in Psychiatry, U. S. Public Health Service

RANDOM HOUSE · NEW YORK

FIFTH PRINTING

COPYRIGHT, 1952, BY EDWARD A. STRECKER · *All rights reserved under
International and Pan-American Copyright Conventions. Published in
New York by Random House, Inc., and simultaneously in Toronto,
Canada, by Random House of Canada, Limited.*

LIBRARY OF CONGRESS CATALOG CARD NUMBER: 52—5553

Manufactured in the United States of America

CONTENTS

BASIC PSYCHIATRY

INTRODUCTION

THERE is an iron curtain between the general public and psychiatry. Of course, a few openings have been made in the barrier by the impact of a segment of the vast coverage of psychiatric topics in the daily press, in popular magazines and in many books. But the area of valid and effective information is still relatively small. Too often the story has been told in highly selective and even distorted fashion. For instance, psychiatrists do not spend their professional lives unraveling the bloody skeins of the psychopathology of sex murders. For one thing, there would not be enough sex murders. In a general way, publicity about psychiatric matters has tended to focus upon a few isolated peaks which do not represent the usual contours of the psychiatric terrain. Certain aspects of psychiatry have been overemphasized and overdramatized. The innumerable important and highly interesting facts and experiences of the everyday practice of psychiatry have been too often slighted and even overlooked.

One unfortunate repercussion has been to create the erroneous idea of a world of mental patients quite alien to and totally unlike the world in which we live. It is thought of as a land of dark and fearsome places, peopled by grotesque and frightening shadows. Of course, all this is quite untrue. Every day of our lives we come into contact with, we meet and talk with, have business and social relations with people who are in some degree psychiatrically sick. And yet it is unlikely that we will be able to detect anything much out of the way.

As for the seriously mentally sick patients, the definite psychotics in the hospices of psychiatry, many years of experience, daily contact with them, living in their midst, has convinced me that they are much the same as we are who live on the outside. Some of the patients are fat, others thin. Some are jolly and fun-loving, others sad and gloomy. Some are optimists; others view their surroundings with deeply jaundiced eyes. Some are sophisticated, mistrustful and suspicious, others far too naïve and trusting. Some patients, many, are truthful; others are unmitigated liars. Some patients would not harm a fly; others have murder in their hearts. In other words, they are even as you and I.

Their world, the world of those who are sick in mind and spirit, is not so very different from our world. The difference is one of degree and not of kind. The markings of behavior are sometimes too heavy or perhaps too faint, but the same behavior, or at least the possibility of the same behavior, is in all of us.

It is good to know that the land of the psychiatrically sick is not too far apart from our land. Many of us, concretely at least one child of every twenty born, is destined to spend some part of its adult life in a public mental hospital. One in ten will be incapacitated by a less severe breakdown. Based on Selective Service examinations, an estimate of psychoneuroses and functional illness would be about 5,000,000 human beings. And this is only a part of the story. Who are the others? We work and play with many of them. Many of them live in the houses of our friends.

It is likely that each one of us knows two or three people who habitually drink too much alcohol. A minimum estimate of the number of pathological drinkers in the United States is 2,000,000. The majority of authorities place the total much higher, one statistician at almost 12,000,000.

The mental defectives, the idiots, imbeciles and morons, constitute an intellectually underprivileged population of not less than three and a half million. Again, many authorities feel that this figure is far too low.

About 7,000,000 citizens have criminal records, and almost one and a quarter million children annually pass through our juvenile courts. Of course, many more are delinquent.

I might go on endlessly giving statistical chapter after chapter of the sad and depressing story—epilepsy, suicide, many other things. And then I might give the astronomical figures of the economic cost. But this book is not of mathematics and dollars. All these things may be found in statistical tables.* What will not be found is the tale of human suffering—much of it needless suffering.

One heavy penalty that has to be paid for picturing a strange and mysterious world of mental disease is that we are afraid of it and shun it. How many of us have visited the public mental hospitals which we support—visited them thoroughly enough to find out what is happening in them? Yet each year more than 100,000 of our fellow citizens pass through the portals of public mental hospitals. Many recover and return to our world, but still far too many live and die in the hospitals. Within the limits of the serious shortage of psychiatrists and other personnel needed, the study and treatment in many

* See "Statistics Pertinent to Psychiatry in the United States," Report No. 7, March, 1949, Group for the Advancement of Psychiatry.

States is satisfactory, and patients are given their fair chance of returning to the world of the mentally quick. Incidentally, for the treatment of all psychiatric patients, in and out of mental hospitals, fewer than 5,000 psychiatrists are available. At least 19,000 are urgently needed. Even this number would mean only one psychiatrist to about each 7,000 of the population.

In many hospitals in this country the care of mental patients is not only inadequate but shameful. It is the price of widespread ignorance—ignorance bred of fear of mental disease. If people really knew, they would not tolerate the kind of care of patients that (as in one hospital) is bought for 49 cents a day for each patient—49 cents not only for food but for the salaries of all the employees of the hospital and its maintenance! Suppose you were that 49-cent patient, or a beloved member of your family—or a dear friend!

As long as we suffer from the evils of ignorance of the psychiatric problem, we shall continue to pay economically backbreaking tribute for the care of a huge increment of chronic mental and nervous illness, much of which could have been prevented. If the public were properly informed and really could be made to understand, it would face the problem realistically, the demand for more money for investigation and research in the area of prevention would be so articulate and emphatic, that the authorities would not dare continue to ignore the urgent need or give it merely token attention.

Finally, insufficient information and lack of clear-cut knowledge lead not only to half-frightened preoccupation concerning the "mysteries" of psychiatry, but also bar a considerable segment of the public from participating in preventive efforts. There are so many simple and helpful things that can be done, particularly in childhood, by parents and others who are in

intimate contact with children! Some of these measures are
not much more complicated or difficult to put into practice
than it is to teach children how to bathe or brush their teeth,
how to take the right kind of food or exercise or rest. In these
areas the public is very well informed. It is tragic that there
should be such large areas of ignorance concerning what may
and can be done to help bring about the maturing of the mind
and personality. In the last analysis, this is rather more important than the growth of the body. Since the body and mind
are inseparable in the unity of functioning, it becomes obvious
that complete maturity can be attained only by total attention
to the needs of the child—not only the physical needs, but,
significantly, the emotional requirements.

For a long time psychiatry has been ready to go ahead
within the limits of the existing personnel. A practical program
is available. But the public must be educated about the plain
facts, not the frills. Then I think it will be eager to help do its
share and accept its responsibilities. It comes down to securing
the potential of emotional maturity for more people, many
more people. If possible, for all people. The nucleus of emotional maturity can only be inculcated during childhood.

Emotional maturity is the most important thing in the
world. In the words of my colleague, Leon Saul, it is truly,
"The basis of mental health, of morality and ethics, of social
co-operation." More than that, "It is the only healthy, long-
range answer to mankind's central problem, namely, man's
inhumanity to man. What helps children develop normally
toward emotional maturity helps mankind make peace and
brotherhood into realities."

Much of what is written in this book describes the penalties
that so often have to be paid for failing to achieve a reasonable
level of emotional maturity. I feel sure that when readers meet

and come to know intimately the patients who walk through
the pages of the book, they will resolve to do all they possibly
can to decrease the far too oft-repeated catastrophe of mental
and psychoneurotic sickness.

☐ 1 ☐ CAUSATION

> Mental diseases are due neither to the wrath nor the favor of
> the gods nor to the possession of the body by demons. Like
> all other human diseases, mental disorders come from natural
> causes, many of which are known and understood.

BEFORE reaching its present high level of knowledge and scientific respectability, etiology (the study of causes) in psychiatry
had to climb up gradually and painfully from the age-old dark
pit of ignorance and superstition. Odds and ends of primitive
thinking, "signs," charms and taboos, are still encountered.
At least once a year, the family of some patient entrusted to
my care solemnly warns me to have the shades of the patient's
room carefully drawn when the moon is at its full, lest the mental symptoms become worse from the influence of moonbeams
(lunacy!). The cessation of the menses still has the reputation of producing mental disease and their reappearance is
believed to be curative. Likewise, pregnancy is said to be endowed with the power of healing the sick mind. Some people
think that bald men and women (if any can be found) are immune from mental illness.

One often hears the glib statement that psychiatrists, compared to other doctors, are smart enough in a way, but "isn't
it too bad that they know little or nothing as to why people
become mentally sick?" Actually, the fund of psychiatric

9

information in the area of causation is as great and often greater than in many other fields of medicine. Some of these truths were realized many centuries ago. When Hippocrates, the father of medicine, stated, "The brain is the organ of the mind," he gave a reasonably valid, though not a complete, explanation of perhaps one-half of all mental diseases. The obvious inference from the utterance of Hippocrates is that when the structure of the brain is diseased, as in paresis, then mental symptoms are very apt to appear in the wake of brain tissue destruction and, in large measure, the mental symptoms result from the tissue disintegration. In both the organic and toxic areas, psychiatrists encounter the same common causes which are part and parcel of the everyday general practice of medicine—syphilis, hardening of the blood vessels, poisons taken into the body or auto-intoxications, poisons created within the body, injuries, upsets in the metabolism of the various organs of the body, disturbances of the ductless glands and many others. Sometimes the preponderance of symptoms shows at the physical level, sometimes at the mental. There are no gods or devils here, just plain facts of everyday sickness.

True enough, there are still too many dimly lit places, perhaps particularly among the "functional" disorders. Yet the majority of these areas, one after another, are being brought into the focus of steadily increasing knowledge. There is no condition about which we do not have at least some serviceable data.

This is not to say that psychiatry in the past has not fallen into error. In common with the other disciplines which study human beings who have many variables, in contrast to the sciences of more exact measurements, like mathematics, psychiatry must be somewhat speculative and experimental. Sometimes it has been led astray by "post hoc, ergo propter hoc" thinking. In plain English, this is the fallacy of assuming that because two things happen in sequence, the second is necessarily due to the first. It is a throwback to the thinking of our primitive ancestors. When, as frequently happened, a member of the tribe disappeared, no doubt in their own crude way primitive men said to each other, "Soon after we saw him last, we heard the angry voice of the gods (thunder) and their fiery tongues were in the skies (lightning). It is clear that he displeased them and the gods destroyed him."

A few decades ago some psychiatrists noted that a few patients were relieved of their mental symptoms after focal infection in the teeth, tonsils, uterus and other parts of the body had been removed. They made the sweeping assumption that mental diseases, psychoneuroses, feeble-mindedness, delinquency and, indeed, just about all mental ills were due to focal infection. Driven by their theory they became very enthusiastic and, eventually, not only teeth and tonsils, but large sections of the colon were removed in the effort to eradicate infection. The majority of psychiatrists did not participate, but, nevertheless, there was a kind of surgical-psychiatric debauch during which many teeth, tonsils, portions of wombs, sections of the large bowel and parts of other organs were deleted. A distinguished psychiatrist of that day remarked, "A number of psychiatrists and surgeons are earnestly engaged in reducing the colons of human beings to semi-colons in a futile attempt to cure mental diseases!"

In 1913, two brilliant investigators, Noguchi and Moore, demonstrated that the living organisms of syphilis were in the brains of patients suffering from paresis. It was an epoch-making discovery. Previously the cause of paresis, a common form of mental disease, was not understood and at best was a matter of vague conjecture. Now, and for all time to come, it is known to be due and always due to the invasion of the brain by syphilis.

Sadly, this great discovery had some unfortunate repercussions, again reminiscent of "post hoc, ergo propter hoc." Psychological investigations fell into disrepute and passed into a state of hibernation. Enthusiastically it was asserted that the answer to all mental disturbances would be found in inflammatory and destructive processes in the brain. It was a vain hope.

Later, spearheaded by Sigmund Freud, the psychoanalytical school penetrated beneath the surface of the conscious mind and made deep explorations. From the depths of the unconscious were brought to the surface great quantities of remarkable and highly significant psychic material. From a careful scrutiny of this material, theories and concepts were derived which will, for all time, influence the course of psychiatry.

Again, unfortunately, the pendulum swung too far. Physiology and chemistry with their precise instruments of research were poorly served by psychiatrists and eventually were practically disregarded. Now, happily, a satisfactory working balance has been restored.

It is unlikely that such serious mistakes will be made in the future. It is now well understood that mental disease is an intricate and complex process involving many factors. These factors cannot be swept together into one neat little heap by any "all or nothing" generalization, however brilliant it may be.

As a by-product, in its search for basic reasons explaining the occurrence of mental illness, psychiatry made a very important contribution to the art of medicine. It is so significant that modern medicine could not be practiced intelligently without constantly employing it. It has been suggested that psychiatrists came upon the principle of the fundamental unity of mind-body functioning, since, lacking instruments of precision available to so many of their professional colleagues, like the cardiographic machine of the heart specialists, they were compelled to use their heads and think things over very carefully. Not so many years ago, all too often, medicine was practiced as though the mind and body were quite separate and distinct from each other. Almost never did the twain meet. Now it is clearly appreciated by every practitioner of medicine that even a very simple physiological function cannot occur without producing reverberations throughout the emotions. Conversely, there cannot be any emotional reaction, even a feeling no stronger than mild disappointment, without it being registered and profiled in every cell and tissue of the human body. If this body-mind interdependence, this entwining of function, is true in health—and it is—then obviously it is equally valid in sickness. It may be accepted without reservation that a person cannot be sick in his body alone or in his mind alone. The impact may be heavier at the body or the mind level, but always *the whole man is sick*.

Fever is generally thought of as a matter of the body, usually due to infection. Yet, fever frequently unlocks the portals of the unconscious mind and there is a pouring out of highly charged emotional material of which the patient was not consciously aware. General anaesthesia is produced by the chemical effect of the anaesthetic upon the brain. But again, often the dykes guarding the unconscious are breached. Perhaps that is the reason why it is not advisable for husbands or wives to be present when their marital partners have to be given ether for an operation. If there is marked underactivity of the thyroid gland, the patient is often dull and apathetic, with occasional explosive outbursts. Conversely, the very overactive thyroid patient is apt to be nervous, jittery and irritable. So do the emotions reflect the things that happen in the body, and, indeed, are part and parcel of them.

During World War II, I saw a young sailor who had been in the sea many hours following the destruction of his ship by an enemy torpedo. This is about all he remembered of the ex-

perience. He was depressed, tense, tremulous and had horrible
nightmares. One day, after an interview with the Navy doctor
who was treating him, he suddenly remembered. Again he saw
the scene in the sea; he was swimming toward the life raft.
A shipmate, his "buddy," in a panic of fear, was clutching him
around the neck, pulling him beneath the surface. In the struggle, his friend was drowned. The patient felt he was to blame,
that he should have saved his buddy's life, even though he
might have lost his own.

Here was an ethical problem in a vivid emotional setting.
Yet, merely looking at the patient was quite enough to make it
evident to anyone that his whole body was participating in and
expressing the intense emotional conflict. His face was chalk
white; he was trembling in every limb; there were violent
pulsations of the vessel of the neck; his pulse was twice as
rapid as usual; he was gasping for breath. Here as always
the body was the instrument for expressing the emotions.

The following very schematic diagram illustrates how uni-
fied is the functioning of the bodily ——— and emotional
- - - - processes in the total man:

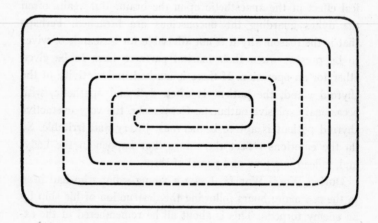

A valid and interesting way of looking at the "causes" of mental disorders is to consider them as:

A. Predisposing

B. Exciting

Predisposing is not the same as precipitating. In the affairs of men and nations alike, precipitating happenings usually are not very serious and often they are quite trivial. When around the United Nations conference table representatives of the various nations deliver harangues with impassioned voice and gesture, it is not likely that these highly dramatic verbal pyrotechnics will produce war. Nor will border incidents or even the assassination of an ambassador, although these incidents may be utilized as "reasons" for war. The actual causes of war are more significant and much deeper—economic, political, ideological and spiritual reasons.

So, too, mental illness is not called forth by a slight fall during childhood, being frightened by a dog, the death of a relative, the failure of a marriage, and what not. These happenings, particularly if they occur soon before the mental or neurotic symptoms appear, are often given undue importance. They have little or none.

A predisposing cause is a very different matter. It is an active element in the equation which, when completed, determines the departure from reality.

Not only in psychiatry but in every realm of medicine, predisposing factors have high priority rating. In the winter, it is a common occurrence for the police to find a human derelict in the gutter of any large city. They take him to the precinct station, "just another drunk." The police surgeon examines him and says, "This man may be drunk, but he also has pneumonia."

Many things were predisposing, including alcoholism, poor nutrition, thin clothing, insufficient food, exposure to cold and inclement weather. All these made the victim and particularly his respiratory tissues vulnerable to one of the organisms which cause pneumonia.

So, too, may a man be predisposed to tuberculosis by a tuberculous ancestry, a frail body, trying indoor work in unhygienic surroundings, too little exercise, sunshine, fresh air and the right kind of food. So predisposed, he may fall easy prey to the tubercle bacillus.

In psychiatry, a predisposing cause prepares the soil for the operation of the exciting cause and renders more likely the occurrence of mental sickness.

Perhaps the more significant predisposing factors are inheritance, the age epoch, environmental factors, occupation and previous attacks.

Inheritance in the past was grossly overrated. When I was a medical student, the course in psychiatry consisted of about thirty lectures. They all repeated the same direful theme. Human beings were either blessed or damned mentally, according to their ancestry. One of the reasons I sought a career in psychiatry was because I did not believe such a sweeping indictment could be true. It is not true. In human disease there are very few conditions which even approximate the Mendelian law, as does perhaps the bleeding disease of some of the former royal families of Europe. In psychiatry usually the most that may be said is that if there is a record of serious mental disease or abnormality in the direct ancestry, then this is a predisposing factor which must be carefully weighed. Not just a peculiar uncle, aunt or cousin, or a rascally grandfather. It is unusual to find a family that does not have a few mental skeletons in its ancestral closets. Sometimes, no doubt in order to hush the inner unconscious voice which might accuse the parents of a young man or woman who is mentally sick of a certain amount of responsibility because of default in the early parent-child relationship, they conveniently shunt the blame on Uncle Jack who was a rake, or the paternal or maternal grandmother (according to whether the mother or father is giving the history) who left her husband and ran away with her lover. Incidentally, I doubt if eugenics would solve the problems of psychiatry. Even if it could be put into general practice, which is very doubtful, then we might hope only to produce a strain of human bovines whose thoughts, emotions and behavior, true enough, would not fall below a certain line, but also they would never rise above a discouragingly mediocre level. Perhaps they would contentedly chew the cud of sameness. Of course, there are people suffering from certain kinds of mental and nervous deviations who should not reproduce because their offspring would have less than an average chance of resisting mental disease.

The age of the patient is an important predisposing consideration. A statistical graph of the incidence of mental disease shows two high peaks: one during the few years following adolescence, the other at the old-age period. The first peak is largely due to the many cases of schizophrenia in young people; their personalities are not tough-fibred enough to meet the hard and fast conditions of everyday reality and they retire, defeated, at least temporarily, into the fortress of make-believe and fantasy. At the other end of the scale, in old age there is a large increment of mental disease, with a depreciation of all mental functions as a consequence of organic deterioration of the brain. At the change of life, the climacteric, in men as well as women, there is a slight rise in incidence. These three peaks represent the natural hazards of age.

Men, like nations, are conceived and born. If they survive the perils of infancy and youth, they come to a strong, lusty young adulthood. After a span of years they attain the climacteric. This should mean what it says, a climax, the very summit of intellectual and emotional powers, which should continue for a long period of time. For a relatively few individuals and nations, the climacteric means just that. But for far too many, it is regarded as the beginning of the end, regression. True enough, the climacteric does bring a triple threat. There is increasingly greater likelihood of organic disease, perhaps particularly of the heart and blood vessels and, in women, of the pelvic organs. Added to this, there is the inescapable fact that more than half of life has been lived and many of its mistakes cannot be retrieved. Finally, there is the ever-increasing threat of deprivation by death of loved objects, family and friends.

For women, the risks of the change of life are psychologically increased by the many old-wives' tales, luridly told, of the dreadful things that happen at the menopause. For one thing, it is supposed to be the time when husbands lose interest in their wives and seek younger and more beautiful women.

Perhaps particularly in our American culture, the situation is somewhat intensified by advertising propaganda which by endless repetition glorifies flaming, slenderized female youth. There is real danger that we may forget that, after all, there is something above the neckline in women which might be of some interest and value.

Nevertheless, in nations and individuals alike, following the onset of the climacteric, there may be a reasonably long-sustained level of maximum efficiency and maturity, intellectually and emotionally. However, eventually and inevitably, old age will make its physical and mental encroachments. The exhausted and senile nation sinks into obscurity. In the human being, there will be increasing deterioration, often leveling to a profound dementia, a psychological death. It is, indeed, a boon to die all over, at one time.

In addition to natural epochal hazards, men and nations are called upon to face many accidental strains and stresses at any time in their life histories. Nations encounter economic, political and ideological crises, and often when they are unprepared and vulnerable. Men and women, unexpectedly too, suffer critical emotional upheavals and anxieties, inflicted by many vicissitudes, from financial reverses to disappointments and rejections in the love life.

The work a person does, one's job, may carry a mental liability. Occupation may operate directly, as when it brings the industrial worker into direct contact with certain poisons, like white lead, mercury, carbon bisulphide (used in making rayon) and many other substances which have a toxic affinity for the brain.

Occupation may predispose indirectly by offering constant and dangerous temptation. In the old days, many bartenders suffered from alcoholic psychoses. Sailors often contracted syphilis and many developed luetic mental disease. In these days, far too many physicians and other professional workers become addicted to narcotic and other sleep-producing and stimulant drugs. Obviously, the serving of liquor in itself carried no mental risk, but it did provide an ever-present temptation to imbibe. Sailing in a four-masted schooner or other ship involved no intrinsic hazard of syphilis. But the old-time sailor was likely to have a girl or several girls in every port of call, many of whom were prostitutes, infected with lues. This was the hazard, not the life of the sea. Some doctors, often overworking under stress, may succumb to the lure of drugs that will give much-needed sleep and then, the next day, they make themselves mentally alert with benzedrine or some other cerebral activating drug. Perhaps familiarity breeds foolhardy contempt.

An achievement of industry is vast quantity production. A

penalty must be paid. Simple, non-creative, monotonous work is not calculated to produce emotional satisfaction in the worker. This is important enough to be discussed presently at more length.

All living things are dependent upon the environments in which they exist and move and, in some measure, are at their mercy. For animals, the threat is largely physical, and often the stake is life. Human beings in many ways have mastered their material surroundings and even regimented them to produce greater ease, comfort and luxury of living. This is notably true in our own country, where living standards average higher than any other land. It is not enough. Man cannot live by bread alone. Beneath the soft surface layer in our culture, there is much that is inimical and threatening. Our culture is too monotonous and patterned. There is a hard, inner core which is ruthlessly competitive. The supreme achievement is industrial, particularly rapid production in great quantities of anything needed, from mousetraps to automobiles. Food is still grown on farms, but much of it is quickly processed, packaged and delivered even to the farthest corners of the world. All this is not to be belittled. In these troubled times of almost universal want, it is saving millions from starvation, despair and anarchy. Nevertheless, the system of quantity production has certain Frankensteinish qualities. Excepting as a hobby, no one in these days makes anything—a chair, a table or a bookcase. There is little pride of accomplishment in standing before an assembly belt and endlessly affixing some small part to skeletons of metal, destined to become automobiles. Often the assembly-line job is too simple to engage and interest enough of the mind. The ego is insulted—belittled. There is too much time for rumination and brooding. It is not a setting which favors contentment, security and emotional maturity. Dissatisfaction, envy and hostility develop. Since at least a third of a man's life is given to his work, for many men we must reckon with occupation as prejudicial to mental health and indict it as predisposing to mental sickness. It is likely that it is a factor of some importance in the production of the tremendous number of disabling psychoneuroses in the population. To these defects in our culture, there must be added the anxiety and fear from living in the shadow of the dread atomic bomb—and now the monstrous H bomb.

Childhood is the time of golden opportunity for the prevention of mental and nervous disorders in adult life. Sometimes the opportunity is fully and wisely used by parents. Sadly, and far too often, the opportunity is forever lost and, instead, during childhood there is deeply etched into the growing personality a large amount of the most serious of all predispositions —emotional immaturity. Almost never can this pattern be wholly eradicated. In adult life, in the face of even minor frustrations, it is very likely to stand out in bold relief in the shape of all kinds of grave emotional maladjustments, psychoneuroses and functional illnesses.

At the proper place, the conditions which prevent the attainment of full-sized emotional stature will be discussed in some detail. But now at least it should be mentioned that the most important determining event in anyone's life is the relationship between the child and its mother, its parents or their surrogates. In this early relationship, there is written in miniature a true forecast of the child's adult emotional life in all its personal and social experiences and responsibilities. Motherhood and parenthood become dual functions. If these are properly fulfilled, the child will be wanted, nurtured, loved, given much affection, protected. In other words, it will be made emotionally secure and have the basis of a sound, healthy personality. Then, gradually and carefully, the child will be emancipated, helped to mature emotional growth, so that eventually it will become a self-thinking, self-feeling and self-acting person. If these basic needs of children are not satisfied at least in minimal fashion, then unconscious hostilities are produced and embedded in their personalities. Later, in adult life, they cannot be faced in consciousness and are camouflaged by guilt and anxieties. All too often, the only path open is escape into psychoneurotic symptoms. Childhood, indeed, is the area of greatest predisposition.

Psychiatry, like other divisions of medicine, has its immunities and its weakened resistances. Unfortunately, there are relatively few immunities from having had a mental illness. There are no immune bodies and other bodily defenses against the occurrence of a second attack, as there are in many childhood diseases, like measles, chickenpox, or in smallpox or shingles. Sometimes in a well-treated psychoneurosis it is true that the patient is so thoroughly insulated against a recurrence by the understanding of himself and his illness he has gained that he is somewhat less likely to become neurotic again, and rather less likely than someone who has never suffered a so-called "nervous breakdown." Generally speaking, mental illness is more like certain kinds of grippe or heart attacks, in which one attack definitely predisposes to more upsets in the future. This is notably true in the manic-depressive psychosis where one episode carries with it a strong tendency to recur.

We have now before us a hypothetically predisposed individual. Perhaps he is only slightly predisposed, in one way or another, but again, there may be many weak links in the chain of his personality armor. Of one thing we may be sure. There is no one who is without some degree of predisposition. In the face of extremely severe internal pressure from inner mental conflicts and destructive external conditions of life, even the soundest personality will yield and break.

No matter how seriously a person may be predisposed, it is

still necessary, before the formula of mental sickness is completed, for his personality to come into contact with an exciting cause. These exciting factors are trigger mechanisms which set off the psychotic or psychoneurotic explosions. They belong either in the category of the preponderantly physical or preponderantly emotional. The qualification *preponderantly* is used advisedly. It is repeated that even when the impact seems to be restrictedly on a physical level, as, for instance, a brain tumor, or solely on an emotional basis, mayhap an unconscious conflict concerning latent homosexuality, nevertheless the response in the shape of symptoms always comes from the total person, and never from a mythical physical or emotional half of him.

There is a long list of physical exciting causes. Only general headings need be given: fever usually due to infectious diseases, disease like pneumonia or malaria perhaps followed by depletion and exhaustion, intoxication due to poisons taken into the body, auto-intoxications, that is, poisons created within the body in the course of some toxic process, perhaps kidney or liver toxicities, decided shifts in the metabolic or "give-and-take" mechanism of any important organ, as, for instance, in the thyroid gland,* chronic diseases like syphilis, tuberculosis or arthritis, a whole group of brain diseases, like tumor, abscess or hemorrhage, head injury, even sunstroke may produce mental symptoms. Some of these physical excitants sometimes take a very heavy toll of the mental health of children. This is true occasionally of both head injury and that inflammation of the brain called "sleeping sickness" (encephalitis). A reversal of the behavior pattern may occur, far beyond the normal "bad" behavior of youngsters. I knew a boy of eight who

---

* Whenever and over a considerable time the waste products (katabolic) exceed the tissue repairing and upbuilding ones (anabolic) the metabolic support of the brain is weakened and mental symptoms may appear.

within a year of an attack of sleeping sickness ran away from home many times, frequently set fires and had to be physically restrained from sexually assaulting his mother. Another boy of six who had had a head injury was barely prevented from hammering carpet tacks into his baby sister's head.

The operation of physical exciting causes is not hard to understand. Often they can be seen and examined. Fever can be recorded by the clinical thermometer. The organisms that cause pneumonia, malaria, tuberculosis may be viewed through the microscope. So, too, may the spirochete of syphilis be seen in a bit of brain tissue taken from the brain of someone who has paresis. An excess of alcohol or bromides or some other poison may be found in the blood by chemical tests. Likewise, many of the industrial poisons may be detected by various laboratory tests. And, so on. All this has led to the idea that here are the really significant causes of mental disturbances, and the things that cannot be seen, like emotional conflicts, which are intangible, seem vague and even mystical. Nothing could be further from the truth. The physical exciting causes are important, but they shrink into relative insignificance when compared to the tremendous influences of those causes which cannot be seen, even through the most powerful microscope— the emotional exciting factors.

If the heart is the dominant organ of the body, then it is not too figurative to say that the emotions are the heart of the mind. When the physical heart dies, life is extinguished. When the emotions practically cease to function as in very deep dementia, then for all intents and purposes the mind is annihilated.

"The emotions are too far-reaching, too important, dynamic and too fluid to be confined within a cage of words. It is not too much to say that they are almost life itself. Emotions activate and energize behavior. They express our ideas. By their

resiliency and almost infinite variation, they vivify and beau-
tify life and create the very joy of living. However highly we
may vaunt our evolution and civilization, it is undoubtedly
true that we are fundamentally living by virtue of our emotions. The painting of a masterpiece; the conversion of a block
of marble into a figure of enduring beauty; the writing of a
great novel; in fact, almost every achievement in the arts is
emotionally rather than intellectually inspired. Large and
small decisions are frequently made on an emotional level,
even though the individual may not be aware of the impelling
force which actuated the 'making-up' of his mind. The meaner
affairs and incidents of life likewise hinge more on *feeling* than
on *thinking*.

"To a large extent everything in the last analysis depends
on the direction in which the emotions exert their pull. The
mass of the people is particularly prone to act this way. Revo-
lutions are awakened; bloody and costly wars are fought; potent historical documents are brought into existence; kings
and queens lose their crowns and their heads; ordinary men
are elevated to high places in response to the electrical current
of feeling which sweeps through the mob. It is true that so-
called intellectuals may use the mob as the chess expert moves
his pawns, but seldom do they succeed in retaining the direction and mastery. Furthermore, they themselves are apt to
find their strength in emotionally conditioned thoughts and
behavior.

"A civilization resting on a purely intellectual foundation
would be almost inconceivable; it would be pallid and anemic,
weak and ineffectual. Great mistakes might not be made, but
notable progress would be wanting.

"It is clear that the emotions constitute a remarkable force
for good or evil. The conduct which they motivate in the affairs
of nations and in the daily lives of every man and woman may

be beneficial or dangerous. In one instance, a nation may be brought to decline and chaos; in the other, a mind may be swept from its moorings. Whenever a force is so gigantic and awful in its potentialities, it should be surrounded by protective barriers and subjected to inhibiting criteria. The only available criterion is the check of the intellectual mind. In other words, human conduct must not only be determined by feeling but it must also be guided by thinking. The moral is 'look before you leap' or, think before you act. The only solution is to restrain, at least partly, impulsive behavior. This is not easy; in fact, it is extraordinarily difficult. Sometimes the emotions spur us on so strongly and so rapidly that they do not give us time to think and, often, the feeling which prompts the act is not accessible to conscious analysis. Nevertheless, effort forms habit. A reasonable amount of self-knowledge plus honest striving will make us eventually, at least in some degree, the masters of what we do, instead of the slaves of unadulterated emotions. If every person could succeed in modifying behavior by thought in the proportion of 25 per cent, human progress and happiness would be immeasurably enhanced and human misery notably lessened." *

Obviously the impact of emotional factors is very heavy and determining. They may be thought of as external and internal. The warp and woof of the external is in the environment, the endless things that life does to us, the acute dramatic blows of fate, the chronic worries that sap resistance. Here are financial reverses, deprivations in the love life, severance from loved ones by death, shaming belittlements, inferiorities and disgrace, ego-degrading failures, and many other blows and insults.

Internal factors are in the unconscious mental life, unsolved emotional conflicts which have come to an impasse. All in all, they are more significant than the environmental hazards.

* From *Discovering Ourselves* by Strecker and Appel (Macmillan Co.).

When compromises fail, these emotional conflicts threaten to break into consciousness, but the personality cannot tolerate them. It is then psychologically mandatory that there be an escape by the route of illness, usually psychoneurotic. There are as many mental conflicts as there are human beings who have them. But in the general pattern may be traced the sharply clashing and seemingly irreconcilable behavior demands of the "I" or self-preservative instinct, sex and the herd or social expectations and requirements. The deeper roots of mental conflicts are in the emotionally immature soil of unsatisfactory early parental and other relationships.

Emotional problems, outside and inside the person, are not rigidly separated one from another. They merge at many points and activate one another, often producing a vicious circle. We all have hidden mental conflicts. Perhaps many of us carry on well enough and make satisfactory adjustments, unless the environment becomes too threatening and disruptive. Then the personality breaks.

After a psychiatrist has made a thorough study of a patient, among other things he carefully estimates the relative strengths of external and internal pressures. Usually, but not always, the internal are the more significant. They are the serious mental conflicts, deep in the psyche of patients, beyond the area of conscious thought and remembrance.

In a way, the material of mental conflicts, and its origin in the life history of the patient, is basic. Perhaps it is comparable to underlying causes of physical disease. The doctor knows that in pneumonia the consolidated lung, cough, fever, bloody sputum, etc., are due to the bacillus of pneumonia. Likewise, in a given case, the headache, vomiting, slow pulse and failing vision come from a brain tumor. So, too, may the psychiatrist know that a patient's symptoms are due to an underlying mental conflict, which is much like a tumor in the psyche.

But the external liabilities are not to be disregarded. I think there is a tendency to belittle them. They occur in infinite variety. Sometimes they are of the trivia.

A spoiled rich young society matron was in a hysterical dither because the butler had given notice. About the only attention this deserved was to try to make her ashamed of her silly behavior. On the other hand, a young traveling sales- man devoted to his wife and their three youngsters, one day while on the road received word that the family car had been struck at a grade crossing by an express train. His wife and the children were instantly killed. That was a somewhat dif- ferent matter.

During World War II we learned that there were emotional overloads heavy enough to break temporarily even the sound- est personalities. Often I saw the human psychic wreckage. Some of the survivors of the torpedoed *Indianapolis* were in the sea without food or water for more than five days. Combat pilots bringing in the "ship" with a cargo of wounded and dead. A sailor trapped in a boiler compartment of a cruiser, he and the "buddy" he kept afloat, the only survivors of twenty-two men. The infantry cowering in foxholes, in the face of mortar fire. All these and many horrors were everyday incidents of the war, frequently in a setting of physical depletion and ex- haustion.

Nor is civilian life exempt from soul-racking dramas.

I was called to see a poor Italian laborer, in his late fifties, because he was depressed and had attempted to take his life by slashing his wrists with a razor blade. He was overwhelmed with self-blame because of this "sin" (suicidal attempt). An- gelo had worked hard all his life, as had his wife. They were devoted to each other. There was one child, now a grown son. They had managed to accumulate almost a thousand dollars for their old age. The Building and Loan Association in which they had the money "blew up" and the savings were gone.

Angelo lost his job. His wife had some vague pains and, at the clinic where she was examined, it was discovered she had an inoperable cancer in the pelvis. At most, she had a few months to live. The son, of whom Angelo and his wife were very proud, was caught in a burglary and sentenced to ten years in the State penitentiary. Then the psychosis appeared. Such psychoses are properly called reactive, indicating that the mental symptoms are due largely to disruptive environmental happenings.

Another patient was a physician, forty-four years old. Over-fatigued from a strenuous practice, he came down with a series of sinus attacks. After battling with this painful condition for several months, at the same time trying to continue his work, he had to give up and go to a Western clinic for several operations and a long period of treatment. When he returned, his wife confessed that she was in love with another man and had been unfaithful to him. One of the two children, a nine-year-old girl, had been falling behind in her school work and behaving very badly. She had been examined by the school psychologist who found her to be feeble-minded. The child had to be put in an institution. The rumor had spread through the town that "the doctor was addicted to drugs" and his practice dwindled almost to nothing.

When I saw the patient, he was tense, worried, anxious and he had a long train of functional symptoms—headache, dizziness, nausea, vomiting, pain in the back and a rapid pulse. Unquestionably, the hard way in which life had dealt with him was a determining factor in the occurrence of the psychoneurosis. Such psychoneuroses are definitely reactive, signifying that the neurotic symptoms are mainly due to severe impacts from the environment.

After examining a patient, the psychiatrist probably does give the illness a name—schizophrenia, reactive depression,

anxiety neurosis or something else. The name is much more
than a label to be affixed to the case record, and filed away
in a diagnostic pigeonhole. In modern psychiatry, a name or
diagnosis is dynamic and provocative. It stimulates intelligent
and skillful thinking and planning. What produced this psychosis or psychoneurosis? How serious is it? What are the
patient's chances for recovery? What plan of treatment will
be most likely to restore the patient to a satisfactory functioning level? All this and much more.

I presume every physician in his thinking expresses the
patient's condition in a formula something like this one:

$$\frac{P + S}{Re} = R_1\, R_2\, R_3\, R_4\, R_5 \text{ etc.}$$

P means Predisposition. It is a kind of measure of the accumulation of liabilities existing in the patient's personality
at the time the illness appeared. Not only or mainly such
weaknesses as were derived from inheritance, but, usually more
tellingly, the long record of vulnerabilities remaining from the
many encounters with the surroundings in which the patient
came off "second best." This from infancy on and particularly
during childhood. Included are unconscious mental conflicts
which could not be solved or even faced in consciousness.

S means Stress. Stress involves chiefly external detrimental
happenings. It may be a single crushing blow, like the sudden
loss by an accident or disease of a dearly beloved wife, husband or child. Or it may be a long-continued emotional drain,
perhaps as in one of my patients. This woman in middle life
had a husband who was not only alcoholic but a drunken brute
who ill-treated her and often made her life well-nigh unbear-
able. The husband did furnish a fair amount of economic support for her and three young children, one crippled by in-

fantile paralysis. Probably unwisely, the wife continued her unhappy life because of the remnants of love that remained, the hope that her husband would stop drinking and the fear of the loss of economic support for herself and the children.

In the formula, Re means Resistance. It is the opposite of predisposition. From inheritance and from the reaction between an individual and the environment, the personality does not solely accumulate weaknesses, but also assets are acquired. There are times and sometimes many times when we come off not vanquished but victorious. Each time the personality is strengthened in some degree. Particularly is this true if we have had a reasonably emotionally secure childhood. The sum of all our personality strengths is equivalent to resistance. It is tremendously important, sometimes in protecting us against a break, sometimes in staving it off for a long time, and frequently, tempering it, so that it is much less serious and we are much more likely to recover.

To complete the formula, the amount of predisposition added to the stress as far as can be determined is divided by the quantity of resistance. The answer is not only the kind of mental or nervous reaction from which the patient is suffering, but also there is available a fairly accurate appreciation of its gravity (R R_1 R_2 R_3 R_4 R_5) and the prospect of recovery. So names or labels mean little or nothing unless they are the keys opening up information as to predisposition, stress, resistance and the outlook for the patient.

In this connection it is worth while to say at least a few words about the important facet of Adolf Meyer's contribution —psychobiology. Here the patient is charted, mentally or even actually on the record. The long line of the patient's life history is divided into years. As far as can be determined from the history, significant events are recorded. In this way, the longitudinal life history is brought into focus.

In my mind's eye I have before me Joan, a young woman twenty-two years old. She whispers to me that she is the "Virgin Queen of the World." She seems to be listening intently and from time to time her lips move as in conversation. Often she laughs in silly, simpering fashion. The patient was one of identical twins and had one brother, two years older. Her parents are divorced. Her brother lives with the father. Joan lives with her mother, who is "nice" and loves her, but is helpless and inadequate. I have changed some of the important happenings in Joan's chronological life history:

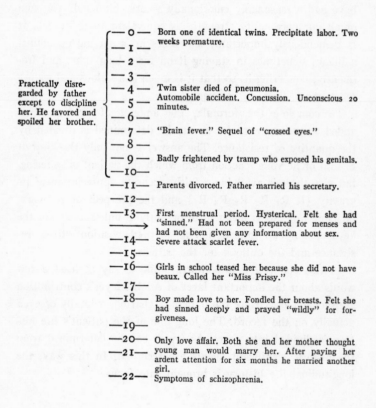

Practically disregarded by father except to discipline her. He favored and spoiled her brother.

— 0 — Born one of identical twins. Precipitate labor. Two weeks premature.

— 1 —
— 2 —
— 3 —
— 4 — Twin sister died of pneumonia.
— 5 — Automobile accident. Concussion. Unconscious 20 minutes.
— 6 —
— 7 — "Brain fever." Sequel of "crossed eyes."
— 8 —
— 9 — Badly frightened by tramp who exposed his genitals.
—10—
—11— Parents divorced. Father married his secretary.
—12—
—13— First menstrual period. Hysterical. Felt she had "sinned." Had not been prepared for menses and had not been given any information about sex.
—14— Severe attack scarlet fever.
—15—
—16— Girls in school teased her because she did not have beaux. Called her "Miss Prissy."
—17—
—18— Boy made love to her. Fondled her breasts. Felt she had sinned deeply and prayed "wildly" for forgiveness.
—19—
—20— Only love affair. Both she and her mother thought
—21— young man would marry her. After paying her ardent attention for six months he married another girl.
—22— Symptoms of schizophrenia.

Such a long-section life history is very valuable. For one thing, it suggests very strongly that if life had been different for Joan or other patients, if they had been better prepared for the crises encountered, if they had been helped to understand them and had been desensitized about them, then they might never have come to the final maladjustments, as Joan came to schizophrenia.

It is clear, too, that this method of scrutinizing a patient's life brings into sharp focus many useful indications for the treatment of the psychosis or psychoneurosis.

Obviously mental diseases are due neither to the wrath or to the favor of the gods or to demoniacal possession. Like all other human diseases, mental disorders come from natural causes, many of which are known and understood and can be successfully treated.

2 | CLASSIFICATION OR NAMING

An unrecorded but highly dramatic and significant event occurred when our remote and primitive ancestors for the first time were able to communicate verbally with one another. At the beginning, their attempts must have been very crude. Yet there can be little doubt as to what they talked about. Their survival was at stake. Then and now, self-preservation was and is the dominant issue. So they took counsel about those prehistoric monsters, much superior to them in size and strength, the mammoth, the saber-toothed tiger and other savage creatures which roamed the surface of the land, swam in the seas and flew in the skies, constantly threatening to annihilate them. In simple, half-articulate fashion, prehistoric men identified them and told each other what they had observed of their habits, their cunning, their strengths and vulnerabilities. In other words, they named and classified them. Armed with this identifying information, they were able with increasing success to outwit and often destroy them. Otherwise, they, themselves, would have perished.

The capacity to recognize, name and classify is not only the basic instrument of science, but also it is the touchstone of our adaptation to the environment in which we live. If we did not have names for things it would be painfully difficult and next to impossible to talk about them with one another, learn more about them and use them advantageously or, perhaps, avoid them. Unless we had such names as kitchen, dining room, living room, bedroom, it would be difficult to build a satisfactory house.

In some fields of human knowledge, for instance, botany, classification is on a very high level. In the humane disciplines like sociology, psychology or psychiatry, we can scarcely expect the same high degree of exactness. They deal with human beings, men, women and children who have much more individuality than plants or flowers and exhibit many more divergences, intangibles and unpredictables. This is notably true in psychiatry. It strives to classify diseases and disorders of the invisible mind or personality functioning not only as the supreme but also the most complex and intricate of all human functions. A very large part of the vast territory of man's psyche still remains to be explored and charted. Nevertheless, psychiatry has made and continues to make, with increasing scientific courage and assurance, large and significant penetrations into the areas of the mind and its workings, the existence of which were scarcely suspected even a few decades ago. So the classification of mental illness proceeds apace.

Naturally, psychiatric classification cannot have an even, level growth. We have found out much more about certain kinds of mental illness than we have about others. For instance, we know a great deal about paresis, a form of mental disease due to syphilis and the subsequent invasion of the brain by the parasite (spirochete) which causes syphilis. We know not only the cause of paresis, but we have reliable tests for its diagnosis. We understand the symptoms; we can predict fairly accurately the patient's chances for improvement under definite treatment, such as malarial or machine-produced fever or penicillin therapy. We can describe accurately what the ravaged brain looks like after death and in the sections of stained brain tissue under the microscope. Comparatively, even though psychiatrists can recognize it readily enough, they do not know nearly as much about the most common psychosis, schizophrenia. Yet both paresis and schizophrenia, together with many other disorders, must be fitted into a single classification list. It is the earnest desire of psychiatrists to keep this list very fluid and flexible, so that as additions are made to our fund of information, old and misleading names of mental diseases may be abandoned and more fitting ones substituted.

There is another good reason for receptive alertness about changing the verbal labels of mental disorders. Psychiatry must still suffer the burden of its conception and infancy in an environment of gross ignorance and superstition, error and prejudice. For instance, the unpleasant word "insanity" still persists even though modern psychiatrists find decreasingly little use for it, excepting perhaps in medico-legal practice, in which it is part of the somewhat archaic language of the law.

Some time ago I had to tell a father that his twenty-year-old daughter was emotionally upset and should have a brief period of treatment in a mental hospital. In spite of my tact and well-founded optimism about the favorable outcome, he reacted with pitiful despair. In his mind, "emotional upset" and "insanity" were synonymous and he cried out, "I would rather have my daughter in her grave than in an insane asylum." In this intelligent and successful man, the old and horrible implications deservedly gathered around the word insanity were still strong enough to annihilate all vestige of reasonable thought.

In three months the young woman made an enduring recovery from her mental illness which had followed the death in combat of her beloved aviator husband to whom she had been married only a few months. Interestingly, the patient's sister at about the same time developed a serious heart ailment as an accompaniment of rheumatic fever. Of course, the father worried about it, but he was able to accept it without too great mental anguish. I suspect it was because he could "see" this daughter's symptoms, the fever, the swelling of the joints and the physical incapacity. They did not terrify him as did the depression of the daughter which he could not "see." Yet today Anna, the "rheumatic heart" patient is seriously incapacitated and will so remain, while Mary, the "insane" patient, is quite well and happy.

Old names die hard, even though they are no longer descriptive or useful. This is always unfortunate, but doubly so in psychiatry, since some of these ancient names have in the course of many years gathered a great weight of barnacle thought and word, encrustations which are belittling and even stigmatizing. In view of much information that has been won and of progress made, they are no longer descriptive or fitting. In psychiatry, a rose does not smell as sweet if it is misnamed.

For instance, epilepsy is a very ancient name. In fact, it was used by Hippocrates. It has certainly outlived its usefulness. Yet I think if the word epilepsy were presented to a cross-section of the population, it would invoke a picture of what epilepsy is still thought to be, a kind of horrible disease in which the victim is forever throwing fits, writhing and twisting and foaming at the mouth. Further, the consensus too probably would be that all epileptics are very unpleasant and even dangerously antisocial people. This, in the face of one of the most brilliant chapters ever written in the history of research, with the fruitful results of several extremely valuable drugs and

other treatments, so that today many patients lead useful and
constructive lives, with very few and sometimes no convulsive
seizures. A better name than epilepsy, for the present at least,
would be "paroxysmal cerebral dysrhythmia" which expresses
a more sensitive and a more readily irritated condition of the
motor area of the brain than is usual.

Dementia praecox is another old-timer, but still hangs on.
It is not an expressive name since there is neither real dementia, as in the mental deterioration of the psychoses of old age,
nor is the disorder restricted to youth. Blessedly, "dementia
praecox" is being rapidly replaced by "schizophrenia," an excellent name, since it describes the principal symptom, the
splitting of the personality in which emotional expressions of
the patient appear to be inadequate and, indeed, at cross-pur-
poses with his thinking.

Just what does the psychiatrist mean when he gives a diagnosis to the patient or the family? In the first place, he may
not affix a definite diagnostic label, but rather use a descriptive
phrase. This does not mean that he has failed to make a diagnosis. Not at all. It may be his sound judgment that a certain
name would needlessly and unjustifiably upset the patient or
the family.

But, suppose after careful study of the situation, the psychiatrist does say, "It is a psychosis" or, "A psychoneurosis,"
or something else. There is no need for being terribly frightened and panicky. At least not until more explanation is forthcoming. After all, a name is a word and words do not have
unlimited coverage. It is true that a psychosis, perhaps schizophrenia, or a psychoneurosis, perhaps anxiety neurosis, may
be quite serious and disabling, temporarily at least. However,
and also, it may not be too grave, and occasionally even
it is very mild, responding in a reasonably short time to

treatment. In psychiatry and general medicine alike, a name cannot be taken without qualification, particularly as it is a common human tendency to picture the worst. Tuberculosis may mean that the bacillus is in the blood stream and a fatal issue is likely. But it may also describe a very small lesion at the apex of one lung with all likelihood of complete recovery. "Heart disease" may mean a type of coronary-artery disease which will be inevitably fatal, but it may also be applied to an almost trivial heart disorder which will have little or no effect on either the span of life or the ordinary activities of the patient.

The analogy is valid for psychiatry. Within the year I saw two boys, each fifteen years old. Each youngster told me about the same story. They both confessed to masturbation and felt remorseful about it. They feared their brains might "soften" (one said "decay"), that they might go insane, that they thought people on the street looked at them in an "odd" way, indicating they knew about the "secret habit." In the mirror they felt their eyes looked "strange." One of the youngsters is now in a mental hospital, receiving insulin and other treatment for schizophrenia. The other is entirely well and happy. He recovered after a few interviews largely designed to correct the aftermath of fear and clear away the debris of misinformation produced on the one hand by a rigid Jehovah-like father who thought and spoke of even the mildest sex lapse in terms of damnation and eternal hell-fire, and on the other by a collection of books and pamphlets, luridly describing the "physical and mental decay" supposedly due to masturbation.

What kinds of mental disease are there and how are they recognized by psychiatrists? There are at least twenty varieties, but fortunately, they rather naturally fall into three groups:

I. ORGANIC

II. TOXIC

III. FUNCTIONAL

In the organic psychoses the symptoms are chiefly, but by
no means solely, due to destruction (often after inflammation)
of the brain tissues, such as the blood vessels and cells. This
large group is made up of such psychoses as paresis, the psychoses due to old age and hardening of the brain arteries,
serious head and brain injuries, brain tumor, sometimes epilepsy, and mental defect (feeble-mindedness) and other conditions in which the brain is actually diseased. In mental
deficiency the inability to function at the average, even minimal, intellectual level results from an insufficient number of
brain cells and other inadequacies of brain structure.

In the toxic psychoses the symptoms are preponderantly,
but, again, by no means entirely, a response to poisons taken
into the body from without, like alcohol or the narcotic drugs,
or to poisonous substances like white lead and many metals,
gases and chemical substances used in the industries; to poisons produced within the body in the course of various infectious and other diseases like pneumonia or acute rheumatic
fever or diabetes; to decided upsets in the functioning of any
of the important organs of the body, as in certain heart conditions when a disease-weakened heart is no longer able to
answer the demand for more blood from the various organs
and parts of the body.

In the functional (an unfortunate designation, since all human sickness is "functional" and it is expressed in terms of
disturbance of function) disorders, the amount of organ pathology which is discovered, even with careful and thorough
examination, is neither sufficient nor impressive enough to account for the symptoms. It is perhaps possible that, as more
knowledge is gained, some forms of actual mental disease, like

schizophrenia or manic-depressive, may pass over into the organic or toxic groups. However, it is even more certain that the many functional disturbances like the psychoneuroses, hysteria, neurasthenia, anxiety neuroses, obsessive and compulsive states, and the long list of so-called psychosomatic conditions, will remain in the functional category, "mental," in the sense that they are the expressions in the shape of all kinds of symptoms of serious unsolved emotional conflicts, hidden in the unconscious reservoir of the human psyche. Indeed, it is likely that the functional group will be added to rather than decreased. Already functional illness makes up more than 60 per cent of the practice of medicine, in general and in the various specialties of medicine and surgery.

I trust that I have not given the impression that organic, toxic and functional are discrete, tightly fenced-in compartments, each with its own special symptoms, never mingling with one another. Indeed, a toxic psychosis in the course of time may become organic. Sometimes, a pathological drinker, after years of repeated toxic alcoholic episodes, delirium tremens, neuritis and others, eventually may sustain permanent brain damage amounting to profound dementia. In one sense, too, a long-enduring functional disorder without solution of a severe mental conflict and with constantly mounting anxiety may result in an ulcer of the stomach or upper intestine, certainly an organic condition.

And by no means are all the symptoms of an organic or toxic psychosis due to the destruction of brain tissue or to bodily poisoning. That powerful, persistent and highly individual psychic structure, the human personality, frequently shows its hand even above the mental leveling of the advanced deterioration in such a definite organic process as senile dementia.

One day I came upon a very little and very old lady on the chronic ward of a mental hospital. She was in her late eighties. Her memory and other mental faculties had been well-nigh

annihilated. She did not know the day of the week, the month
or the year or even where she was. The brain destruction had
drawn an iron curtain between her and the outside world and
she did not have even the foggiest notion of the stirring events
that were happening. She scarcely knew her own name. She held
a pillow tightly clutched to her withered breasts. She whispered to me, "My baby." Before I left the hospital, I read over
her history. She had never married and had always passionately loved babies. The symptom of the pillow-baby was
scarcely due to the shrinkage and loss of cell functioning of
her senile brain. It was the persistence and satisfaction in
symbolic fashion of a long-lasting, deep but unfulfilled wish
to have babies.

A diagram is appended which in purely schematic fashion
illustrates by means of the double-pointed arrows and open
spaces between the compartments that they are not rigidly
separated from each other. Toxic symptoms may appear in
organic conditions, and vice-versa. Functional symptoms may
show in both organic and toxic reactions and the reverse.

The clusters of dots ⊛ indicate symptoms derived from
the personality markings of the patients and give a relative
idea of their frequency distribution in the organic, toxic and
functional groups.

Sometimes, but infrequently, a psychiatrist, even after a painstaking study of a patient, is not able to make an exact diagnosis. He may honestly say so to the patient or the family. It need not be a matter of great concern. Treatment is not too much hampered and patients may get well even though the exact diagnosis remains elusive. It is not scientific to attempt to force a square peg of symptoms into a round diagnostic hole. The intensive review of the conditions which would not fit any of the known diagnostic patterns may lead to new and valuable data and an extension of classification.

A friend of mine, formerly a distinguished professor of medicine, at the end of each year gave a clinic on "Damfino's Disease." In it he discussed the patients whose conditions he had not been successful in satisfactorily diagnosing. It was a very enlightening clinic.

3 | EXAMINATION AND SYMPTOMS

Not so many years ago, an appointment to visit a psychiatrist was something to be concealed—not exactly disgraceful, but still better not divulged. Probably there would be embarrassing questions from intimate friends. Acquaintances would be apt to raise their eyebrows. There might be looks of sympathy, or even jocular remarks.

About fifteen years ago, a very prominent and wealthy man called me on the telephone for an appointment. I gave him an hour. "Fine," he said, "and now I want to reserve and pay for the hour before and the hour after I am to see you." I said that would not be possible. No appointment. A month later, I did see the gentleman in the usual way. His explanation for wanting the unusual appointment was that he did not wish to run the risk of encountering anyone who might recognize him.

In these days, while some people still regard a psychiatric appointment as something to be kept quiet, many more do not feel a bit ashamed of it. And some people boast about it. In some social circles, what "my psychiatrist said to me" has edged "my surgical operation" out of first place as a fascinating conversational topic.

Contrary to general opinion, the objective of a psychiatric examination is *not* to discover the condition of the patient's mind. It is much broader than that. The purpose of a psychiatric examination is to come to an opinion about the condition of the patient who is being examined, body and mind together. They cannot be separated. They are one.

Naturally, and in keeping with the usual practice in other fields of medicine, the psychiatrist begins by wanting to know something about the history. He is apt to ask about the chief complaint, though he is unlikely to use those words. More likely, after he has put the patient at ease, he might say, "What seems to be bothering you? Tell me about it."

The psychiatrist is hopeful that the patient will begin to speak freely and discuss his problems as he sees them. The patient who does this will never have a more intent and interested listener than the psychiatrist. Nor will he ever have a better opportunity to talk without interruption.

Many patients have difficulty putting a finger on the chief complaint. It may be very vague and general. "I just feel so tense." Others readily recite their most troublesome symptoms. Perhaps headache, indigestion, nausea, vomiting, insomnia, trouble with concentration. At the early cross-section, the psychiatrist has little or no way of knowing what this array of symptoms might mean. They might indicate some very serious organic disease, like cirrhosis of the liver, or even brain tumor. They might be explainable on the basis of a serious matrimonial problem, perhaps the eternal triangle. They might be the frontispiece of an emotional conflict reaching far back into childhood. Or, as in a lawyer in whom a peptic ulcer subsequently developed, they might be the physical expression of fear that his thefts from a trust fund would be discovered. These and many more things. At this stage, while the psychiatrist may have some leading thoughts, he tries not to guess.

Sometimes a decidedly sick psychotic patient may not have any complaints. He may feel fine and say so. Occasionally, that may mean he has completed a plan to kill his brother, whom he believes is persecuting him. Incidentally, the smaller proportion of patients seen by the psychiatrist in his office and in the clinic are markedly psychotic.

If the patient tells his life story freely (which is desired above all else), then the psychiatrist will not badger him about the details of the history. They will emerge gradually and the data will group themselves into the history of the present illness, the past history and the family history.

As the psychiatrist sorts out the facts he has gathered, about the illness, he scans them with a practiced eye. They should build up into a careful chronological account of the sequence of the appearance of the symptoms and their nature. Attention is closely focused upon the onset. If the onset was abrupt and dramatic, it is rather more favorable than when the withdrawal from the realities of everyday life was gradual, sometimes almost imperceptible.

The incidental setting at the time of onset may be very significant and explanatory. One of my patients, the very intelligent wife of a physician, at forty broke down with a very unfavorable-appearing type of paranoid psychosis. There was a tremendous number of delusions and hallucinations. Her enemies were simply swarming about her, torturing her with all sorts of bizarre and fiendish devices. For one thing, they were shooting thousands of tiny celluloid arrows into her brain cells from a "powerful violet-ray machine." The history revealed that at the time she began to lose her grip on reality, she had been reading a very lurid detective mystery. The "celluloid arrows" and other fantastic incidents from the book simply merged into the beginning of the psychosis and colored the symptoms. The patient recovered in a few months.

Severe emotional insults from the environment deserve careful consideration. From the logbook of my Navy experiences during World War II, the words of Jack, a Navy pilot, from his unconscious memory, spoken during a hypnotic trance: "I remember now. God! I turned to say a word to the 'kid.' He was dead. Machine-gunned through his head."

Jack had combat fatigue which had blotted out his conscious memory. The "kid" was his buddy, they had been close friends from the time they were aviation cadets.

And this from the records of my civilian practice, from a woman who had "forgotten," but who was tense and filled with anxiety, spoken to the accompaniment of uncontrollable sobbing: "Oh, I remember. It all comes back now. It was Mary's [her only daughter] fifteenth birthday. She came to me and told me she was pregnant. I think I fainted. I am ashamed. I should have comforted my child."

So, in the history of the illness, there may be similar and many other buffets and frustrations which take heavy toll of the personality and sometimes seem to invite the plunge into the unreality of nervous and mental disease.

The ancestral record, the family history, may be obtained early or late in the study of the patient. Some patients, and more particularly their families, feeling that the illness is readily explainable on the basis of an aunt who had idiocyncrasies, or an uncle who was hopelessly alcoholic, make all this clear in the first few minutes of the interview. Almost invariably the psychiatrist's answer must be, "No, it is not the uncle or the aunt." I have stopped counting the number of times I have told alcoholic patients that they cannot blame their pathological drinking upon inheritance from an alcoholic father.

Not to say that the account of the family, direct and collateral, can be safely disregarded. The psychiatrist is interested in every item of information that will contribute to his better understanding of the patient. He will want to know the familial record of psychoses and psychoneuroses, suicide, mental defect, epilepsy, alcoholism, drug addictions and many other conditions. Sometimes, but comparatively infrequently, the question of direct inheritance must be weighed, as in juvenile paresis, when there is a history of parental syphilis, and in certain types of epilepsy, feeble-mindedness, and manic-depressive. More often than not, the highlights of the familial neuropsychiatric picture are significant, because of the shadows they cast upon the family life and environment. Some years ago, I treated a girl of nineteen for what, at first glance, looked like malignant schizophrenia. She had lived with her father, a ne'er-do-well, and her mother, who had schizophrenia. Her symptoms reproduced those of her mother, silliness, grimacing, hearing voices, ideas of reference, stuporous spells. After a few weeks of hospital treatment, a bright, attractive young woman with an I.Q. of 120 emerged from the shell of mental symptoms. After her recovery, she made up some preliminary educational work and then entered a nurses' training school. For more than ten years she has been doing excellent psychiatric nursing.

With a reasonably co-operative patient, and perhaps with the assistance of the family, the past history passes in review before the psychiatrist. There are thousands of patients, but never are two histories alike. It is the oft-told but always new story of man's age-old struggle with conflicts inside himself and threats from the environment. There are the experiences of childhood, at first often concealed behind the iron curtain which shuts off the unconscious life from conscious memory. That iron curtain must be lifted, at least partially, for the happenings of childhood never cease to exert an enormous influence on every thought, feeling and act of adult life. Then there are the preponderantly physical occurrences, the diseases, the injuries, sometimes with calamitous aftermaths. And then the emotional disappointments, frustrations, deprivations, sometimes abruptly explosive, sometimes slowly but surely breaching the psychic resistance. In the life history of the patient, there is contained the entirety of his responses to the psychosomatic onslaughts and liabilities of life—and its assets.

As a result of the constant interaction between human beings and the environments in which we live, something is shaped that is called the personality. It cannot be defined. The extent of its territory is too vast to be fenced in by words. Besides, it is ever changing from cradle to grave.

The human personality will be referred to many times in this book. At this place, at least, it should be mentioned that it is the most powerful determinant of behavior. If it were possible to record permanently at any given instant the ever-changing personality, it would be a composite but precise picture of all previous life happenings, great and small, every thought, every feeling, every bit of conduct. And the reaction to all these things. The central core of the human personality is carried over from the ancestry. This at birth. Then rapidly, early in life, and more slowly as years are added, layer after layer is placed around this central core. Here are only a few of the ingredients that are contained in the personality—physical build and distinguishing characteristics, intelligence with its kaleidoscope of thoughts, indifferent, base and noble, emotional traits, enthusiasms, often constructive, ideals, sometimes almost godlike. But in the same person, perhaps also bias, prejudices, shameful and bloody intolerances, habits, sometimes binding like a vise. There are interests, hobbies, drives and tendencies. There is energy output, sometimes tremendous, sometimes trifling. There are aggressive and submissive traits. There are tension and anxieties. There are hostilities, often dating back to childhood, and since they cannot be tolerated in consciousness, they are covered over by feelings of guilt. There is the selection of a vocation and of avocations. There is social responsibility. There is the potentiality of success or failure in life, of happiness or misery, and many other things: The degree of emotional maturity is the measure of the stature and grandeur of the personality or of its insignificance. Indeed, there are more things in the earth of each one of us than are dreamt of in our philosophies.

I have not mentioned sex. Next to self-preservation, it is the most powerful part of the human personality and, indeed, it is a part of self-preservation. Someone once said, "Why all this dither about sex? Animals have a sex life and don't get neurotic about it." In the first place, we are not sure that they may not become neurotic about it. More importantly, human beings are not guinea pigs.

There will be many references to sex in subsequent chapters. From the angle of the past history it is important to know about the first conscious contact with sex. The setting in which it occurred. Whether it was upsetting. The attitude in the home about sex during childhood. Curiosity about sex. When and where sexual information was obtained. Growth of sex interest. Menstrual periods and the preparation given before their appearance. Sexual habits. Masturbation. Sexual fancies and fantasies. Sexual dreams and auto-eroticism. Homosexuality and other sexual deviations. What was the attitude toward marriage? How hard was it to leave parents and home? If married, how old when married? The difference in ages of husband and wife? What was the attitude toward pregnancy and childbirth? And toward contraception? How was the physical and mental health during pregnancy? During labor and afterward? All this, and much more.

Too much ado about sex? Probably not enough. The clinical terrain of the psychoses, psychoneuroses and functional disturbances is criss-crossed by many trails. Not all of them can be followed back to their original sources. But enough of them can be traced that we know without doubt that sex, ignorance and misinformation about it, frustrations, incompletions, fear and guilt very often were the points of departure from the straight road of reasonable adjustment and mental health.

Often very practical clues are revealed by items of historical interest. For instance, if the patient has had a course of treatment, "medicine given into the veins," it might suggest syphilis. Perhaps the mental illness is paresis. Or a history of taking large doses of bromides ("I am afraid much more than the doctor ordered. It quieted my nerves") over a long period of time raises the thought that the symptoms might be largely due to bromide intoxication. A "mental blank" for which the patient is amnesic might mean the "petit mal" of epilepsy. A musician in a great symphony orchestra occasionally "dropped" a few notes. Only the conductor detected it. The musician had petit mal. Or physical symptoms which come and go quickly—blindness, deafness, loss of speech, paralysis, loss of sensation, etc., may prove to be hysteria. And so on.

All in all, the history is far from being a cut and dried affair. "John Smith. Age 29. Father died of stroke at 69. Mother living and well. Had the usual diseases of childhood. No operations. Married. No children. Happy. Now complains of headache."

No! The history should be much more than that. If thoroughly taken and carefully and wisely interpreted, it is a rich mine of information. Particularly in psychiatry has history-taking become a fine art. Perhaps this is because psychiatrists do not have many instruments of precision and, therefore, cannot depend on tests, diagnostic short-cuts or exploratory operations.

Perhaps it may seem that my hypothetical psychiatrist has been so intent upon the history that he has mislaid the body of the patient. There might even be the fear that if he does not soon examine his patients physically, then it might be too late, at least for those patients whose symptoms are due to serious organic conditions, perhaps heart disease. There need be no concern. The patient's body is studied from the very beginning. Sometimes this is done at the first session, at least in preliminary fashion. Many people feel reassured when they see the familiar instruments of the doctor, the clinical thermometer, the stethoscope, the blood-pressure machine, the reflex hammer.

There are many reasons for making a thorough physical examination, which will be stressed later. At this place, it is sufficient to say that no conscientious psychiatrist, or, for that matter, any doctor would think of treating any patient for any condition unless he was familiar with the physical state of the organs of the body.

The examination will be as extensive as the situation requires. It may take weeks, or even longer, and may include many laboratory studies.

Sometimes the physical study may yield direct and conclusive information. Complaints of the patient do not carry labels, "organic" or "functional." Symptoms which at first glance appear to be functional, brought to the surface by unsolved, unconscious mental conflicts, may be the result of many and divers organic diseases, arteriosclerosis, syphilis, intoxications, bodily infections, a great variety of metabolic disturbances.

I remember the case of a patient, a lawyer, fifty-five years old, which almost tripped me. His neurasthenic and hypochondriacal symptoms were so detailed and so complete that I jotted down a notation, "psychoneurosis, neurasthenia." Fortunately I put a question mark after the note. He had a great variety of sensations, pain in the heart, headache, "twitching," spots before the eyes, noises in the ears, insomnia, and so on. Particularly was he tired, worn out. But his fatigue was highly selective. Too tired to take his wife out socially or talk to her, or, "worse," to listen to her conversation. Not too tired to play bridge or golf with the boys, to go to stag parties or to engage in certain extramarital activities. "These things divert me. Make me feel better."

My hasty and unscientific first opinion seemed to be substantiated by an emotional problem, which the patient discussed freely. He was tired of his wife. "She nags." He referred to her unflatteringly as "a boring old frump." (In reality, she was a pleasant, intelligent, long-suffering and rather attractive woman.) He was "in love" with a "beautiful blonde" whose charms he described in detail.

Increasingly he brooded over his symptoms. What did they mean. Heart disease? "Am I going to have a stroke? I know I'm a very sick man." He felt that he should go to a sanitarium at once. "I want to be in close touch with doctors. Suppose I have a heart attack. I might die."

I did make a neurological examination, I am afraid without much thought of turning up anything significant. But when I flashed a pupillary lamp into the eyes, the pupils did not become smaller. They did not change size at all. When I tapped with my reflex hammer the tendon below the knee, the foot kicked up over a wide arc. There were marked tremors of the tongue. And many other signs.

I ordered examinations of the blood and spinal fluid. They

were both strongly positive—syphilis of the brain. The patient did not have neurasthenia. He had paresis.

No psychiatrist is so skillful, so experienced, so penetrating in his diagnostic vision that he dare neglect the examination of the bodies of his patients.

An experienced, skilled psychiatrist usually can make a mental examination without the patient being aware that his mind is being examined. Asked to recall the experience, the average patient probably would say, "It didn't amount to much. Just sort of a conversation. I guess I did most of the talking." Yet, the examination which seems so easygoing and casual is being carefully directed by the psychiatrist, and he is avoiding certain pitfalls. Above all things, the psychiatrist is not a bristling questionnaire. "What day is this?" "Are you happy?" "Are you sad?" "Are your enemies ganging up on you?" "How much is 35 x 18?" No, not at all. An occasional question, perhaps, and a little leading when the patient is very hesitant but not too much. It is worth repeating that the most satisfactory mental examination results from letting the patient tell his *own* story in his *own* way. Often I say to patients, "Let's forget what your family said; just tell me how you feel about it." The patient will not find the psychiatrist stern, rebuking, judicial in his manner, but, rather, interested, helpful, kindly. Of course, the psychiatrist is studying the patient, but quietly and unobtrusively. And he remembers that the patient is also observing him.

Chimpanzees are not human beings but sometimes they are quite intelligent. A noted animal psychologist prepared a room filled with toys for his highly trained "chimp" whom he was studying. He then tip-toed from the room, softly closing the door behind him and then applied his eye to the keyhole in order to observe how the "chimp" would react, what he would do with the toys. Somewhat to his surprise, he found the eye of the animal peering at him through the keyhole from the other side of the door.

For many years I have been teaching my students to observe carefully. In these days there are so many instruments of precision with which to measure symptoms of illness that we are in some danger of losing our powers of observation. Something like this has happened to our sense of smell. Compared to that of animals, it has atrophied, and in human beings, the brain organ of smell is relatively small. We no longer need a keen sense of smell, with which to detect creatures who might prey upon us. As most of us live our lives, such dangerous animals are safely confined in strong cages in zoos. Unfortunately, those humans who prey upon their fellows have no distinctive odor.

Students of detective fiction may remember that the great Holmes chided Watson since, although he had ascended the stairs in the Baker Street lodgings many times, yet he had never observed how many steps there were. When I taught neurology, I presented an annual clinic of patients to illustrate the gaits due to various brain diseases. I included a blind man, a friend of mine. The students, watching his feet carefully, made all sorts of diagnoses, implicating practically every part of the brain. Not a single student noted the wide open, sightless eyes of the blind man and realized that his stumbling was due to the blindness. They failed to observe.

There is so much to be observed. The general appearance of the patient. Is he well-groomed or untidy? How does he hold himself? Stiffly, tense, nonchalantly? Does he talk much or little? Does he gesture? Are his movements purposeful, in touch with the surroundings? Or aimless? These are only a few of the many things the trained and alert psychiatrist notes and stores in the books of his memory.

Manner of speech has significance. I have learned that sometimes ladies who pour out a veritable cascade of words describing the marvelous virtues of their husbands may be far from satisfied with their marital partners. Shakespeare knew. These ladies protest too much.

Sometimes slips of the tongue have meaning, and, in the psychoses, a tremendous amount of psychiatric information may be acquired even when the patient does not utter a single word.

For instance, there is *negativism*. It is a kind of almost automatic muscular resistance to any attempt on the part of the examiner to move any part of the patient's body. If the finger is placed on the eyelid to raise it, immediately a strong downward pull is encountered.

Then there are *mannerisms*. They are odd, bizarre, exaggerated, over-adorned ways of doing ordinary things. One of my patients salaamed deeply at every third step. Another walked sideways. Another flipped his food into his mouth from the end of his knife.

Catalepsy is an extremely interesting symptom. The arms or legs and even the head may be placed in awkward, strained positions which may be maintained for a long time. Catalepsy has physical, chemical and psychological implications. A drug, bulbocapnine, injected into a cat, makes the animal cataleptic. Mice may run over its belly; but the cat does not move its paws. In deep hypnotism, the subject becomes cataleptic.

Perhaps catalepsy has something to do with perplexity. Mice, who are easily trained, may be conditioned to two distinctively marked apertures. They learn quickly that if they jump through aperture "A," very nice tidbits of food await them. They learn quickly, too, that behind aperture "B" there is an unpleasant wire contrivance which tangles up their legs. So, they won't jump through "B." When the gadget is switched so that "A" becomes "B," they jump hopefully, anticipating food, only to be fooled by the wire trap. So they refuse to jump.

When a current of air is turned upon them, they roll off the platform, circle about it madly, then turn over on their backs in a cataleptic stupor.

A pig was accustomed to a machine which, when the pig pressed a lever, rolled out an apple. But the machine was adjusted so that when the usual lever was pressed there was no apple. There was an unpleasant electric shock. Finally, an apple could be poised on the pig's head, but it was so cataleptic that it would not tilt its head to drop the apple into its mouth. Perplexity? Frustration? Human beings are not pigs, but they do have a good deal in common.

In extreme degrees of catalepsy, there is *cerea* (waxy) *flexibilitus*. The limbs, when put into odd positions, give the impression of being made of wax.

A few years ago, I was presenting a schizophrenic patient to my students. He had an interesting psychosis, and in my teaching enthusiasm, I made many gestures. Suddenly there were peals of laughter from the students. Just behind me stood the patient with a blank expression on his face, vigorously sawing the air with his arms. He was faithfully reproducing my gestures, not because he wanted to mock me, but because he could not do anything else but imitate me. He had a symptom called *echopraxia*. *Echolalia* is imitation of what is said.

Sometimes a patient, although mute, may show *automatic obedience*. Shown a sharp needle and told to protrude the tongue so that the examiner can thrust the needle through it, one may witness the play of the muscles about the mouth to keep the tongue in, yet inevitably it slowly emerges.

Patients may exhibit *psychiatric stupors*. They are stuporous conditions which, as far as can be determined by exhaustive examinations, are not primarily due to bodily disease. Sometimes the stupor is so profound that not only is there no reaction to painful stimuli like a needle thrust, but there seems to be a complete suspension of thought, feeling (emotion) and movement. Stupors often seem to be symbolic of death and the awakening from the stupor symbolic of rebirth. It is interesting that patients are often much improved after emerging from stupors.

The stupor may not be as deep as it seems. At least I gather this from my former patient, Laura, now an oft-cited case. Laura had been stuporous for almost two years. During all this time she was mute, took no food voluntarily and had to be fed through a tube. She lay curled up on her bed in an attitude of complete flexion, her arms folded upon her chest, head down, her knees drawn up almost to her chin. For all the world she looked like a foetus in the womb of the mother. I took a small group of graduate students to her room, demonstrated the patient's attitude and explained to them that this was what Sigmund Freud meant when he said that in certain psychoses the patients in their bodily attitudes were expressing an unconscious wish to return to the mother's womb. A few minutes after I left the room, the head nurse came hurrying after me. She said, "Excuse me, Doctor, Laura has spoken." It was an event. The first speech in two years. I asked, "What did Laura say?" The nurse replied, "Laura said, 'Did you ever hear such damn nonsense in all your life?' "

In a few months, Laura was well and lived the remainder of her life outside a mental hospital.

The stream of thought never ceases to flow. In waking life and in sleep it goes on. Speech is the expression of thought. However, psychiatrists soon come to realize that in all human beings, sick or well, speech is used as much or even more to conceal thinking as to reveal it. I like to think first of a patient's speech in general terms, its amount, its speed, its pressure or force. I like, too, to compare these things to the blood stream as governed by the dominant organ, the heart. In thought and speech, the directing, governing force is the emotions. By no means is this restricted to neuropsychiatry. In normal everyday mental life, the mood is the mainspring of thought and speech. It is the accelerator and the brake. A good, happy mood lubricates thought and usually produces a free flow of speech, enriched by association of ideas. A melancholy mood tends to limit thought and speech and induces a poverty of associated ideas with depressive content.

Incidentally, this is a good place to state and emphasize the fact that *there are no symptoms of psychoses and psychoneuroses which may not be found in miniature in normal mental life*. The difference is in degree and not in kind. Potentially, mentally, like the Colonel's lady and Judy O'Grady, we are all sisters under our skins.

But degree is highly important. For instance, in the thought and speech of many psychoses, there are alterations (not brief, such as might happen to anyone, but long-sustained) which go far beyond, above or below, very generously placed normal limits. For instance, in the excited phase of manic-depressive psychosis, the thoughts and speech of the patient, at the mercy of rapidly shifting emotional reactions, are tossed about like a frail craft in a gale of wind. The patient starts to speak about something, anything, but immediately it is obvious from what he says that his thoughts dart about with lightning-like rapidity, this way and that, stimulated by what he sees and hears and by ideas that crop up from his excited mind. Usually he is never able to complete his thought. This is called *distractibility*.

Of course, many of us in our everyday thinking are somewhat distracted. Rarely is the course of a thought to its goal straight and true like the flight of an arrow. But, usually the distractions are relatively few and we are able to bring a thought to its conclusion in a reasonable time. With the hope

of illustrating the difference between average thought and
speech and that which is psychotic, I have appended a diagram. The unbroken line represents the average normal; the
broken one pathological distractibility. The dots indicate places
at which the current of thought switches at the command of
stimuli picked up from the environment by the special senses,
particularly hearing and sight or dictated by inner thought
stimuli.

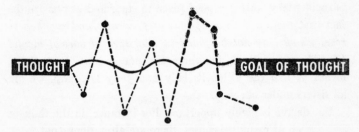

Sometimes distractibility may reach such a peak that speech
sounds like delirium, a salad of words, often only syllables,
disjointed odds and ends of phrases, inarticulate noises. This
extreme of distractibility is called *flight of ideas*.

Strangely enough, the very same manic-depressive patient
so distractible and flighty, may, in a few weeks, scarcely speak
at all. Thought becomes slower and slower like the waters of
a very sluggish stream, and may even dry up into *mutism*.
These depressed patients, when asked a simple question, "Do
you feel any better today?" sometimes delay the answer so
long that one thinks they could not have heard or did not understand. Finally, after a long time, the patient replies in a
simple, low-toned monosyllable, "No." The material which
adorns thought, association of ideas, is temporarily exhausted.

There are many other disorders of thinking and its vehicle,
speech. In schizophrenia, the expression of thoughts appears
like discrete islets upon the surface of the sea of the mind.

lacking connection with each other, *dissociated* thinking. They are connected deep below the surface of the mind, just as islands rising above the sea level are linked together on the floor of the ocean. We can see only the peaks.

Usually, in the same psychosis, schizophrenia, *neologisms* may be encountered. They are "new" words or phrases which have special significance only for the patient. One of my patients complains of the "corines" which produce annoying sensations in his chest. Another speaks of the "dartleroid," a machine which tries to steal his thoughts.

Speech may be garrulous and repetitive. I know an old chap approaching senility who was once a big-game hunter. His friends have heard of his exploits so many times and in such infinite detail that, when they see him approaching, they silently steal away.

In obsessive-compulsive neuroses, patients may be obsessed with one line of thinking and be compelled to speak in a certain way, "against my will." Sometimes this may be very embarrassing. I knew a lady of gentle birth and rearing, who from time to time was compelled to emit a stream of filthy and obscene speech. Finally, she had to eschew all social activities until she recovered.

In conditions of mental confusion or deterioration, the speech may be rambling and hard to follow, and in delirium, it is often incoherent. This does not mean that it is meaningless. Whether it can be penetrated or not, everything a patient does or says has significance.

A noted psychiatrist was examining a woman patient in her bedroom. She seemed quite unco-operative. Her speech consisted of disjointed phrases and she did not answer any questions. The psychiatrist listened more closely and then heard her say and repeat many times, quite distinctly, "rubber ears." At the same time, she looked intently at the bedroom door. His curiosity aroused, he walked to the door and opened it softly. To his amazement, the patient's husband was standing there. Obviously he had been eavesdropping.

The internist would not be satisfied merely with knowing the speed and pressure of the patient's blood stream. He must know much more than that. So he takes samples of the blood and examines it in test tubes and under the microscope for its coloring matter, not only the number of red and white blood cells, but their size and shape, to see if they are distorted by disease, poisons in the blood and many other things. So, too, is the psychiatrist not content with merely observing the stream of thought in a general way. He, too, wants to know what is in it. And whether its content is abnormal. Many interesting things may be found. Illusions, hallucinations, delusions, ideas of reference, obsessions and compulsions are only a few of them.

Illusions are common enough in normal everyday life. I suppose I am not the only person who, trusting to the evidence of my eyes alone, would believe firmly that the magician actually did pull the rabbits from the ears of someone in the audience. Alone in a house at night, one may readily mistake the noise of a prowling cat for a burglar; in a forest, the bare limbs of a tree for a skeleton, the rustling leaves for the stealthy approach of a beast of prey.

There is a famous haunted house in Sussex. A gentleman wagered £100 that he would sleep one night in the ghost-ridden chamber of the haunted house. He placed a loaded revolver under the pillow, went to bed and promptly fell asleep. At about two A.M., he awoke with a start. By the pale light of the moon filtering in through the casement window, he saw a white, ghostly, shaking hand at the foot of the bed. Trembling with fear, he grasped his revolver, aimed, pulled the trigger and shot off his own big toe.

It is obvious that illusions are deceptions by our senses, shaped and activated by moving emotional reactions.

Illusions are common in many psychoses. They may be seen in pure culture and they reach their crescendo in alcoholic delirium tremens. Here, with the background of stark, naked terror, the patient screams, attempts to hide his head and begs for protection from the horrible, ravenous animals and huge insects which he sees swarming up the side of the bed and over the bedclothes, seeking to devour him.

Perhaps the basic difference between the "normal" illusions of everyday life and those of the mentally sick is that in the former, when logical proof is furnished, usually the illusory-founded belief is relinquished. I understand, and indeed the magician explains it is a trick, so I know rabbits are not being pulled out of someone's ears. When, during daylight and with quieted emotions, the tree in the forest is examined, it is seen readily enough that what looked like a skeleton was merely the limbs of the tree divested of foliage by winter's frost and winds. And so on. But the mentally sick do not so readily abandon their illusions and hallucinations. Even when no one else can hear the "scratching noise" at the door, the patient not only hears it but clearly distinguishes the whispered voices of his "enemies" plotting to cut his throat. And, even though it is demonstrated that it is merely a shadow upon the wall cast by a piece of furniture, the patient still insists it is the Virgin, miraculously appearing before him to tell him of the great mission he is to perform on earth.

For some unknown reason, novelists commonly write "hallucination" when they mean "delusion." "He suffered from the hallucination that he was Napoleon." That would be a delusion. A delusion is a gross false belief of which more anon. A *hallucination* is a sensory deception. Hallucinations are very closely akin to illusions, in fact, I believe so closely akin that they are the same. The difference is largely theoretical. Illusions have a stimulus or starting point in one or more of the senses. Something is actually seen or heard, but the sound or sight is misinterpreted, as it were, metamorphosed, perhaps into "an angel sent from heaven" or "the voice" of the plotting enemy.

In a hallucination, it is assumed that the process is entirely imaginary, without any sensory foundation whatsoever, no starting point of initiation in hearing, sight, smell, touch or taste. This I do not credit. For one thing, we have more than five senses. There is the muscle-joint sense which helps us maintain our position in space, the vibratory sense, the sensations which penetrate our consciousness from the various organs of the body, etc. Because we cannot always run down the sensation which is misinterpreted is scarcely sufficient reason for the assumption that there was no sensation. Some years ago, I studied a group of patients who believed they had various animals, snakes or insects in their stomachs. The "proof" of these delusions were carefully described sensations: the animals scratched, sucked, clawed and bit—hallucinations. Careful laboratory studies revealed inflammatory conditions of the stomach, and decreased amounts of hydrochloric acid. I believe the misinterpreted sensations came from these conditions.

Hallucinations, like illusions, may occur in practically any psychosis, with the exception of paranoia. They are particularly prominent in toxic-delirious states and in schizophrenia.

I promised to say more about delusions. I shall do so descriptively, reserving for another place a discussion of how delusions are formed and shaped.

It is not enough to say that a delusion is a false belief—even a gross false belief. Many people (even psychiatrists) tenaciously cling to obviously erroneous doctrines, even in the face of irrefutable evidence that they are wrong. Yet they cannot be labeled delusional off-hand, and this is particularly true if many people subscribe to the same belief. Someone said, "No man is happy without a delusion of some kind—delusions are as necessary to happiness as realities." Theoretically, fine-spun arguments about the difference between mistaken opinions and delusions might be indefinitely continued. Practically, however, psychiatrists usually are not puzzled. When a patient pulls down a forelock of hair, drapes his arm across his chest, and says, "I am Napoleon Bonaparte," there is not much room for argument.

There is a great variety of delusions, and they may involve anything ever conceived of by the mind of man, anything upon earth, beneath the earth or in the heavens above. Perhaps at one end of the scale are grandiose delusions. Said one of my patients, who had paresis, "I am the strongest man in the world and the richest. I own all the diamond and ruby mines. Everything belongs to me. Even the planets. I have 10,000 wives and millions of children." (Why multiple wives and innumerable children should be regarded as a blessing is difficult for me to understand.) It is said that de Maupassant lovingly regarded the pebbles on the paths of the grounds of the sanitarium in which he was a patient as his children.

At the nadir of the scale are delusions which belittle the patient. A sweet little old lady begged to have the doors and windows of her room sealed since she was "only a small mite of dust." She feared that a puff of wind would blow her away. Many patients deny their own existence.

Once I made a study of depressive and self-blameful delusions and found in many of them an interesting touch of the grandiose. A woman who believed she had sinned beyond redemption and would be horribly punished as she deserved (so she said) used to tell frequently how she would be boiled to death in a kettle, but always she specified that the kettle would be made of solid gold!

Sometimes delusions may be curiously prophetic. A long time ago in New York, I saw in consultation a prominent financier. He was pacing up and down his library, tremendously tense and anxious, in a panic of fear. Suddenly, he stopped before me and shouted, "Why, Doctor, I tell you we will even go off the gold standard." This was years before such a possibility had been seriously considered.

It might be objected that since we actually did go off the gold standard, this was scarcely a delusion. But it was. The premises from which the conclusion was drawn were quite fallacious and psychotic.

So, too, one of my alcoholic patients attempted to murder his wife because she was "unfaithful." Actually, the wife *was* unfaithful. But the "proofs" the alcoholic husband adduced were delusional. "Voices" told him about it. Odds and ends of trash which had been in the house for years, and imaginary footprints on dust-free floors were his "clues," left there by his wife's lover. He could smell cigar smoke, proving that "he" had hurriedly departed just before the husband came home. He detected the odor of the hair tonic which "he uses" on the pillow of his wife's bed. And so on. Actually, his wife's lover did not smoke at all and had never been in the patient's home. While the wife was untrue, yet the husband was as delusional as though she had been faithful. Perhaps almost as delusional as a patient 83 years old who stealthily followed his wife, 81 years old, every time she left the house, because of an unshakable belief that she was on her way to a house of assignation!

It is hard to believe, as will be developed at another place, that these and many other extravagant delusions have roots in common with many false opinions such as we ourselves hold and which may be highly respected in the market place.

Ideas of reference attach undue and usually erroneous significance to casual happenings and incidents. They have their counterpart in everyday life. Many people who are not at all mentally sick read into a slight change in someone's facial expression, the shrug of a shoulder, a small gesture, the intonation of a voice, meanings that were not intended. And they may worry needlessly: "I wonder what he meant by that."

It is not at all unusual for women to remark, "I knew by the look in her eyes that she knew just what I paid for this hat and I could tell she didn't like it." And they may be right.

The ideas of reference of the mentally sick step far beyond these "normal" limits. Literally anything in the environment —routine things like the voice of a radio announcer or a commercial or a newspaper advertisement or a book a fraction of an inch out of place on the shelf—is grist for the mill of the sick mind and is endowed with elaborate hidden meanings. They are "warnings," "signals" to the "gang" to get ready to "close in on me," signs of derision attempting to "third degree me," "broadcasting their lies that I am a sexual pervert." As one would expect, ideas of reference are quite common in paranoid psychoses.

Obsessions are dominations of the personality by a thought, which literally takes possession of the mind and cannot be exorcised. "No matter what I do or how hard I try, I can't drive the thought of death out of my head."

Compulsions dictate behavior which cannot be inhibited even though the patient may try strenuously to control his actions. Thus, an intelligent gentleman, certainly a sane and sound man, *had* to hop over every thirteenth step even though he fully recognized the futility and silliness of his compulsive act. Another patient, a poor working girl, was *compelled* to walk at least a mile out of her way to and from work in order to avoid passing a florist shop. Obsessions, compulsions and *phobias* or fears, which dictate all sorts of bizarre behavior and avoidances (fears of being alone, of crowds, of riding in any moving conveyance, of dirt and germs, etc., etc.) may determine very elaborate rituals of conduct.

Johnson, who loved to walk along the roads and lanes of rural England, was compelled to tap every fence post he passed with his stick. Often he tried to pass one untapped, but he suffered so much physically and mentally that he was forced to retrace his steps, find the post he had missed, and tap it. As soon as he did this, his symptoms—sweating, rapidly beating heart, trembling and anxiety—disappeared like magic.

I had a patient, an able-minded and successful executive, who until he recovered was compelled to go through a most elaborate ritual each night before retiring. Every article of clothing he removed had to be folded and put away "just so." He had to bring out each piece of clothing he was to wear the next day, arrange and place it, again "just so." His shoes had to be under the edge of the bed, on an even line, which he aligned with a ruler, many, many times. The rituals often consumed two or more hours and made his life burdensome. Before he could sleep, he would get out of bed as many as a dozen times, and inspect every bit of clothing to see that it was precisely placed.

Obsessions, compulsions, phobias are cover-up or camouflaging symptoms. Strange as it may seem, they protect the ego and represent on the part of the patient an unconscious choice of the lesser of two evils. The greater evil would be the appearance in consciousness of the material which has been repressed or pushed behind the portals of what is remembered. If such material suddenly reappeared in the memory it would be a calamity for the personality. However, the obsessions, compulsions, phobias, etc., are hostages to the present, symbols of what is for the time being, at least, safely tucked away beneath the blanket of the "forgotten," protectively forgotten because the person could not live psychologically with the memory of it, without great distress.

In a broad sense, obsessions, compulsions and phobias are part of a heavy burden of ignorance and superstitions which human beings have carried from the time of those dim ages, long before the dawn of recorded history. Every man worships at the altars of some strange gods. Each one of us has a pet superstition. Perhaps it is Friday when it falls on the 13th day of the month, or lighting three cigarettes from one match or walking under a ladder or spilling salt or the assurance that comes from knocking on wood. Of course, we don't believe such foolishness, but it is just as well not to take a chance! From time immemorial, children coming home from school have played the game of "last tag" and "not stepping on the crack." Dire calamities are in store for that youngster who is tagged last or who steps on a pavement crack.

The emotions have been sufficiently headlined so that it is easy to understand that a reasonably accurate determination of the state of the emotional life is *the important* part of the examination. The emotions are the very life-giving essence, the animating, activating principle of the human personality. Frequently, upon their condition, their viability, their energy, the degree of their survival in the psychosis, there rests the verdict for or against the patient's recovery. In mental disease, every shading of emotional life is portrayed, from exhilaration of such a degree that it seems to be at the very peak of human happiness to depression so deep that the agony of mind is beyond description. In profound dementia, such as is sometimes seen in very severe senile psychoses, the emotions practically die. That old person is no longer responsive to personal or public events, even though they be direful calamities causing widespread suffering. In the psychoneuroses and functional disturbances, there is usually anxiety.

It might be restated that a good way *not* to arrive at a satisfactory conclusion about a patient's emotional state is to assail him with a barrage of questions: "Are you happy?" "Are you depressed?" "Are you irritable?" That is not the way we determine the emotional condition of our friends. Without asking a host of queries, we are often acutely sensitized to the fact that they are happy or blue, irritable, bored, ashamed, angry, jealous, scornful, worried, distrustful, frightened, etc. Sometimes, in a small intimate social group or in the family circle, a sensible person will admonish the too-eager questioners: "Don't bother Bill, anyone can see he is upset about something."

How do we read the emotional barometers of our friends? In much the same way that the psychiatrist reads those of his patients. He judges by such things as the facial expression, the attitude, the gestures, many other things. Particularly are the eyes significant. "The eyes are the windows of the soul" is trite, but true. The intonation and cadence of the voice may be more revealing than the spoken words. Perhaps you have heard someone who was in the grip of a blue mood say, "Oh, yes, I'm happy, *very happy*." You knew at once from the tone of voice that he was very miserable.

Of course, the psychiatrist is a trained observer. He readily notes such signs as pallor or flushing, sweating, dilatation of the pupils, throbbing of the blood vessels of the neck, clenched fists, rapid, shallow breathing, etc. And he can supplement his observations by various examinations, such as blood-pressure readings.

I have heard people say that they would be afraid to go to a psychiatrist; he would be sure to find something. "Just like

the eye specialists. You never come away without glasses."
Actually, psychiatrists are quite pleased when they find that
nothing much is wrong. For one thing, they all have more work
than they want. In the matter of the emotions, as elsewhere,
much more leeway may be expected from a psychiatrist than
from the average lay person.

Before the emotions can be labeled "sick" it is necessary
that the reaction has continued for a reasonably long period of
time. In almost everyone's life, there may be found isolated
instances of murderous rage or jealousy, depression with a few
suicidal thoughts, deep but passing suspicions. If they have
strong reasons in back of them, are relatively brief and are not
translated into serious behavior, then often they mean very
little.

We are so accustomed to the accommodations of our consciousness (sensorium); it orients us so correctly in space; it
is so prompt in furnishing us with the evidence by which we
recognize ourselves and our friends; and it is so unfailing in
giving us accurate time bearings and relationships that we seldom remember that the binding threads of consciousness are
readily severed. Normally, they are parted by sleep, when the
conscious mind is in abeyance. So, too, when a general anaesthetic is administered. Likewise in hypnotism. Fever, intoxications and infections cloud consciousness. So do deteriorations
due to brain diseases.

When the consciousness is impaired for one reason or another, we can no longer depend upon it to receive and interpret correctly the messages from the outside world brought by
the special senses. Then we are *disoriented,* either partially or
completely. No longer are we able to place ourselves accurately
in space. No longer can we clearly recognize our friends, even
our relatives. We might even be uncertain about ourselves. No
longer are we sure of time, of the day, month or even year. In

short, we are at sea, loosed from our conscious moorings, disoriented. And so, too, are many patients disoriented, notably in the toxic and organic psychoses.

Edwards wrote of memory, "The secret of a good memory is attention, and attention to a subject depends upon our interest in it. We rarely forget that which makes a deep impression on our minds."

By no means is this constantly true. Each one of us has repressed things that happened to us, particularly during childhood, things too painful to remember. It would shame and belittle us to have them openly before us on the table of consciousness. It is much more comfortable to live without them. This kind of active, purposeful forgetting is *amnesia.* Functional amnesia* is a gap in the memory, usually involving a limited span of time. The remembrance of what occurred during a certain time period is blotted from the memory because it cannot be faced in memory without too great anxiety and distress. Often, in functional illness, it becomes necessary for the psychiatrist to part the veils of consciousness, so that he and the patient may together view the repressed material and that the patient may learn to live with it in comfort.

Sometimes it is the remote memory that is impaired, sometimes the recent memory, things that happened perhaps only a few minutes before. This is very likely to occur in old people, who are forever "losing" their spectacles, or even their teeth.

There are many interesting memory disturbances. In a condition called Korsakoff's psychosis, sometimes found in alcoholics, particularly when there has been a deprivation of vitamins, there may be *falsification of memory*. Events which possibly did occur in the past are woven into the present.

---

* There is a variety of amnesia which is organic, due to brain injury, or disease. It is usually permanent.

I was demonstrating such a patient to my students. Because of his illness he had been bedridden for months, was emaciated and his muscles were so wasted that he could not move his legs. Thinking to bring out memory falsification, I said, "Where were you last night?" Somewhat to my embarrassment, the patient replied promptly, "You know where we were, Doc. Atlantic City, of course. Don't you remember all the night clubs we visited? And the girls. I think you liked the little, fat blonde one the best."

Often it is advisable for the psychiatrist to test the counting and calculation capacity of the patient, his writing, spontaneously, by dictation and from copy, the degree of attention, school and general knowledge and familiarity with current events. All of these tests can be made without being too mysterious about it and without too much formality. Either attitude may frighten a mental patient or make him suspicious.

In making these tests the psychiatrist has in mind the intellectual equipment and educational background of the patient. He would not carry out his examination on the same level for a patient who had had only two or three years' schooling and for a Phi Beta Kappa.

If there is reason to think that the intelligence of the patient is subnormal or less, then the intelligence level may be accurately measured by a selection from a large series of tests.

Often special studies and examinations add very helpful information. There are word-association tests, the Rorschach, hypnosis, sodium pentothal interviews, dream analysis and many others. These are "uncovering" techniques. In other words, they are designed to uncover, gain access to material in the unconscious mind of the patient, material of which the patient is not consciously aware and, therefore, cannot reveal clearly to the psychiatrist in the usual interview. Sometimes this material is called "conflictual," since it has to do with the nature of the hidden mental conflict. Often is it necessary to bring it up from the depths into the daylight of consciousness, so that it can be viewed and studied and helpful treatment may be devised.

All in all, as the patient tells his story and his troubles, there come under the focus of the psychiatrist's trained observation, understanding and interpretation, the abnormal constituents in the stream of thought. They have much significance for the psychiatrist, as much significance as do the distorted and diseased blood cells and other evidence in the blood stream as it is viewed and studied by the internist.

4 | THE ORGANIC PSYCHOSES

THE CELLS, fibres and tissues of the brain are tough and resistant, made to withstand terrific assaults. But they can be seriously and permanently damaged and even destroyed. Their destruction is final. In man, the brain cannot heal and resume its function as do the skin, muscles and other parts of the body. There is another grave hazard. In the comparatively small area of the brain, weighing on the average only about 1300 to 1500 grams, there is concentrated the representation of all the functions of the body and mind. An area of destruction, so small that in many other parts of the body it would be inconsequential, in certain places in the brain, would have very serious consequences. There may result blindness or deafness, paralysis, loss of sensation, aphasia, in which the word needed to express a thought in the mind cannot be uttered, or perhaps a simple request like, "Put out your tongue," is not comprehended. There may be serious interference with a lowering of mental capacity—thinking and judgment; this is one reason why the outlook for complete recovery of the patient who has organic mental disease is not very bright. The result is very apt to be some degree of deterioration or dementia, and "dementia" defines an uncompromising situation. It implies a downward step in mental functioning which cannot be retraced.

Even though in the organic psychoses, more often than not, the psychiatrist can scarcely hope to cure his patients, yet he can speak with considerable assurance about causation. His scientific position here is as strong as in any field of medicine. Often he can predict with accuracy just what will be found in the brain after death, at autopsy and under the microscope.

I could glibly recite the "causes" of many of the organic psychoses and somewhat convincingly prove the list. I could say truly enough that the symptoms of paresis cannot appear unless the brain has been invaded by the spirochete of syphilis, nor senile and arteriosclerotic psychoses without old age changes in the tissues of the brain, and notably hardening of its blood-vessel walls, nor the valid symptoms of brain tumor without the actual growth in the brain.

This would be correct, but it would leave too much unsaid. We would be left with too many perplexing questions on our hands. Here are a few: Of all the many people who contract syphilis, why does only a relatively small number, less than 5 per cent, develop the mental disease, paresis? How significant is old age in the production of senile psychoses? Some people show mental deterioration in their fifties, but I know a lady of eighty-seven who is bright and alert, with very little memory failure, and I have known many other very old people who were quite clear-minded. Indeed, comparatively young people, even in their early forties, may show advanced dementia—so-called presenile dementia. Why is it, too, that sometimes in brain tumor there are prominent mental symptoms, in other tumor patients, none at all? The mental symptoms do not give a great deal of help in determining the location of the tumor within the brain.

In World War I, in the campaign in Mesopotamia, a British officer was shot through the frontal lobes by a machine-gun bullet. He made a good recovery, but soon after he ran off with a brother officer's wife. Before this he had been the soul of honor, subscribing to and living according to a very high moral code. A group of London neurologists presented this case as proof that man's ethical function, his moral sense, resides in the frontal lobes of the brain. But an eminent neurologist objected, "I am not convinced, since no proof has been advanced that there was anything wrong with the lady's frontal lobes."

So, one cannot afford to be glib about causation in the organic psychoses. We do know the principal reason, the spirochete in the brain, the hardening of the brain blood vessels or what not, but that is far from being the whole answer. Much more than that must be worked out. This is true in every area of medicine. To say that the bacillus of Koch is the cause of tuberculosis is right enough, but it leaves much unsaid.

Perhaps we can define an organic psychosis as one which cannot occur unless there are pathological changes in the brain structure. This does not mean that when there are pathological changes it is inevitable that there be mental symptoms. A friend of mine, an eminent neurologist and psychiatrist, studied the brains of twenty old people. Ten had had definite mental symptoms during life. Ten had had no mental symptoms. There was just as much pathology in the brains of those who had been free of mental symptoms as in the ones who had been mentally sick.

In addition to paresis, senile psychoses and brain tumor, there are many more organic brain diseases in which mental symptoms may occur—brain hemorrhage, thrombus or plugging of a brain blood vessel followed by softening of the brain tissue supplied by the vessel, meningitis, inflaming diseases like encephalitis (sleeping sickness) which, after the inflammation has subsided, may leave in its wake a path of damaged brain tissue, injuries to the brain, Huntington's Chorea, which is not St. Vitus' Dance, but a very serious chorea of adult life which runs in families and in which eventually there is very profound dementia, etc. I include epilepsy, even though it has not been finally determined whether it is primarily due to structural or toxic factors.

The mental symptoms—the clinical pictures patients show in the organic psychoses, not only what they think, say and do but how they think, speak and act—are the result of three pressures:

1. The pressure of the havoc wrought in the brain by the disease and the impairment of mind function resulting;

2. The pressure from each individual's personality.

Almost always some previous personality traits survive the holocaust. I have noted in many old people with mental symptoms, even in those whose defective memories restricted them to a small orbit of daily life, without personal, time and space connections, that some remnant of previous personality traits still remain in their manner. In other words, those who earlier in life, when the tide was at its flood, were amiable and gentle are apt still to be sweet and mild in their old age, when the tides of physical and mental life are at their ebb. Those who when young were mean, irritable and suspicious are likely to be meaner, more crotchety and more suspicious in their senile mental enfeeblements. Once in a sanitarium, I asked two old ladies with senile dementia the day of the week and the date. One said, "I'm ashamed I can't remember. Is it all right?"; the other, "None of your damned business. Find out for yourself."

Too rarely do any of us remember that all through our lives

and the way we live them, we are weaving the patterns for the kind of old age we are going to have.

3. Too often, the significance of the pressure from the environment in shaping the symptoms is disregarded. The environment, that is, the people in contact with the patient who has an organic mental disorder almost never understand and carry out intelligent and helpful programs. One mistaken attitude is that of oversympathy. No matter how outrageously the patient behaves, it is overlooked and even encouraged. "Poor Granny, she has nothing left in her life. Let her do whatever she wants." Not only is this bad for the environment, but also it is not good for the patient. Almost never is a person completely without some degree of capacity to learn a few simple lessons of habit and behavior, particularly in the early stages of the mental illness. Learned and established then, they will serve to make life much more bearable for the patient and those who look after him.

The environment, again the people in it, too often are totally indifferent toward the patient and sometimes even cruel. They act toward him as though he were in a vacuum, totally cut off from every human interest and desire. Negatively, in their attitude they pay no attention at all to the sick person. Positively, they make unpleasant remarks about him in his presence, plainly show their annoyance at the least trouble he makes for them, threaten to put him "away" and, all in all, make it very clear they heartily wish they were rid of him. Naturally, the mentally confused patient becomes more confused and blindly hostile, and unconsciously he retaliates by behaving worse. I have seen some old people in whom the idea that they were being poisoned by their families had some foundation. They were being poisoned, not by drugs, but psychologically.

In many areas and not always among those who are at a

low cultural level, the general social attitude is cruel beyond
words. This is still notably true in epilepsy. Too often, the
epileptic is socially stigmatized; the mark of the outcast, the
untouchable, is put upon his brow. I have wondered whether
in some people this archaic attitude did not represent an inner
fear that they, themselves, might become afflicted and that
the gods will be so impressed by their condemnation of others
that they will withhold the curse from them.

Perhaps this symbolic diagram will illustrate the effect of
the three pressures, the brain disease (— — — — —), the personality (•••••••••••) and environment (ₒₒₒₒₒₒₒₒ), in producing and distorting the condition of the patient with organic
mental disease.

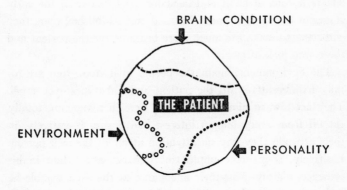

Obviously, it would not be possible to describe all the organic mental disorders. It is not necessary. There is a pattern
which holds true. It does vary in degree. There may be merely
a slight reduction in mental capacity and judgment, scarcely
perceptible, excepting that the person becomes rather bore-
some and a bit repetitive in conversation. At the other end of
the pole the patient may have a well-nigh complete abolition
of all the mental faculties with such complete deterioration

that he knows little more than his own name and not always that.

1. *Causation.* That part of the cause residing in the brain disease is usually clear-cut and ascertainable by various examinations, physical, neurological, studies of the brain waves, x-ray, blood, spinal fluid, etc.

The careful physician, in obscure cases, at least, before he decides that the condition is functional, that is, due to unsolved mental conflicts, exhausts the information to be gained from examinations. Even after careful studies, an occasional mistake may occur.

An Irish servant girl, a devout Catholic, suffered from convulsions which certainly looked like epilepsy. However, since thorough examinations revealed nothing, and since the convulsions occurred only on Fridays and were always ushered in by the patient's smelling burning meat, it was decided that the condition was hysteria. The patient died in a convulsion and post-mortem examination revealed a tumor in the smelling lobe of the brain.

2. *Mental Capacity.* Generally there is a history of personality change, followed by increasing weakness of memory, especially for things that just happened. This is the stage of mislaying all sorts of articles, so annoying to the patient and his relatives. The patient becomes less prompt and less secure in following the passage of time and in placing himself accurately in regard to people he knows and to familiar surroundings. Judgment becomes very much impaired. The details of a situation may be recognized accurately, but the conclusion arrived at may be astonishingly false. An old gentleman who for years had gone each day to the public library stopped his visits because he noticed that when he entered the reading room, the people were all reading intently. He felt that this signified they were no longer interested in him, didn't care

what happened to him and would rather he stayed away. The niceties of social situations are no longer appreciated. A man in the midst of a conversation with several friends suddenly and noticeably wet himself. Such an accident might occur, but the mental deterioration was revealed by the fact that he was not in the least embarrassed. It was the beginning of paresis. Commonly, in those who had been careful and even fastidious, there is increasing carelessness in dress, spots all over the clothes, buttons left unbuttoned, unkempt hair, unpolished shoes, dirty nails and hands, etc.

3. *Emotional Reactions.* The emotional reactions seem to be foreshortened, losing in depth but spread out in thin, shallow fashion. Patients may become violently angry or weep profusely because of some trivial happening. One man "raised the roof" with a storm of vehemence and abuse because his daughter-in-law said she might vote for one of the Democratic candidates in a local election. He had always been a Republican.

The horizon of the emotional life retreats more and more as the mental capacity decreases. With the restriction of interests on the outside, the self assumes even greater significance than is usual, and that is saying a great deal. Family calamities and public catastrophes are apt to elicit only a minor chord of emotional response. But anything pertaining to the self may call out a major emotional reaction, as in a patient who flew into a violent rage, smashing the dinner dishes, because his coffee cup had not been filled to the brim. *He* wanted it that way, even though he invariably slopped it over the table cloth.

4. *Ethical Behavior.* The ethical and moral level is in some degree lowered by the brain damage and resultant deterioration. This is serious. A man or woman who has led a long life of constructiveness, integrity and honor may, because of the weakening of inhibition in an organic psychosis, undo it all in

a few weeks, not only dissipating his material resources, but dishonoring himself and disgracing his family. Sexual advances in public, perverted practices and indecent exposure before children are not uncommon. In the early stages, the patient may become the victim of unscrupulous "gold diggers" of the opposite sex. The last scene of the play of life may be a sad, sorry spectacle.

A man I knew who had great wealth and had led a fine, constructive and philanthropic life, at the age of 87 was almost victimized by an unscrupulous female servant. In fact, the attending physician and the family, by good fortune, intercepted a marriage which in an hour more would have been a *fait accompli*. The woman had almost fastened the bonds of marriage around his fortune, by flattering his mythical sexual prowess.

Sometimes, organic mental patients make wills which they never would have thought of making in their right minds. Members of the family, perhaps sons and daughters who have loved them unselfishly and been devoted to their interests, may be cut off without a penny and the money left to some adventuress or unscrupulous gigolo or for some dubious purpose, like a home for indigent cats.

It is not only expensive to try to break a will, but often it is impossible. The time to break a wrong will is when it is made. The opinion of one or more honest, competent psychiatrists, carefully recorded, will at some future time mean much more to the Judge Surrogate than hypothetical opinions of psychiatrists who did not know the patient when he was alive.

5. *Decreased Tolerance to Alcohol and Drugs*. With a brain whose function is handicapped by organic damage, the personality is much more vulnerable to alcohol and narcotic drugs. Even in small amounts they may produce confusion and even

mild delirium. Sometimes this is taken advantage of by black-mailers. A man in the early stages of arteriosclerotic deterioration was induced to go to their hotel room by "a nice man and his wife" who had picked an acquaintance with him in the hotel lobby. In the room, the man treated him to a couple of drinks. Then the "husband" made an excuse and left the room, saying he would return shortly. When he did return, the "wife" was in tears, her clothing was torn and disarranged and between sobs she said she had been sexually assaulted. The patient was so confused by the alcohol he had taken that he said he did not know what had happened. He thought he had fallen into a doze. Fortunately, the couple had a police record and were frightened off by the family attorney.

I have sketched a pattern of the organic psychoses; purposely a little worse than the average picture, but still far from being extreme. When the throne of the brain is shaken and weak, there is likely to be chaos of its subject functions.

Paresis. On the basis of admission to public mental hospitals, paresis and other brain syphilis account for about 10 per cent of mental diseases. Of course, paresis cannot occur without the presence of the living spirochete of syphilis in the brain. The spirochete in the brain looks something like this:

This fact is far from sufficient to enable us to write Q.E.D. after the problem of paresis. It is to be repeated that only a comparatively few of the many thousands who contract syphilis develop paresis. It may be added that certain areas of the brain must be invaded and become diseased before paresis results. Other parts of the central nervous system may be attacked, producing a picture with or without mental symptoms, for instance, the meninges of the brain (syphilitic meningitis), or the spinal cord (locomotor ataxia). But these are not paresis. In certain parts of the world, French Indo-China and other places, syphilis was rampant, but the natives rarely developed paresis. However, colonial settlers were not immune. The North American Indian had syphilis long before Columbus discovered this continent, but apparently did not become paretic until his white brother persuaded him to live on reservations, in hogans instead of tepees, and sent him to school and college. On plantations, syphilis was widespread among the Negro, but paresis did not make its appearance until he began to live in urban centers and partake of industrialization. Now paresis is as common in the Negro as in the white man. Is it true, perhaps, that paresis is one of the penalties we pay for our highly geared, competitive industrial civilization?

It has been asserted, but certainly not proven, that there may be certain strains of the organism of syphilis which not only convey syphilis, but also carry the potentiality of paresis. I know of one authentic record which would seem to lend some color to this theory. Three sailors on the same night visited a house of prostitution in Hamburg and consorted with the same prostitute. All three contracted syphilis and, some ten years later, all three became paretic. But one case is not enough to make fact out of theory, any more than one swallow makes a summer.

The living spirochete lies dormant in the body for a long time, anywhere from eight months to thirty years (average, about fifteen years) before it makes its trek to the brain. What determines this migration, and what biological law and factors in the particular individual determine the spirochete to etch in the brain the pattern which means paresis?

Is it the strain and stress of modern civilization? Is it alcohol? Perhaps nutritional disorders with insufficient vitamins? Or, perhaps head injury? These and other factors may be influential, but we do not know.

The modern physician bases the diagnosis of paresis on a triad of symptoms:

A. Physical and neurological signs;

B. Mental symptoms;

C. The examination of the blood and spinal fluid.

The neurological signs are interesting. In many, but by no means all patients, there may be such signs as loss of expression in the face, a kind of "washed-out" appearance, differences in the size and shape of the pupils of the eyes, sometimes with failure to react to light but with normal reaction when the vision is accommodated to distance; shuffling gait, tremors, very much increased tendon reflexes, as in the exaggerated upward kick of the foot when the knee tendon is tapped, tremulous handwriting, often with mistakes in spelling and omissions of words and phrases; perhaps convulsions. The convulsion, which may be the first outward sign of paresis, may be exactly like the convulsion of epilepsy or an apoplectic stroke and, occasionally, may be mistaken for them.

In some patients the speech is thick and slurred. Sometimes test phrases are used to detect the slurring—like, "Round the rugged rock the ragged rascal ran." I had an associate who was very enthusiastic about test phrases, and spent considerable time contriving "tongue twisters" of ever-increasing complexity. However, he abandoned the practice, when after exhibiting some of the phrases he had invented before his students, his own tongue became so badly twisted that he slurred his speech as much as any paretic patient.

The mental symptoms of paresis are far from being uniform. Early in the psychosis there are apt to be irritability and a general slowing of mental processes, with faults of memory and capricious errors in judgment. Preoccupation with bodily functions and overconcern about them, a clinical picture closely resembling neurasthenia, a functional neurosis, may be the most prominent early symptom. Such a case was cited in an earlier chapter.

As the disease progresses, the mental symptoms become more characteristic, but I should say characteristic for the person who has the paresis, rather than of the paresis itself. Somehow the general public, and often medical students, have the idea that every paretic patient is grandiose, has mental pockets lined with gold, uranium and priceless gems, with an unlimited supply of beautiful and good-natured wives and myriads of attractive children, and with such physical and mental prowess that on one day the patient can easily win the heavyweight boxing championship and the next day preside with distinction at a United Nations conference. Some paretic patients believe they have and can do all these things, but many more do not. The patient may be tearful and depressed, filled with self-blame for imaginary wrongdoing, perhaps harboring gross bodily delusions: stomach sealed or the head filled with sawdust instead of brains or suspicions with delusions of being hounded and persecuted by a ruthless gang of enemies. These and many other clinical pictures derive their colorings not from the paresis, but from the previous personality pigments of the patient. If there is a distinctive mental coloring, it is the drab gray dementia, from the engulfing of all the mental faculties. Eventually this may so degrade the mind and personality that the patient is more vegetative than human.

Each year I present an "X" Clinic to my medical students. They are far enough along in their studies so that they are able to recognize the various forms of mental disease. I give the histories and demonstrate the mental symptoms. The students are not familiar with the result of the physical or laboratory examinations. One patient may be a man eighty or more years old, obviously demented. He does not know he is in a hospital, says the year is 1880, that Theodore Roosevelt is President. His memory is so defective that he does not remember having had breakfast less than thirty minutes before. The students promptly diagnose senile dementia.

The next patient is forty years old, one-half the age of the first patient, and yet, he is even more deeply deteriorated. He has no idea of the day, date or year and vaguely ventures that it is summer, although it is snowing outside the clinic window. He has been in the hospital six months but has never been able to find his bed at night. Five years before he was in an automobile accident, sustaining a fractured skull and being unconscious for two hours. The majority of the students diagnose "Mental Deterioration due to Head Injury." A few think it is "Pre-senile Dementia."

The next patient is a boy nine years old. Since he could not progress beyond the first grade, cannot add 2 and 3, cannot spell "house" and says vaguely that this is "Merica," the students agree that he is an imbecile.

The next patient, a woman twenty-five years old, is in a state of great physical and mental excitement. She is here, there and everywhere in the clinic amphitheater, gesticulating dramatically, impersonating a grand-opera singer, but very badly, profane in her speech and signaling out the students for critical and lewd remarks. Her thoughts seem to travel with the speed of an express train, but never reach their goal, being switched about this way and that, by what she sees and hears in the clinic. In the short time she is before the students, she registers in her face and bodily movements a kaleidoscope of emotions—good humor, hilarious laughter, sadness, a wild outburst of weeping, irritability, anger, murderous rage. The students are unanimous in pronouncing it "Acute Mania."

The next patient, also a woman, is fifty-two years old. She is deeply depressed, frantic with self-blame and declares she should be stoned to death for her "horrible sins." She points to her chest and moans, explaining that her intestines are tightly wrapped around her heart, lungs and, indeed, all her organs. The students decide she is suffering from "Involutional Melancholia."

Then, a patient, a man forty-three years old who has had several severe convulsions, in one of which he bit off the tip of his tongue and fractured his jaw. The students think he has epilepsy.

They diagnose the next patient schizophrenic, on the basis of the symptoms he displays—an odd, stiff gait, many mannerisms such as forking his index and middle fingers and pressing their tips to his eyeballs, and telling without any emotional reaction a rambling, disjointed story about the "tigelites" who extract the thoughts from his head, change their shape and put them back again with a machine.

The students could not see much mentally wrong with the last patient. Neither could I. Perhaps he was a bit vague and occasionally mildly confused, but not more than may be seen in a tired person.

*The patients, all seven of them, had paresis.**

* The child had juvenile paresis which may follow inherited syphilis.

Never have I given this "X" Clinic in which the percentage
of the correct diagnoses exceeded 20 per cent. One important
factor, the all-important factor, had been withheld from the
students—the result of the examination of the blood and spinal
fluid. If the students had had that information they would
have diagnosed every patient correctly.

In paresis, the Wasserman test of the blood or an equivalent
test is positive in 90 per cent of patients who have not been
treated, and the spinal fluid is positive in practically all untreated patients. This is supported by certain chemical and
microscope examinations: the globulin is positive, the total
protein is about 75 and there are 50 or more small round cells
called lymphocytes, which normally should not exceed fifteen.
Even more significant is a gold color test of the spinal fluid,
called the gold curve. Reduced to a symbolic graph, a gold
curve test positive for paresis would look something like this:

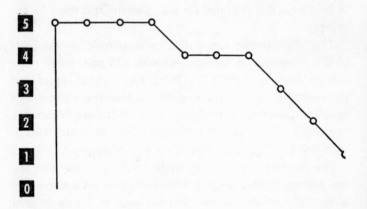

The gold curve reaction in a normal spinal fluid would be
flat, like this:

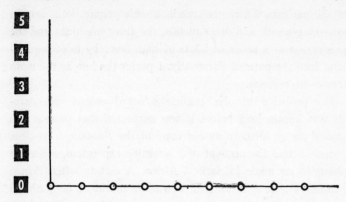

If I were to write a formula for the diagnosis of paresis, I would give the examination of the blood and spinal fluid a value of almost 100, the physical and neurological symptoms 50 to 60, but the mental symptoms not more than 15 to 20. In untreated patients, it is entirely possible to make a correct diagnosis of paresis without seeing the patient.

There are still some persons who hesitate to give the psychiatrist permission to draw a little spinal fluid from a relative who is sick, fearing it is a serious and even dangerous procedure. It is not. It is a simple, routine matter, taking only a few minutes, done hundreds of thousands of times a year. Not only is it mandatory in order to make a diagnosis of paresis, but it yields valuable information in many other nervous and mental diseases.

Only about three decades ago there was practically no treatment for paresis. After a few years or less, paretic patients died in pitiful condition, ravaged in body and debased in mind.

Now there is a variety of treatments available which, if the paresis is not too far advanced, will produce considerable improvement, sometimes close to recovery, in 60 to 70 per cent of the patients. There are certain arsenic preparations, certain salts of bismuth and other metals, the fever machines and the production of a series of bouts of high fever by injecting malaria into the patient. Personally, I prefer the last as the main treatment reliance.

It is probable that the beneficial effect of malaria upon paresis was known long before it was suspected that paresis was caused by syphilis. In an old copy of the *Edinburgh Review,* I came across the account of a scientific expedition, reporting observations made in darkest Africa. A certain witch doctor habitually sent some natives, who came to him to be conjured for their bodily ills, to a swamp infested with malaria-bearing mosquitoes, with instructions to remain in the swamp overnight. From the careful description by the doctor in the party, it seemed altogether likely that the sick natives had paresis. And this before the time that it had been demonstrated that paresis was due to syphilis and could be improved by malarial infection.

Recently, careful experimental work with penicillin has shown promise. Perhaps one day the wonder drug or one of the group to which it is related may conquer paresis as completely as it has vanquished many other infections. Recently a new preparation, procaine penicillin in oil and aluminum monostearate, was given to 100 patients. It cured both syphilis and gonorrhea in less than 5 days. It is given in a moment, without discomfort or after effects, and costs 48 cents a dose!

Naturally, in addition to whatever specific therapy the psychiatrist gives his paretic patients, he also does everything possible, by increasing the nutrition, particularly the vitamin supply, and by putting the patients under favorable conditions, to bring them to their physical optimums.

There are two opportunities for the prevention of paresis

and one of them is golden. The simple formula, "No syphilis— no paresis," is valid—and sadly neglected. This is largely due to ignorance. Of the five great evils that afflict mankind, Poverty, Ignorance, Disease, Crime and Legal Entanglement, ignorance probably is the worst.

Nevertheless, if syphilis is contracted, there is still a good chance of avoiding by early and energetic treatment the calamity of paresis.

Senile and Arteriosclerotic Psychoses. The two poles of life, infancy and old age, are appealing in their helplessness and should call forth the utmost in scientific and humane study and care. Babies and the aged (whether they are old by reason of the chronology of their years or because of advanced hardening of the blood vessels of the brain) are fragile. Modern medical science has turned in a brilliant record in the matter of prolonging human life. In only a few decades, life expectation has been increased, somewhere between ten and fifteen years. But unless we find a way of prolonging the life of the mind and the personality, infinitely more precious than the body, then the lengthening of the life span becomes a curse rather than a blessing.

You will remember in *Gulliver's Travels* the description by the master satirist, Dean Swift, of the unfortunate "Struldbrugs" who were destined never to die, but who did not escape the physical and mental infirmities of old age:

"When they come to fourscore years . . . they are not only opinionated, peevish, covetous, morose, vain, talkative; but incapable of friendship, and dead to all natural affection, which never descended below their grandchildren. Envy and impotent desires are their prevailing passions . . . At ninety . . . they have no distinction of taste, but eat and drink whatever they can get without relish or appetite . . . In talking they forget the common appellation of things, and the names of persons, even those who are their nearest friends and relations."

I have long since been convinced that many old people could be spared the ordeal of senile mental disturbances or at least the debacle could be deferred for a long time. After a long, active and often trying life, the brain cells of old people are "tired." Without being too artificial about it, or encasing them in glass houses, it is still possible to give them a reasonable amount of insulation against the too stern rebuffs and sharp vicissitudes of life. It is not possible, nor would it be wise, to conceal from the oldsters, family and world problems and troubles, but they need not be painted in the darkest and most somber colors. And, the good things in life should be stressed and even dressed up a bit. There are a few good things left in life.

I knew an old man, whose only son made what on the surface looked like a very hazardous marriage. The young woman was a waitress in a down-at-the-heels restaurant. Not that this was anything against her, but there were some "soft" spots in her past life. She had previously been married unhappily, and her former husband had committed suicide. She had one child.

My patient's wife and her sister endlessly fretted and fussed and scolded the old man, blaming him and insisting that he halt the impending marriage, which it was predicted would bring down horrible disaster upon everyone concerned. There was nothing the old man could do other than worry, which he did in full measure, without cessation.

Surprisingly the marriage turned out very well. The former waitress proved to be a loving, mature and capable wife—a fine helpmate. But by this time the old man's mind was permanently darkened by the shadows of senile dementia.

Serious and sometimes even relatively slight physical accidents and illness often seem to precipitate senile mental symptoms, particularly if unwisely handled. Unless it would be decidedly dangerous, it is a good plan to get the old patient out of bed, at least from a flat to a sitting position. For some reason not satisfactorily explained, the development of mental symptoms seems to be favored by long continuance of the flat position in bed. Particularly does this seem to be true in fractures of bones.

Old brains do not withstand well the narcotic effects of alcohol. This is not to say that quite small amounts of good liquor are harmful. Indeed, many doctors feel it may be mildly helpful. One of my professors in medical school used to say: "A man more than 65 years old, who does not take a little good brandy is almost as foolish as the young man who takes too much."

Unquestionably there is some familial influence in determining the time when the minds of old people break with mental symptoms. There are families in which in as many as three or four generations there is likely to be a rather consistent departure from the mental realities of life, perhaps in the early sixties. I have known some families in which the family "pattern" was regarded as inflexible and an air of hushed and gloomy expectancy pervaded the home whenever one of the family approached the fatal age—and long before. Once, I visited such a family at the time when Aunt Jane was nearing the turn of sixty. Everyone looked at poor Aunt Jane as though they expected her to break out in a cackle of insane laughter at any moment. Years later, I was delighted to learn that Aunt Jane lived to the age of 73, bright, alert and free from mental symptoms, until two weeks before her death, when she was knocked over by an erratic bicyclist.

Fatalistic attitudes are always unfortunate and almost always unjustifiable. More often than not the expected fails to happen. Even though there may be family tendencies toward early old-age mental breaks, yet there is no scientific rule about it, and it is far from inflexible. Certainly the situation is not improved by an almost ghoulish anticipation.

Incidentally, the general public attitude toward advancing years is an illustration of bad mental hygiene. In all of us it is too much dominated by the actual count of years. On this basis, too, industry makes too rigid employment distinctions. Old people themselves fall into one of two erroneous attitudes. One group has no acceptance at all of the increasing measure of their years. They try to outdo youngsters in sports and other activities, take large amounts of sex hormones and not infrequently, on a broiling hot day, drop dead on a golf course. There is considerable narcissism in this. One lady I knew, on her sixtieth birthday, had every mirror removed from the house.

The second, and larger, group submits too readily to the psychological tyranny of their age. They are the people who would like to do this or that, join in the fun, but "no, after all, I am no longer young; it wouldn't look right." Often they are quite capable of participating physically and mentally, but psychologically they have sentenced themselves to being old. There is a way to grow old gracefully. In order to accomplish it, there must be emotional maturity. Mature people live each epoch of their lives with satisfaction and pleasure to themselves and others. With reasonable adequacy, they meet its responsibilities. When they pass into another epoch, they bring into it from the previous one, the good and useful things they have learned. They are prepared to take the best things from the new and older life period. These are the people who really mean and feel it when they say, "It was fine being 20 or 30 or 40 or 50, but I wouldn't want to go back to it now." Perhaps in these thoughts there is contained the most reliable protection against the mental ravages of old age.

I have a feeling that one day further researches into the chemistry of food and the vitamin needs of the body will make a telling contribution, not only in adding more years to the span of physical life, but also in prolonging the life of the mind. Certainly babies and old people need different kinds of food and at different times than those in the full bloom of life. For one thing, it is wise for old people to eat small amounts of food, but at frequent intervals.

The symptom pattern of senile and arteriosclerotic psychoses has been outlined in the organic psychoses pattern.

The treatment is one of masterly inactivity. This does not mean that there is nothing to be done. Indeed, there is a great deal to do. It does mean that the patient should not be subjected to unnecessary annoyances. I knew a sweet old lady, mildly deteriorated, with memory failure. But she was cheerful, kept herself clean and neat and enjoyed helping with the household tasks. All went well until her society-minded daughter insisted on "fixing her up" and making her look "prettier." Among other things, this involved blueing the old lady's hair and arranging it in elaborate coiffures. The gentle old soul never rebelled, but she used to try to hide, in order to escape the attentions of her daughter.

There are many practical things to be done, a thousand and one medical chores, perhaps relieving an irritated skin or hemorrhoids or bladder irritation, or seeing that the teeth are well brushed and cared for, the patient's body kept clean and the clothes neat, etc. The doctor who considers himself superior to seeing that these considerations are carried out does not belong in the honorable Guild of Hippocrates.

It is amazing how much we all think of the "creature comforts" of life, and see that we get them for ourselves, and yet how often we forget to see that our old people have them. We should be sure that they, too, are comfortable and secure as to food, heat and cold, common dangers. Too often we do not remember that the old, mentally dulled patient no longer is vigilant in the functioning of his sense of self-preservation. There should be available proper, easily digested food and enough body and bed clothing to protect against cold. Old people chill easily. They mislay all manner of things, and we should not be too impatient about helping find them. They may readily trip and fall. Or choke on too large a piece of food. Sometimes one of their fears may be that their small possessions, precious to them, might be stolen at night. So, they may wander about the house at night, perhaps lighting matches to find their "things." Their memories being very short, they may forget to blow out the matches, setting the house or themselves ablaze. They may wander away from home, taking up with strangers and telling them interesting but usually untrue stories of ill-treatment by the family.

Medicines of various sorts are often needed, vitamins, suitable laxatives, for insomnia small doses of carefully selected sedatives, perhaps a little good whisky. The attending doctor will know what is needed.

Possibly nicotinic acid is directly helpful, particularly if the factor of hardened brain vessels is prominent. Some years ago I had a patient, 83 years old, who had played such a prominent role in world affairs that I dare not describe him more closely for fear of identification. He had been hopelessly confused for many months, not even knowing he was living in his country place nor recognizing his own sons and daughters. There was nothing much to be done, other than good nursing and attention to the ordinary body needs. I did prescribe nicotinic acid. One of the daughters felt that the small spark of mind remaining might be kindled if her father moved into his town house, which he always liked. Within a few weeks, the old gentleman improved amazingly. The confusion cleared, he recognized his family and the surroundings, enjoyed the newspaper and visits from his cronies. The remission lasted almost ten months. Then he relapsed, but fortunately died a few weeks later.

Often the mental symptoms are severe enough so that treatment in a mental hospital is mandatory. However, I do not believe that nearly all the old people in hospitals are sick enough mentally to be in them. Sometimes the reason is economic. All the adults in the family have jobs and there is no one to look after the old person. But by no means does this account for all the patients.

We need to adopt a more middle-of-the-road policy toward our old people. Not to the extent of the ancestral worship of the Chinese. After all, we cannot live in their pasts with the older generation. But the cynical disregard of helpless old age by the enslaving dictatorships of our day is not good either. Nor is the problem solved by the vote-getting expediency of old-age pensions. Two states have had to make dangerous curtailments of budgets for education and other urgent purposes because almost 80 per cent of the income is earmarked for old-age pensions. What is needed is personal, not political, attitudes, a decent interest and regard for the needs and rights of old people. This is of the essence of true democracy.

Senile patients die of varied causes. The machine of the body is worn out, and vital parts, the heart, kidneys, liver, etc., give way. The most common cause of death is terminal pneumonia, "the friend of the aged."

On the basis of admissions to psychiatric public hospitals, the mental symptoms of old age and hardening of the brain blood vessels account for about 17 per cent of all mental diseases. So, it is a serious problem.

Epilepsy. Epilepsy, the once "sacred disease," has been taken out of the hands of the gods by modern science. It is still heavily encrusted by ignorance and superstition. Practically every drug on the official list, and many not on it, too, acres of herbs, all sorts of substances including the secretions and excretions of domestic and wild animals, have been given in the past, in the vain effort to appease the convulsive wrath of the gods.

During the war, on one of my tours through the South for the Army, I came across a pathetic little chap from the mountains of West Virginia, who though both feeble-minded and epileptic, had slipped through the sieve of the draft. He confided to me that he had eaten the "mess of mice Mom fried for me to cure dem fits," but, sadly, "I still gets the fits." I had him promptly discharged from the Army.

Among the innumerable superstitions which epilepsy has acquired, I have always felt a Chinese one was the most appealing—certainly more appealing than touching the king's ring, which persisted well into the Middle Ages. The tiny garments of children are hung on the housetops so that the winds may blow away the evil spirits which have entered the bodies of epileptic children. In another version, the clothes fluttering in the breezes make mute supplication to the gods to return the soul of the child of which the convulsions have robbed him.

By no means all, or even the majority, of epileptic patients have mental symptoms. Furthermore, epilepsy does not rule out average and even superior intelligence. Indeed, among genius, in art and letters and perhaps particularly in music there is quite a sprinkling of epilepsy. It is probable that Julius Caesar had the disease. At least, when Mark Antony, before the populace of Rome, tried to crown him Emperor but desisted since the temper of the crowd was obviously against it—

the great Caesar, in his frustration, fell to the ground and foamed at the mouth in a fit.

A considerable part of the convulsive apple has to be cut away before we come to the core of true or so-called idiopathic epilepsy. In other words, many convulsions have satisfactory explanation in various conditions and diseases—hydrocephalus or "water on the brain," meningitis, head injury, uremia, diabetes, lead poisoning, alcohol, certain disturbances of the ductless glands, etc. I think, too, that sometimes local irritations may be at fault. I have records of a number of children in whom convulsions ceased after they had been circumcised or, in another group, given proper glasses for markedly defective vision.

The core of the problem of convulsions is idiopathic epilepsy, a bad name (though rather better than "the falling evil") for "paroxysmal cerebral dysrhythmia." Freely translated, this means a periodic disturbance of brain beat or rhythm. Here is another way of putting it: It is possible to produce a convulsion in anyone, for instance, by injecting enough water into the veins. We all have a convulsive discharge level. In those people who have epilepsy, the motor area of the brain discharges into activity much more readily and with much less irritation than is usual. It takes much less pressure to pull the trigger. Just exactly why this is so we are not sure, but certainly inheritance cannot be excluded.

True epilepsy is likely to show its hand early in life, the bulk of it appearing before twenty. Convulsions in middle life or later usually are due to other conditions.

The discovery of electroencephalography has gone a long way toward throwing scientific light on the dark areas of epilepsy. It is a method of studying and recording the beat or waves of the brain. It is of very great value in epilepsy and is helpful in the diagnosis of many other brain conditions. It is a test of considerable sensitivity, since it was found to be definitely positive in 60 per cent of the parents of epileptic patients, who did not have the disease themselves. In this country, Lennox, Gibbs, Cobb, Davis, Forster and others are to be commended for their splendid work in electroencephalography. We have their permission to reproduce the graphs of samples of brain waves.

During the convulsion of "grand mal" or convulsive epilepsy:

During the time there is no convulsion:

The "little sickness" or "petit mal" which, although there may be but a brief period of unconsciousness, without convulsion, is nevertheless true epilepsy; the graph comes out something like this during the attack:

And between attacks it looks like this:

In psychomotor epilepsy, during the seizure:

And between attacks:

Of course, the electroencephalogram is not infallible. Nothing is. When it is positive, it is very likely to be diagnostic, but sometimes it may be negative, even though epilepsy is present. If possible the psychiatrist wants to observe the convulsion. It is a distressing sight.

The convulsion is chiefly marked by loss of consciousness. If there is a warning or "aura," like a burning sensation in the head, or a pain in the pit of the stomach, or a feeling of gaiety, whatever it may be, it is the last thing the patient remembers. He goes down as though sandbagged, wherever he happens to be, and may seriously injure himself in the fall. There may be the epileptic cry. He convulses first with stiffening and then writhing and twisting of the limbs. He may froth at the mouth and if he bites his tongue, as often happens, the froth is bloody. The patient is blue in the face, the breathing is labored, the eyes are apt to roll upward and their pupils do not react to light. Often control of bladder and bowels is lost. The convulsion may occur at any time without warning, often at night. Usually the patient sleeps following the seizure, and does not remember what happened during and for some time following the convulsion.

I think I have never witnessed a convulsion in the street without the appearance of the little chap, perhaps a plumber's helper, who knows just what to do. Exuding self-confidence, he rings the bell of a house in the neighborhood, and borrows a little salt and a spoon. Returning swiftly, he more or less, usually less, deftly puts some of the salt on the back of the patient's tongue. By this time the fit, which lasts only a short time, is over anyhow, and the first-aid chap turns to the admiring crowd, sometimes remarking, "It's easy enough if you know just what to do."

Actually, there is nothing to be done. Once a convulsion has started, no power on earth can stop it. It is a good idea to loosen the patient's clothing and insert a roll of soft cloth between the jaws, so that the tongue is not bitten.

The motif of the convulsion of true epilepsy is the loss of consciousness. In major hysteria, the convulsion may sometimes closely simulate that of epilepsy, but the consciousness is not completely annihilated. A noted French neurologist remarked that a hysterical woman about to have her convulsion selected a soft spot in which to fall, and while convulsing observed the surroundings from "the tail of her eye" in order to note the effect upon the audience. By no means does this mean that the patient is pretending to have a convulsion. She is not. Hysteria is a definite and serious neurosis, not pretense.

In a hysterical convulsion, the color and breathing are not likely to change, the pupils of the eyes react normally to light, generally the tongue is not bitten, only rarely is bladder and bowel control lost. Often the patient emerges bright and alert from the convulsion, remembering it and what happened after it.

The epileptic has been so maligned in his personality that I hesitate to call the roll of his personality vices, even though they sometimes are present. He has been described as egotistical, conceited, emotionally unstable, filled with notions of imaginary physical ills, a sickly sentimentalist, hypocritical, unable to adapt to his environment, cruel, sadistic, irascible, impulsive.

Surely God never made anyone that way, and I doubt if the brain condition in itself could produce such a monster. The more likely is it that at least some of these traits are in each one of us, part of the decor of our unconscious minds, kept closely cloistered by inhibition, from breaking out too openly into conscious behavior. Too often is the unfortunate epileptic regarded as socially beyond the pale. Probably, unable to hope to achieve the acceptance by his fellows, he has nothing to gain by keeping some of the undesirable personality traits under cover. I feel sure from my own professional experience, because of the brilliant advances made in the treatment of epilepsy, that the examples of the more serious personality difficulties are much rarer than formerly.

Epileptic patients often are subject to mental upsets. Probably, the mildest form is periodical ill-humor. It means about what it says, periods of bad humor raised to the nth degree, lasting a few hours to several days. At these times, some patients may be so evil-tempered that in speech and manner one must tread more softly than the rustle of an angel's wings, in order to avoid a temper explosion. I always think of this ill-humor as symbolized by an early colonial flag which bore a coiled serpent with bared fangs, ready to strike and the inscription, "Nole me tangere" (Touch me not!). Not that epileptics have a corner on bad humor.

When mental symptoms take the place of a convulsion, as they do from time to time, they are spoken of as epileptic equivalents. There may be dream or twilight states in which the patient is confused and dream-like in his behavior, delirium with hallucinations, delusions with a content of ecstasy, often religious, anxiety, etc.

Sometimes, too, patients may be very suspicious and paranoid. Again, one may not be too sure how much of this is due to the epilepsy and how much to the social odium under which the patient labors. Even outside the area of epilepsy, if we regard anyone as unclean and untouchable, we can scarcely expect him to be filled with feelings of kindliness and beneficence toward us.

Epileptic fugue states are interesting and very important legally. A fugue state covers a varying period of time for which, later on, the patient has absolutely no memory. Usually a fugue lasts only a few hours or at most several days, but occasionally it may cover a long time. I knew of a patient who traveled from New York to London where he worked for a period of six months, supporting himself and as far as could be determined, behaving normally. Suddenly he "awakened" and was in a panic of fear at finding himself in a strange land, not remembering leaving the United States, or, indeed, anything regarding his activities during the half year.

During the fugue, patients may, and I think usually do, act normally enough. However, they may misbehave and even commit serious crimes—sex crimes or murder. My belief is that the crime is not so much in the epilepsy as in the personality of the person who has the epilepsy. Each of us has a certain minimum ethical code which we rarely transgress. Even in post-hypnotic behavior, the subject will not carry out suggestions made when he was hypnotized if they are too definitely opposed to his moral standards.   ,

However, if a crime is committed during a fugue state by an epileptic, he is not legally responsible and cannot be found guilty. After World War I in France, frequently I testified as an expert in court-martial trials. In one instance, as was the practice, a "human chain" was sent across "no-man's land" to the enemy lines, attempting to secure and bring back military information. There were five soldiers. They held hands and, on their bellies, inched forward slowly. More than halfway over, suddenly one of the five, a boy of eighteen, gave a loud shriek. Immediately this drew the enemy fire. Two of the five were killed. The other three, including the boy who had made the noise, got back to our lines safely.

In war, this is very serious. I talked with the prisoner and examined his records. There was some account of convulsions in civilian life. The boy claimed he did not remember anything about the incident in "no-man's land." Maybe he lied. I am not sure. In any event, I testified that probably he had epilepsy and should be acquitted. He was, and was subsequently sent to a hospital for study and treatment. Possibly I made a scientific error but there was a reasonable doubt and my conscience is easier.

There is a very dangerous equivalent, "epileptic furor," fortunately not common. When I was a very young man, in fact just recently added to the staff of a psychiatric hospital, I had an experience which left me with a great deal of personal and physical respect for epileptic furor. About two o'clock in the morning, I was called by the head night nurse to come see a patient who was "disturbed." I went to the patient's hall, and with all the valor of youth and ignorance, was just about to unlock the door of a room from which came a terrific din. But the old and experienced nurse tactfully intervened, "Doctor, why not look in first?" In those days, mental hospitals had little peepholes in the doors of patients' rooms which could be opened separately. I opened it, and looked in. I saw about six feet two inches of a young man, about 190 pounds of solid bone and muscles, in an epileptic furor. He had wrenched off a poster from his bed, solid mahogany, weighing about fifty pounds. He stood in the middle of the room brandishing it furiously. The room was a shambles. My patient had demolished into splinters every bit of movable furniture and was now turning his club with energy and enthusiasm upon the walls. Fortunately, the old hospital had four-foot walls, and ·the door was thick, solid oak.

I looked at the nurse and the nurse looked at me. I said, "I don't think anything particular is to be done." The nurse said, "Thank you. I think your judgment is wise."

The next morning the patient was as gentle as a lamb.

Epilepsy may darken the mind with the deepest dementia. I believe this is due to the terrific impacts upon the brain of frequent convulsions. Certainly it is becoming less common, since more skillful treatment has come into general use. The old-time deteriorated epileptic was very much like the type of pugilist who had little defensive skill and earned his living by being battered into insensibility time after time.

The span of life is somewhat shorter in epileptics than in non-epileptics, but not much shorter, again thanks to modern treatment. Occasionally patients die of status epilepticus, in which one convulsion follows upon the heels of another. Efforts to halt the convulsions are usually but not always successful.

The brightest page in the treatment of epilepsy was written by pharmacological research. Originally bromides were the only drugs available. Often they did lessen the number of convulsions, but too often they had to be given in large doses. The patient paid the penalty in terms of mental dullness and stupidity and ran the risk of bromide poisoning.

Next, phenobarbital came into common use. It was, and still is, of great value. It can be taken over a comparatively long time with only minimal risk of intoxication. And frequently it decreases markedly the number of convulsive and petit mal attacks.

Then dilantin was discovered. It is an interesting example of satisfying a request to find a drug that would help epileptic patients. Putnam, Merritt and others answered the call and produced dilantin. It was a notable addition to the physician's weapons in the battle against epilepsy. It has advantages and disadvantages. It does not make the patient sleepy and "dopey." The majority of patients can take dilantin for a long time, and usually the number of convulsions is reduced. Sometimes, too, it is useful in combating the mental "equivalents."

Dilantin does have drawbacks. Some patients are allergic to it. It may produce skin rashes, headache and dizziness. In one patient, who at first examination seemed to have a brain tumor, the symptoms promptly disappeared after the dilantin was stopped.

The discovery of dilantin spearheaded further research and a number of useful drugs were worked out—glutamic acid, tridione, phenantoin, paradione and others. Each of these had an area of usefulness in the treatment of epilepsy. Tridione seems to be very helpful in severe forms of petit mal, as are both paradione and glutamic acid.

These drugs have added immeasurably to the treatment of epilepsy. They have removed the blight from thousands of human beings and given them the chance of leading useful and happy lives, on reasonably even terms with their fellow men.

Much is to be done besides giving medicines. Incidentally, of course, any medicine given in epilepsy must be ordered by a physician. Medicines given upon the advice of friends or at the behest of patent-medicine propaganda are very likely to give more trouble than help, and may lead to disaster for the patient.

Special diets may be of some value. Many physicians permit the patient to take a full, regular diet and to add to it by generous "snacks" of carbohydrate foods between meals and at bedtime. The idea is to keep the blood sugar at a satisfactory level and this may decrease the number of seizures.

It is an excellent idea to keep the patient's general health at a high level, in other words, to try to keep him physically and psychologically well. Hunger, fatigue, colds, constipation, emotional upsets—all seem to favor the occurrence of the "spells." Mild and gradually increasing exercises, like walking or golfing, are good. Long swims in deep water, strenuous mountain climbing, flying airplanes, riveting, or any occupation carried out at considerable heights above ground level are not wise, unnecessary temptations to the gods of mishap. Alcohol, if used at all, should be taken only in small amounts. Otherwise, the patient may lead a normal social and occupational life. Sometimes, patients and their families think the doctor is being fussy about trivial things. He is not. Usually, his suggestions have a background of sound scientific information and practical experience.

Every epileptic patient needs a philosophy toward his illness and toward life. One should begin by giving him a simple and understandable explanation of what epilepsy is and what happens in it. Given skillfully and kindly and at each patient's intellectual level, such explanations divest epilepsy of much of its horror, superstition, belittlement, shame and stigma and definitely elevate the morale of the patient. Then, there should follow an equally lucid explanation of why certain medicines and treatments are ordered. There are many analogies. For instance, in diabetes, insulin may be given, the diet changed and the mode of life somewhat altered in order to keep the blood sugar on an even keel, thus steering safely away from the complications of diabetes, notably the danger of coma. So, in epilepsy, the use of certain drugs and other treatments with some modification of the physical activities of life and a little soft-pedaling of its emotional stresses, act together in stabilizing the cortex of the brain, making it less "jittery" and less likely to discharge into a convulsion at small pressures from the physical and emotional trigger of life.

I have a friend, not a psychiatrist, just a good, conscientious doctor (not that being a psychiatrist precludes this) who is doing a fine piece of work for his epileptic patients. Among other things, he gathers them together for an hour once a week. Under his wise and kindly guidance, they discuss the problems created by their epilepsy with one another. Each time they go forth with broader understanding and renewed faith and courage.

The place to begin the education of the epileptic and block the formation in the personality of a cynical and embittered attitude toward people and life is during childhood in the home. Too often, parents are motivated by the mistaken notion of shielding the child from embarrassment and distress, and he is isolated from all contact with other children. Inevitably, he develops a feeling of guilt, for does he not have a shameful thing to hide? His parents must think so, or else they would let him play with other children! This pattern is deeply impressed into his personality. Around this core, there is rapidly laid down layers of unhappiness, inadequacy, mistrust and suspicion. And when this personality, illy prepared for the give and take of adult life, does meet social unfriendliness, as is sadly often true, then the personality becomes hopelessly distorted and the epileptic attempts to strike back at society.

Modern science has acquired enough information to be able to map out a project, tentatively at least, for the prevention of epilepsy. Such a program does have in it a segment of eugenics. How large this segment is, no one knows with surety. Certainly a smaller segment than was thought true a few decades ago, when the leading thought was that people were either saved from or doomed to convulsions by their ancestral records. Nevertheless, it is true that a nucleus of idiopathic epilepsy is inherited. To forbid the marriage of epileptics would not give us an epileptic-free world. It has been shown, according to electroencephalographic tracings, that as much as 12 per cent of the population who have never had any signs of epilepsy at all, nevertheless in their brain patterns do show a predisposition. Perhaps we can say this much: If there is clear evidence of idiopathic epilepsy in the direct ancestry, then definitely there is a greater hazard of the offspring being epileptic than if the family record were clear. But many other factors are involved. If the question arises in a contemplated marriage, the counsel of an authoritative physician should be sought.

A program of prevention must extend beyond the confines of idiopathic epilepsy. All conditions which produce convulsions are under careful investigation and already many measures have been taken to abolish or, at least, lessen the threat. Medicine and surgery and all of their specialties are interested and have contributed toward prevention. For instance, obstetricians, by refining and perfecting their techniques, have greatly reduced the number of head injuries during birth, and thus lowered the toll of convulsions.

One half a million epileptics in the United States is a conservative estimate. The economic and social loss is enormous.

This, then, is the story of the organic psychoses. More details might be given, but the chief actors have been identified and the parts they play, in these so often the closing scenes in the drama of mental life, have been described. The brain is and can do many things. But, first and foremost, it is an organ of the body, like the liver, spleen, heart or stomach. Like them, it consists of tissue and like them, too, it has a function to perform, albeit a highly specialized and complicated function.

As in other organs, too, when its tissue is destroyed or damaged by disease or injury, then at best it can perform its function only in a very halting fashion. Then the shadows of mental deterioration descend and envelop the mind.

5 | TOXIC PSYCHOSES

Lᴵᴷᴱ all living things, human beings are vulnerable to poisons. Indeed, in many ways we are more vulnerable than other creatures. For one thing, our bodies are more highly organized and more delicately balanced. For another, we have achieved the supreme in the development of living structure—the human brain.

The brain is infinitely more complex and has a much wider range of function than any man-made machine. For instance, the working of human memory is truly amazing. Here is a perceiving, sorting, filing, indexing and cross-indexing system which usually gives immediate and correct answers, as it were, instantaneously pulls out the right card, often for seventy years and upwards, and without unusual attention and care. Machines with far more limited function, for instance the machine in the Bureau of Standards used for measuring the expansion of metals, cannot perform their function unless the conditions are exactly right. The machine must be sealed in a vacuum, the temperature carefully adjusted and guarded against the slightest stir of air. And yet, compared to the machinery of the human brain, with its many cells and pathways, working separately and at the same time in perfect unison with one another, all inconceivably intricate—the metal-measuring apparatus is like a child's crude toy. Of course, there are astounding man-made machines, based on the principles of the new science of cybernetics. These machines do answer questions accurately. But they do not think, even though some scientists rather naïvely go so far as to insist they do. After all, they have to be made and operated by the brain of man. And nothing more comes out of the machine than is put into it.

Naturally, like any machine, the human brain must be supplied with fuel. The basic source of its fuel power is the blood which the heart pumps into the brain. And, naturally, too, if the blood supply is poisoned, then the function of the brain is distorted and mental symptoms may appear.

From the standpoint of the probability of mental symptoms due to poisoning, the human brain is vulnerable to a triple threat.

First, poisons are often taken into the body more or less deliberately. Apparently from time immemorial human beings have found it necessary to dull their brains with a great assortment of poisons, in order to escape facing the unpleasant and forbidding aspects of the realities of their situations in life. Then follows a long train of dangerous narcotic and excitement-producing drugs, like morphine and cocaine. Finally, at the end of the procession is a large and motley collection of so-called "harmless" drugs. They are taken freely by millions of people without much more thought than goes with drinking a glass of water. These drugs are far from harmless. They produce a large amount of human misery. Presently I shall discuss them.

Many workers in various industries are exposed to a great

variety of chemical poisons, solids, liquids and gases. It has been known for a long time that the brain is very susceptible to white lead and other metals. With the rapid expansion of civilian and military industries, the list of mental-symptom-producing poisons has grown to formidable proportions. The extant threat comes from radioactive substances used in making atom bombs. In view of the physical and mental horrors of the bomb, it certainly begins to look as though our nuclear physicists have created a Frankenstein.

The second prong of the triple toxic threat comes from poisons created within the body in the course of almost any infectious or other disease. The brain may give way under the impact of toxic blows from all sorts of sickness, sometimes even from such seemingly minor affairs as grippe. In fact, it may be taken as axiomatic that whenever the body is sick, toxic, then in some degree the mind (of which the brain is the executive organ) becomes involved in the process. It is in this area that the practice of medicine in all its specialties and psychiatry constantly cross paths. One day a doctor is called to see a patient sick with pneumonia. There is fever, some difficulty in breathing, blood in the sputum. The patient is mentally clear enough. But in twenty-four hours he may be wildly delirious. The fever and the toxicity from the infecting bacillus have increased apace. The patient now is not only a medical but also a psychiatric problem.

Finally, a serious threat to the integrity of brain functioning comes from a definite and continued upset in its metabolism. The brain is the highly efficient and faithful executive of the needs and desires of the body. For instance, it sets into motion physical movements from the simple lifting of the least finger to a complicated and masterly rendition of a great musical classic. It puts into effect promptly those safeguarding and sometimes life-saving movements, like jumping out of the path of danger of a fast-approaching motor car. It operates a check or inhibition against excessive and waste motion and other harmful behavior. It provides the needed activity of nerve cells and tissue which goes into thinking, from the thinking of the simplest thought to that genius thinking from which is shaped the eternal grandeur of art and literature—or the building of empires—or great inventions serving men and easing their labors.

The brain can make all these things possible provided its metabolism, the give and take between its upbuilding and destructive or waste products, is not too much disturbed. And, it is disturbed, its balance is decidedly shifted and it loses the support it needs, if the body or any organ or system of the body is unbalanced in its particular metabolism. This happens when the waste products from badly balanced functioning continue to exceed tissue repair and restitution. Then the brain is seriously compromised and handicapped. It cannot respond normally. It does the best it can, but it reacts in halting and distorted fashion. This means mental symptoms.

Suppose the heart is very badly damaged from acute articular rheumatism during childhood. It is constantly in the position of trying to do more work and give more blood than is safe. The heart overworks and does not have the opportunity of recouping its strength. Then gradually its function becomes weaker. And the brain loses much of the support of the heart. The patient is likely to show mental symptoms. Perhaps he becomes confused and suspicious, interpreting casual happenings in the sickroom as inimical and threatening. So, in any organ or part of the body the thyroid gland, kidney, liver, blood, etc., if the metabolism shifts too much to the debit side, it becomes increasingly harder for the brain to produce normal thinking and behavior.

The chances of the physician's uncovering the offending

poisonous agent are overwhelmingly favorable. Often the general physical examination reveals important leads. Even the non-medical public is more or less familiar with bodily and mental evidences of poisoning. People know that "the horrors" or delirium tremens is likely to occur in alcoholism. From reading murder fiction, if not from other sources, they discuss the pin-point pupils of the morphine addict, the dilated pupils of the cocaine slave and the sex crimes of the marihuana smoker.* They identify the bulging eyeballs, trembling, overactivity and excited irritability as revealing disease of the thyroid gland. When they hear that a young pregnant woman who has been "heavy" and a bit confused has had a convulsion, women who have had children may ominously shake their heads and murmur, "kidney poisoning." Often they are quite right. The other day in court, I overheard a lawyer whisper this remark about an eminent counselor who was addressing the jury very effectively: "K is very keen this morning, but pretty jumpy. He must be taking benzedrine." And so on.

Naturally, doctors are more skilled in discovering tell-tale physical and mental signs of poisoning and in evaluating them correctly. Furthermore, they have available batteries of ac-

* While "reefer" smokers may indulge in sexual orgies and commit sex crimes, yet marihuana does not specifically produce such behavior. During the War, I was a member of a Commission, the objective of which is still secret. We had the opportunity of studying the effect of many narcotic and other drugs. I examined a number of marihuana smokers. Their "parties" were not particularly bestial. They smoked the cigarettes, played soft music on the victrola, drank cheap wine with a low alcohol content and indulged in phantasy dreams. Of course, there is no doubt that the use of marihuana is deteriorating and degrading to the personality. But with marihuana, as with many drugs, the previous make-up of the person is the determining factor in motivating criminal behavior. Cocaine is one exception. I have examined a number of murderers who sniffed cocaine habitually and "nerved" themselves with "snow" to gain courage to kill. Fortunately, the splendid work of the F.B.I. has practically abolished cocaine traffic in this country.

curate tests, chemical and microscopic, by means of which the majority of poisons taken into the body can be identified. Toxicity produced within the body in the course of many diseases, too, does not very often elude the questing eye of the expert. In many conditions, the source of the poisoning may be viewed under the microscope, as, for instance, the parasite of malaria or the bacillus of tuberculosis—or in the reaction seen in the test tube as in certain kidney infections. When the toxic mental symptoms arise on the basis of disordered metabolism in this organ or that, tests too may track down the basic situations, perhaps the breathing or metabolic test in overactivity of the thyroid gland, liver and kidney function tests, the electrocardiogram in heart disease. All in all, it is exceedingly likely that the physician will be able to put his diagnostic finger on the source of the poisoning.

Sometimes a simple test or two makes clear a confusing psychotic illness. Some years ago I was called to see a young woman who worked in a stocking factory. She was mildly confused, mistaking the day, the date and place. At home she acted as though she were in the factory. She sat in a chair making the motions she was accustomed to make in her daily work and from time to time stopping to chat with an imaginary fellow worker. However, the confusion frequently lifted and she placed herself accurately in her home surroundings. During the confused periods, she spoke of a "great flock of pigeons" flying about her head. She could hear the rustle of their wings and their "cooing" calls. Sometimes she appeared to be frightened and complained that "they" accused her of immorality and were trying to destroy her mind. I had her admitted to the Psychopathic Pavilion. There, on the day of admission, she passed into a catatonic stupor. She did not move, speak nor eat. Her limbs could be placed in strained, awkward positions which were retained for long periods of time. When she was stuck with a sharp needle, she gave no sign of pain, not even the flicker of an eyelid.

Adding to these symptoms, the fact that the patient had always been introverted and shy, did not have any close friends, never went to parties and never had a beau, made it likely that the psychosis might be schizophrenia. This was my preliminary opinion. As was my custom, I ordered certain laboratory examinations.

To my surprise, the blood showed 300 mg. of bromide in each 100 c.c. There should not be any bromides in the blood. Here was the answer to the riddle. With the administration of ordinary salt and a few other simple treatment measures, the mental symptoms disappeared.

When questioned, the patient told of taking frequent and large doses of a certain patent medicine containing bromides for her "nerves." She expressed great surprise that this should be of any importance. "It's only bromides. It quiets your nerves. All the girls take it. It can't hurt you, can it?"

This leads me naturally to some description of the appalling attitude of the public regarding so-called "harmless" drugs. Millions of people, particularly in this country, take them in the most nonchalant manner. Legislation regarding their sale is very uneven. In some states it is fairly strict, but in others they can be obtained readily enough without prescriptions.

There are no "harmless" drugs. Even aspirin, millions of tablets of which are taken for the slightest twinge of pain or even mild discomfort, can do harm if taken too often and in too large amounts.

I knew an eminent professor who every morning took a massive dose of epsom salts to clear out his bowels and "start the day right." He should have known better. He so depleted his body tissues that he became weak, forgetful and confused and had to undergo a three-months' hospital treatment consisting of rest, vitamin-rich diet and the establishment of a new and less drastic bowel routine.

I need not recite the lengthy list of drugs which are taken with gay abandon and little necessity. I will mention the long series of barbiturates and benzedrine. The barbiturates are sleep-producing and benzedrine is a brain excitant. Both are habit forming. Both have a proper area of usefulness. The physician knows that area and will prescribe them if and as needed.

I know many people who started innocently enough, one barbiturate capsule, taken on the advice of a friend, in order to get a good night's sleep. It worked like magic. Soon another restless night came along. Again the little capsule did the trick. But, after a time, one capsule did not suffice. Two had to be taken. And later on three and more. The seemingly harmless hypnotic drug had sprung the trap and the person was caught. By no means is he always successful in extricating himself. Sometimes an overdose, desperately taken to insure sleep, brings death. Sometimes, and not infrequently, there is suicide.

In my experience, the barbiturate drugs and benzedrine are often taken by the same person.

I knew a brilliant young physician who had a gallant and constructive war record. In the African campaign he sustained multiple shrapnel abdominal wounds. After a long period of treatment in a military surgical hospital, he made a good recovery and was given a medical discharge from the Army. From time to time, he did have considerable discomfort from abdominal adhesions.

He returned to private practice and soon was highly successful. He overworked tremendously and it was not unusual for him to be seeing patients or poring over his records after midnight. He was a fine-grained, conscientious man and worried about his patients. Soon he began to have restless nights, with more wakeful than sleeping hours.

He started to experiment with a mild barbiturate preparation. Apparently he stepped up the dosage rapidly and soon was taking large amounts. In the mornings he had a hang-over, felt dull and stupid and scarcely able to get through his morning office hours and hospital rounds. Then he resorted to benzedrine to keep awake and alert. In a few months he was taking amazingly heavy doses of both the narcotic and excitant drugs.

From the history it would appear that the mental symptoms began with mild confusion. His secretary and his associates noticed that occasionally he was a day or two off in his count. Several times he went into another office, thinking it was his own. None of these things seemed remarkable. They were explained by the fact that he was a very busy and tired man.

At luncheon with his fellow physicians, he talked more freely than before. He said he was going to Washington as the F.B.I. wanted to confer with him about certain information he had picked up during the war in Europe and Africa. This sounded reasonable enough.

But in a few days a medical friend from an adjoining office found him intently examining a .38 caliber loaded revolver. The same day a patient reported that he had given her a large handful of amytal and seconal capsules, saying, "Here, take these, all of them. They will help you." Of course, psychiatric help was sought. At first, he refused to go to a sanitarium but finally agreed to try it "for a week or two."

There his inhibitions disappeared and he told fantastic stories. He said he was head of all the espionage work in this country and all over the world. The President wanted him to accept a commission as Lieutenant General, but he had declined. He was under the constant protection of the F.B.I., as evilly disposed nations had put a fabulous price on his head. Sometimes it took him several hours to travel a few city blocks, since the streets swarmed with enemy agents seeking his death and frequently he had to dodge up an alley to change his disguise. Once he had performed a post-mortem examination on a super-spy whom he had shot to death in a gun battle. The idea was to discover highly significant information imprinted on the spy's brain. He alone could find, read and interpret these "last thoughts." This message was so important that enemy agents engaged the F.B.I. men in a gun battle in which many lost their lives, while he calmly completed the autopsy. He had warned his wife that if she gave any information about him over the telephone or in any other way, he would have to kill her. (His wife confirmed this threat.)

After a long period of treatment, the patient recovered and is now trying to rehabilitate himself and return to practice.

I have given only a sampling of the devastation and chaos wrought in a fine mind by "harmless" drugs. Apparently, benzedrine has such a fascinating reputation that in several high schools it was found that some of the youngsters were removing the contents of benzedrine inhalers, and chewing them to extract the drug!*

The toxic psychoses are contained within a pattern of basic symptoms. The consciousness to which is anchored the binding threads that tie us to our environment is disturbed. There is likely to be increased activity of movement. Misinterpretations of messages from the outside world through our senses, illusions and hallucinations commonly occur. The boundaries of the pattern of the typical symptoms are very flexible. It takes a skilled psychiatrist to understand that a little uncer-

* From time to time, I have testified as an expert for the U. S. Postal Service in their campaign to stop the sale of fraudulent medicines. Strangely enough, people can become addicted to taking substances which have no more effect than water.

tainty and mental fumbling in placing one's self in regard to persons, place or time, with some restlessness and perhaps occasionally misinterpretation of what is seen or heard, all of which may be observed in some mild toxic conditions, may be of the same stripe as a severe delirium, in which the patient is completely out of this world as far as the recognition of even his own family and familiar places, like his home, are concerned, in which he thrashes about so wildly that he may have to be restrained to protect him from serious bodily injury and in which the patient screams and shrinks away in stark terror from the horrible creatures of his illusions. The pattern of symptoms is the same, but there are innumerable gradations in degree. So, too, is there a vast difference between a rifle shot and the explosion of an atom bomb.

Here is an average picture. A poor, hard-working immigrant tailor, forty years old, had a discharging ear. Other than applying a few home remedies, he paid little attention to it and kept on working. In a few days he felt very flushed and hot, had headache and the pain in the ear was so sharp that he went to a clinic. The clinic doctor found a fever of almost five degrees, with middle-ear infection, threatening to involve the mastoid. He had him admitted to the hospital.

In a few days, the little tailor began to waver in his consciousness. Often he thought he was in the tailor shop and industriously went through the motions of operating a sewing machine. These periods were relatively brief in duration and again and again, he would place himself correctly in "the good hospital." Sometimes when his wife visited him, he did not recognize her and shrank from her, frightened. But usually before she left, he knew her, was quite affectionate in his language and asked anxiously for the children. Once he said tomorrow would be "X" day (a Hungarian holiday which comes in the summer). He readily admitted his error when the falling snow outside the window was pointed out to him.

Often when he was going through the motions of sewing, he would busily brush away something. Later it appeared that these were "imaginary" cotton bastings, showers of them which "those who hate foreigners" were strewing over his work. Several times he complained that the ward nurse had called him "a foreign pig." He had "overheard" his fellow patients whisper that she was a spy in the employ of "those who hate foreigners."

The patient's emotional reactions were very fluid. He cried a great deal. As various delusional thoughts swept briefly through his mind, his face expressed in rapid sequence unhappiness, irritability, anger, distrust, fear and, occasionally, satisfaction.

With removal of the infection, sulfa drugs and general vitamin and upbuilding treatment, the tailor made an excellent recovery.

I am always dubious as to a basic toxic condition when with delusions, illusions and hallucinations, the consciousness remains clear and alert. It is more likely to be schizophrenia or some other psychosis.

A young colored man was brought to my City Hospital Service by the police. With great difficulty they had coaxed him down from a telegraph pole which he had climbed almost to the top. Since he did drink to excess and heard voices, the first diagnosis was "alcoholic hallucinosis." He related his experience easily and naturally. "It was such and such a day (given correctly), about three o'clock. I was walking along the street and suddenly God said to me, 'Sam, I want you to climb that pole.' And I clumb a ways. And God said, 'Climb higher, Sam.' And I clumb higher. And, when I stopped, God kept on telling me to go higher, until I clumb near the top." "What then, Sam?" "Well, God said, 'Sam, I want you to climb to the top,' and I said, 'God, that's going too far.' "

Sam had schizophrenia.

In making a diagnosis of toxic psychosis, the physician has the advantage of noting general signs of bodily poisoning, perhaps fever, headache, constipation, weight loss, increase in the number of white blood cells, tremors, inco-ordination, nausea, vomiting, skin rashes and many other signs. Then there are particular signs which point to the seat of the toxicity, perhaps paralysis in infantile paralysis, the distinctive rash in scarlet fever, the "ague" or chills and fever of malaria, the swelling (edema) from fluid, in heart and kidney disease, and a long list of many other distinctive signs.

The outlook for recovery in the toxic conditions is excellent. There are, of course, exceptions. The poisoning may be overwhelming. Or there may be addiction to a narcotic drug like morphine, which cannot be broken. Or the source of the toxicity may be a disease which in itself is death-dealing, as in the final stages of cancer.

Theoretically, at least, all the toxic mental reactions due to poisons taken into the body consciously are preventable. After all, there are far less dangerous ways of softening the impact of reality than by taking large amounts of alcohol and drugs. It is good self-discipline and strengthening to the ego not to reach frantically for a pain-relieving tablet at the slightest tinge of discomfort.

Great strides have been made in the prevention of industrial poisoning hazards. Naturally, as with all of us, familiarity breeds contempt, and workers grow careless. Sometimes, nothing more than thorough physical cleanliness is required. Of course, many infectious diseases are not preventable, but many of them are, by vaccination and various immunizing sera. And, if the diseases do occur, even then prompt and thorough treatment lessens the likelihood and reduces the severity of toxic mental symptoms. Periodic health examinations may reveal a tendency to this or that metabolic disorder, and often effective safeguarding measures may be taken. And, even if the metabolic disturbance does occur, then often reasonable observance of a physical and psychological regime may restrict it to safe territory. The brain is a very precious organ. It opens up for us an infinite number and variety of satisfactions and pleasures. It stands a great deal of abuse, but, of course, we cannot expect it to function normally if we permit it to be poisoned.

All in all, the physician does a good job in the management of the toxic mental reactions. It may not seem so to the observer, but he is following a careful and logical plan of treatment.

The first step is to remove, if possible, the poison. Sometimes this is simple, sometimes extraordinarily difficult. It may amount merely to placing the patient in a situation which cuts off the supply of alcohol. It may mean giving some substance which will neutralize the poison, as, for instance, salt in bromide intoxication. On the other hand, a surgical operation may be necessary. In certain cases of thyroid toxicity, part of the thyroid gland must be cut away to remove the source of poisoning. Recently tried, radioactive iodine is very promising. And in osteomyelitis, or perhaps abscess formation in various parts of the body, the pus must be evacuated surgically, and so on.

Almost always the physician makes every effort to dilute the poisonous substance. He may increase the fluid intake and promote elimination by stimulating the bowel, kidney and skin functions.

Since poisoned bodily tissues throw a heavy strain on the heart and blood vessels and hinder the free performance of their functions, the physician skillfully supports the life-giving organ by carefully selected medication.

Since, too, the poison takes heavy toll of the nutrition and strength of the body, usually there is ordered a generous diet with sufficient vitamins and perhaps upbuilding tonics. If the situation is serious, transfusions of blood may be life saving.

The physician focuses a critical eye upon the insomnia which is usually present. Here is a problem of nice medical judgment. Sleep is necessary. Hypnotic drugs in sufficient dosage will produce sleep. Also, they add another toxic agent to a body already overburdened with poison. The nicety of judgment involves using a minimal amount of the least harmful hypnotic drugs and, as far as possible, the employment of other sleep-producing measures—hydrotherapy, wet packs and long-continued baths in water at a neutral temperature. Skillful, tactful nursing may create a psychological atmosphere which favors sleep. Not like a probationer nurse who awakened one of my patients from a much-needed sleep, to be sure she had actually been asleep, so that she could record it in the night report.

The doctor and competent nurse pool their resources in the psychological management of the patient. No matter how delirious the patient, they never feel that calming reassurance oft repeated is to be neglected. The soothing human voice and behavior, trained not only in what to say and do but also in how to say and do it, often have power over the terrors which come when some poison draws a curtain between the mind and its environment.

Thoughtful, well-trained psychiatric nurses are ever on the alert, but not too obviously, about the danger of suicide. Suicide is much more common in toxic psychoses than is generally realized. In Philadelphia some years ago I made some observations regarding suicide in toxic psychoses. Not only were they more common than was supposed, but they occurred more often in patients in general hospitals than in those in mental hospitals. Psychiatrists and psychiatric nurses, by their experience, were more alerted to the danger.

A specific medicine or treatment is one which actually cures a given disease, like quinine in malaria. There are not many specifics in the practice of medicine. However, in recent times, brilliant researches have produced from the treasure box of pharmacology penicillin, the sulfa drugs and many other antibiotics, which often deal incisively with the organisms and toxins causing many diseases. Psychiatry shares in this scientific benefaction. The use of these substances not only saves many lives which formerly would have been lost, but also they have decreased the incidence of toxic mental reactions, since they may put a period to the course of many diseases before they seriously involve the brain and its functions.

While chronic alcoholism is primarily a psychological disturbance, yet it does involve the organs and tissues of the body, including the brain and entire nervous system. Delirium tremens, acute alcoholic hallucinosis, which is a kind of delirium in the sphere of misinterpreted hearing rather than vision, alcoholic polyneuritis, Korsakoff's psychosis and alcoholic dementia are only a few of the conditions with marked mental symptoms in which a tidal wave of toxicity overwhelms the brain and its connections. True enough, modern investigations have demonstrated that often alcohol sets the stage, but the real damage comes from the lessening of food intake and notably from the vitamin starvation. Alcoholics engaged in serious debauches, sometimes consuming several quarts of whiskey daily, are not interested in food and the body and brain are deprived of adequate nutritional supply.

Modern treatment deals very satisfactorily with many of these grave complications of alcoholism by supplying much-needed potent vitamins and other substances.

Delirium tremens in the days when it was treated largely by sleep-producing drugs and physical restraint had a mortality as high as 20 per cent. Today, treated more rationally, with a minimum of sleep-producing drugs or none at all, and injections into the veins of insulin and certain vitamins, the delirium is often stopped in its tracks. Experimental work with oxygen inhalations makes it likely that this will prove to be a valuable method of treatment. I have not seen a delirium-tremens patient die for a long time. God and science are good to alcoholics.

Incidentally, as I have indicated, the content of delirium tremens belongs in a cabinet of horrors. Such grotesque and terrible creatures as are described by the patient could not have existed even in prehistoric ages. In many years of experience, I have observed only one instance in which the content of the delirium was not horrible.

Pat, a young Irishman and a chronic alcoholic, had had several attacks of orthodox delirium tremens. Again, he had been drinking heavily and not eating and was sitting in the kitchen of his house, sunk in a semi-drunken torpor. Suddenly he called upstairs to his wife, "Mary, come down right away, we have a fortune in our hands." His wife came into the kitchen and Pat eagerly pointed out to her a blank space on the wall: "See what is there on the screen. Scenes from foreign lands. I put them on the screen just by thinking about the countries. We'll patent it, Mary, and then we'll be on easy street." But Mary looked at the wall and at her husband, and then took him by the ear and marched him to the city hospital.

When poisons have been introduced into the body from without, as in addictions, there arises the question of how quickly to withdraw the drug. Alcohol may be stopped at once. The popular idea that the patient should be tapered off or else there will be serious consequences is not founded in fact. Tapering off does more harm than good.

In fact, with the exception of morphine and perhaps some of the other derivatives of opium and cocaine, the habit-forming drug may be abruptly withdrawn.

It well may be that research work now being carried on by Dr. Harris Isbell, Director of Research at the U. S. Public Health Service Hospital at Lexington, Kentucky, may change the current attitude that barbiturate preparations may be withdrawn rather abruptly. Dr. Isbell feels that the barbiturate addict undergoes a much more agonizing period, with a greater threat of death, than other drug users. In his experience, the morphine or opium addict, during withdrawal may be nervous, sleepless, nauseated and so forth, yet the withdrawal is accomplished in about five to seven days, and the patient almost never dies during this period. However, the barbiturate addict has a much more difficult time. Among other things, he may have psychotic symptoms, convulsions, and fall and injure himself. Usually the withdrawal period takes two to three weeks, but it may last as long as three months. At the beginning the addict is usually given eight to twelve of his favorite barbiturates daily and the dose is then gradually reduced to one pill each day. If the patient becomes seriously agitated, the former dose is resumed. At the Public Health Hospital, bromides and paraldehyde are being used to support the patient during the withdrawal period. Even with morphine, gradual decrease of the dosage over a long period of time is not good treatment. A few days should suffice, the number of days depending somewhat on the average daily dose and the physical condition of the patient.

It is true that a morphine habitué suffering from real signs of withdrawal (withdrawal symptoms may be exaggerated or even simulated) does not present a pleasant picture and there is the temptation of taking him out of his misery by ordering a dose of the drug. The temptation should be resisted unless there is danger of serious physical collapse. The patient whose dosage of morphine has been stopped is apt to yawn prodigiously and his eyes run tears. He sneezes frequently. There are restless movements and often severe sweating and chills. The patient may suffer from abdominal cramps, vomiting and diarrhea. The speech may be thick. If withdrawal symptoms do occur, they usually appear about forty-eight hours after the cessation of the morphine and last from five to fourteen days.

The permanent recovery rate in morphinism and other potent narcotic drug addictions is not very high. The difficulty does not come so much from dealing with the drug, but from the inadequate and ineffective personality of the drug-taker. Too often, the personality structure is too immature and weak to support the mature determination and courage needed to conquer the habit.

When the addiction is the result of a very serious situation entirely beyond the control of an individual who has a basically sound personality, then the outlook is much more promising.

A former professional colleague of mine, a distinguished gynecologist, now dead, developed a serious infection of the right hand from an operation he performed. Before the days of penicillin, the infection rapidly spread up the arm, which became enormously swollen. The surgeon felt the arm should be amputated but my friend elected to take the chance on his life rather than risk his professional career by the loss of his right arm. The infection and the surgical treatment were excruciatingly painful over a period of almost six months. The surgeon ordered morphine to relieve the pain and the patient was on a dosage of six grains daily (one-quarter grain is the usual medicinal dose). Finally, both the life and the arm of the patient were saved, although the last and the ring finger and the adjoining part of the hand had to be amputated.

Within less than six months, with very little psychiatric assistance and only ten days in a sanitarium, my friend broke the morphine habit and had a highly productive and successful career until his death, fifteen years later. It was typical of his high courage that he said to me that the loss of half his hand was a blessing in disguise, since he was able to make a much more extensive and thorough pelvic examination than when he had a whole hand.

It must not be assumed that the things a delirious patient says or does come from the drug or poison. They come from the cloistered precincts of the patient's psyche. The drug or poison merely pulls the trigger. The conscious mind is loosed from its moorings. The critical, restraining, inhibitory function becomes disorganized. The guard is down. The locks are opened and often a stream of words pours forth from the recesses of the personality, expressive of thoughts and feelings so deeply hidden that their existence was not even suspected by the conscious mind.

A man who had periods of alcoholism, when in his cups, would act with undue physical familiarity toward his fellow drinkers and make very disparaging remarks about women. Several times, while very drunk, his lewd speech and gestures revealed with brutal frankness an unmistakably strong latent homosexuality in his make-up. In his sober times, he lived a heterosexual life with his wife and was rigidly and even violently intolerant of any social tolerance of homosexuality. "Horrible" and "foul" were his gentlest words for it.

A woman of forty, whose selfishly possessive semi-invalid mother had kept her chained for many years to nursing her, until the chances of making a life of her own were lost, came down with acute articular rheumatism. In her delirium she referred to "that evil female spirit who would not die so that I could live." Sometimes it was "the black cat who sucked away the breath of my life."

A man in his fifties, sick with malarial fever, would surreptitiously cover the hand of his nurse if she rested it on the bed as she sat at his side. After recovery, curiosity prompted the physician to trace down this act, so often performed in the delirium. The patient then remembered something from his childhood which he had completely forgotten. He had been devotedly attached to his mother, who died of a long, lingering tuberculosis. He could not bear the sight of her pitifully thin hands, so when permitted to see her, he would in some way contrive to cover them with the bedclothes.

According to statistics, toxic psychoses represent about ten per cent of mental diseases. I have little doubt that the actual number is three or four times as great. The statistics are based on the records of public mental hospitals. Many of these patients are treated in general hospitals, in sanitoria and in the home.

It is to be emphasized that in no field of practice can general medical men utilize the teachings of psychiatry more profitably and find greater opportunities for prevention and cure than in the toxic mental reactions.

6 | "FUNCTIONAL" SICKNESS

In this explanatory discussion, I am compelled to use the word "functional" in its common but far too restricted sense. All human sickness is functional, that is, the organs and parts of the body do *not* perform their functions satisfactorily as they do in health. This is true, whether or not there is inflammation or destruction of the tissues of the brain, or any of the body organs or parts. However, "functional" is usually, albeit too narrowly, used in the sense of illness due to unsolved emotional conflicts. Of course, since the *whole* person is in the grip of the conflict, the body cannot do its job properly, just as it could not function as it should if there were a growth in the stomach or a tumor in the brain, instead of a serious mental conflict.

Using "functional" in this restricted way, for purposes of explanation, how is the psychiatrist able to identify a patient's symptoms as functional? Certainly not by the kind of symptoms. Headache, backache, nausea, vomiting, skin rash, indeed the whole list of the complaints patients make to their doctors appears in case histories routinely and indifferently, as to whether the pathology is in terms of actual tissue as in cirrhosis of the liver, or less concrete, but just as real, pathology hidden behind the portals of the unconscious psyche, perhaps a repressed sexual trauma of childhood.

As a medical student, I was told not to worry about how to distinguish symptoms, headache or what not, the organic (the professor called these "real") from the functional symptoms (the professor called these "imaginary"). I was informed that the organic or "real" symptoms could be seen and demonstrated, like, for instance, vomiting or a skin rash or blood in the stool. Conversely, the functional symptoms, or "imaginary" ones, were not demonstrable or objective. They were subjective. They were the things of which the patients complained, perhaps backache. The inference was that unless the doctor could "prove" the backache by some chemical, x-ray or other test, then it would be safer to assume that there was no backache. The patient was one of those queer "hypochondriacs," a creature of imaginary ailments, and nothing much could be done about it.

I have often reflected that if I had put the objective-subjective teaching into practice, I would have done irreparable harm to many hundreds of very sick patients. Of course, the whole idea was silly and archaic. In an anxiety or other neurosis, the rapidly beating heart, perhaps 140 beats per minute, is just as real as if there were a diseased heart. And the vomitus can be seen just as plainly, whether it comes from a psychic rejection of pregnancy or from a liver toxemia in a pregnant woman. The skin may be as flaming red when it expresses a mental conflict as it is in scarlet fever. And so on.

I am glad, too, further to disbar from the precincts of real scientific thought the oft-repeated fallacy that the patient who has so-called organic disease is a much sicker person than the one who is *just* "functional." In the course of years of practice, I have seen many patients with severe psychoneuroses. Personally, I would prefer to have a so-called organic disease, even if moderately severe. For one thing, there is usually less suffering. The sharp lancinating pain of appendicitis is not pleasant, but I would accept it rather than undergo long-drawn-out and baffling anxiety and tension. Furthermore, even with considerable allowance made for a more intelligent attitude toward nervous illness, there are still many, far too many, blind spots of ignorance and even intolerance. It is still too often sadly true that if one can point to something that may be seen through a microscope or in a test tube or revealed by some test, then one is considered legitimately and "respectably" sick—otherwise not.

Finally, if there is any question remaining as to how sick a person may be functionally, let me say that occasionally, though rarely, a patient may die of a psychoneurosis. At least, they may become so depleted and vulnerable, as a result of very severe unsolved emotional conflicts, that there is no longer enough resistance to overcome some chance complicating illness.

Perhaps I may sum up what I have written by saying that sickness is sickness. Always, all of the patient is sick. Always does sickness upset and distort the functioning of the organs of the body. Perhaps the chief difference is that in organic disease, the disturbance of function is chiefly at the level of damage to the tissue of organs; in functional disease, unsolved mental conflicts are at fault.

It is true that usually the pathology of organic disease may be more definitely visualized and localized. But by no means is this constantly true. It is not so very unusual to find discrepancies between the diagnosis during life and the findings at autopsy. At autopsy there may be more extensive involve-

ment of organs than was realized or the location may be somewhat different than was diagnosed. Occasionally, too, pathology may be revealed that was not even remotely suspected.
Medicine is an art more than a science.

Where is the pathology of irreconcilable emotional conflicts,
the pathology of the psyche, psychopathology? Of course, it is
in every cell and recess of the body and mind of the patient.
Perhaps the psychopathology can be more readily visualized
as being located in that area of the human personality which
is "not-conscious." Here is a deep, almost bottomless reservoir
with many levels, containing some traces or remnants of everything that has happened to the individual in his lifetime and
his reactions to these happenings, perhaps even only thoughts.
Many psychoanalysts would regard this as a very minimum
estimate of the material not easily accessible to conscious, deliberate thinking. They feel that they have demonstrated by
plumbing the depths of the "not-conscious" mind that material
may be recovered, easily identifiable as having its source while
the individual was a foetus in the womb of the mother or even
reaching back through many eons of time, into the dim, his-
torically unrecorded experiences of primitive man.

In any event, there is a heavy line of demarcation, but not
completely closed, between the conscious and "not-conscious"
mind. The conscious mind is the mind of awareness. It is the
mind that says, "Good morning" and "How are you?" It orients, places the person correctly as to time, place and identity,
and its content is useful in ordinary business and social conversations. Even at this level, it frequently reaches down into
the "not-conscious" for help in associating and elaborating
ideas. It says and does many things, but, of itself, it is not
able to view the deeper reasons for the saying and doing. Altogether, it is a shallow compartment.

The "not-conscious" mind is very deep with many levels.

Superficially, there is a level from which, with a little effort, "forgotten" things can be reclaimed and brought into consciousness. Deeper, there are levels from which material can be brought into the open only with strong labors of recall. Then there are sensitive areas scattered throughout, from which seep through interesting little slips of speech and behavior, the significance of which is not realized by the person who makes them. From time to time, a patient says to me, with great emphasis, of his wife, "She is a very good woman." Or a

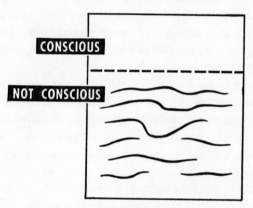

A diagrammatic visualization of the mind

wife of her husband, "He is such a considerate man." Fine, laudatory remarks, but the speakers are unaware of the fact that there was a paradox in the words of the statements and the deep, obviously regretful sighs that accompanied them. Every physician occasionally receives an unsigned check from a patient. Perhaps sometimes it is a not-conscious evaluation of the value placed by the patient on the services rendered.

Then there are many deep layers of "not-conscious" mental activity. These are tightly sealed compartments, but their coverings may be pried off, perhaps by delirium, anaesthesia, drugs, in dream life and, as an important treatment technique, by the free association of psychoanalysis. And in every person's psyche, there are things in the subterranean depths which never come into the light of consciousness. Probably it is better that they do not.

It is scarcely necessary to validate the existence and operation of a "not-conscious" mind. In the outpourings of delirium (seemingly irrelevant babbling, but actually fraught with deep meaning); when inhibitions have been removed by an anaesthetic or by various drugs; in hypnosis, the waters of consciousness are stilled, and much flotsam and jetsam are churned up from the depths and revealed in the stream of unconscious thought and act.

In dreams, we walk in the valley of the unconscious. Often the things we "think" and "do" are very frightening. We may see strange people, including ourselves. Much of the dream content, many dream figures are adequately disguised. It is fortunate. Otherwise, our ego would be hopelessly belittled and shamed.

An added proof comes from the work of the psychotherapist and particularly the psychoanalyst, who by his skilled interpretation of the "random" unsupervised spoken thoughts of patients and their dreams, strip off many coverings of the hidden mental life, so that the patients may know themselves, the first step toward recovery.

Finally, perhaps I may borrow an analogy from the physical sciences. Anything that has once existed, even a scrap of paper, while it can be destroyed, cannot be effaced as though it had never been. By tearing it into bits, by burning it, by subjecting the ashes to heat, to acids and alkalies, by pressure, it can be changed so that it no longer can be recognized as the former scrap of paper, but always something remains. So, too, is it with a human experience, act, or even a thought.

The liver, a muscle or any organ of the body is composed of cells that are chiefly instrumental in performing the function of the organ. They are bound together by connecting tissue. In the field of human behavior, perhaps we can accept the word "complexes" as a name for basic psychological "cells," promoters of conduct, good, bad, indifferent. Each one of us begins to imbibe complexes with our mother's milk, and early in our lives we soon accumulate a vast number of them. They concern all sorts of things—politics, religion, the length of women's skirts, marriage preferences, blondes, brunettes or redheads, baseball or golf. Indeed, anything under the sun. Less in our boasted logic and far more in our complexes are to be found the sources of our likes and dislikes, our loves and hates, our interests, our prejudices and intolerances, the fine things we do in our everyday lives and the ignoble and base ones.

The reasons we give for our interests and hobbies are usually high-sounding, plausible and fallacious. The range of human activities is limitless—collecting stamps, or coins (I mean old coins), voting the Republican or Democratic ticket, taking poor orphaned children to the circus, promoting parties to swell the fund for research and treatment of "polio," eating pistachio ice-cream. These things and many others are no less interesting, creditable and constructive, even though we do not know fully their derivations and inspirations. Actually we do not. The nucleus of the behavior drives which they activate and inspire in adult life were imbedded into our personalities when we were at our mothers' knees, long before we had enough intelligence even to know and recognize pros and cons, much less make decisions. I know enough about a certain great physician to realize that his decision to study medicine had the determining emotional motivation of the sorrow and distress of his adored mother at the death of his older sister of diabetes, when he was four years old. He has made valuable contributions to the treatment of diabetes. I know an intelligent man who spends considerable time and effort in promoting the idea that children should not be taught any prayers, even a simple "Now I lay me down to sleep" since, as he states, it damages their developing egos and will make them too dependent. Actually, I think his attitude was laid down in his childhood by his rigid and righteous, hell-and-damnation father: no music or dancing, no bright colors or laughter and long knee-racking hours spent in gloomy family prayers.

Many of our complexes lead us to satisfactory enough behavior. At its lowest rating, interestingly time-passing pursuits and avocations, at its highest, useful endeavors and occupations, philanthropies and perhaps the noblest, most unselfish and even saintly lives.

Every complex demands and must have its day in the Court of Human Behavior. In some shape or fashion, it *will* be heard, expressed in our everyday speech and actions. And, often, it may be expressed directly and easily enough. After all, there is nothing out of the way in collecting stamps or old coins, being a baseball fan or working for local option. At worst, sometimes enthusiasts in this or that movement become too enthusiastic and bore their friends. At social gatherings, I never discuss psychiatry unless I am convinced that the group earnestly desires to hear about it. Otherwise, I prefer to talk about sculpturing, the fourth dimension, the H bomb, or something about which I do not know anything.

There are two conditions which constitute a bar to the expression in conscious behavior of trends emanating from our unconscious complexes. The first condition is that the conscious recognition of the nature of the complex would be unpleasant and even shameful and repulsive to the total personality.

The second condition, which usually follows the first, is that the complex put into action would sin against the social code and bring down upon the head of the sinner the condemnation and retaliation of the herd, his fellow men. After all, the conscious behavior response to collecting stamps, or coins or even betting mildly on horse races is socially acceptable enough. To give rein in behavior to a strong latent homosexual drive or an incestuous desire of a son for his mother is not acceptable. Society would brand the transgressor as unclean—a moral leper. The law would seek to punish the offender.

Perhaps the appended diagram may serve to illustrate the situation:

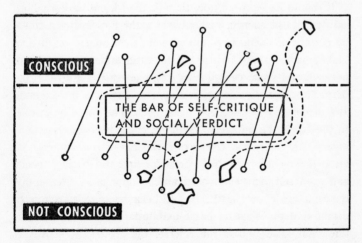

The small circles ° ° ° ° represent "normal" complexes. The conduct flowing from them is personally and socially acceptable. Therefore, they may appear in the stream of everyday conscious behavior, unchanged in form. The behavior resulting from the complexes ⟁⟁⟁ would be outlawed by the individual and by society. Therefore, seeking expression in unconsciousness, as they must, they are blocked by the bar of self-critique and the adverse social verdict, and they must be camouflaged ⟁⟁⟁ before they can appear in conscious behavior in passably acceptable form.

It may be repeated that every human being has complexes seeking expression in behavior, which, if uncensored and uninhibited, would be indicted at the bar of personal and social judgment. The unconscious psyche is the terrain upon which conflicts are fought and there are strong power drives from the ego with its self-preservative demands, from sex often socially unruly in its desires, from an unconscious but canny estimate of the balance between the amount of aggressiveness that the herd or society will accept.

It should be repeated, too, there is the Id, not only a powerful dynamo of energy, without which the human being would be pallid and ineffective, but also it is the source of instinctual demands asking for immediate gratification, irrespective of personal and social consequences. In one sense, the Id is primitive man, primitive in aggressive ego demands, in sex urges and in defiance of the herd social code. The opposite number to the Id, is the Superego, civilized, cultured man, containing among other things a conscience, capable of pronouncing adverse judgment upon "bad" behavior and stimulating "good" and even self-sacrificing, ideal and noble conduct. Naturally, the Superego closely scrutinizes Id behavior, recoils from, condemns and punishes its baser manifestations. Often it is too intolerant. The Ego is the referee, the arbiter. It strives to keep the Id within reasonable personal and social bounds. At the same time, it asks the Superego not to be too severe and unrelenting in its expectations and judgments. Not infrequently, the Ego is caught in the pincer movement between

Id and Superego. The Ego, too, must maintain itself. It is the *person* as presented to public view, to his fellow men. Therefore it must not be either too blatant or too belittled. These, then, are the contending forces. This is the battleground. All human behavior, even ordinary everyday behavior, is the result of a compromise in the psyche. The vast majority are reasonably satisfactory compromises. But the fields of human conflict also are bestrewn with compromises, pathological, sick compromises which sacrifice some of the hold on reality, but as little as possible in the circumstances. Still something of mental health is relinquished.

Perhaps what has been said, I hope not at too great length, may be briefly summarized:

A. In addition to the conscious mind, there is a mind in every human being whose content and operations are beyond the horizons of consciousness.

B. This mind may be and actually often is the seat of extremely important pathology, psychopathology, determining human illness.

C. Such psychopathology results from irreconcilable drives, dictating opposing kinds of behavior.

D. Failing a reasonably satisfactory compromise, an impasse results. An irresistible force has encountered an immovable body. Such an impasse cannot continue. It would mean a psychological catastrophe, perhaps a major psychosis. However faulty it may be, a compromise must be found. Often some of the inner pressure is removed by changing or converting the emotional conflict into signs and symptoms, perhaps headache, nausea, vomiting, rapid beating of the heart and innumerable other symptoms, which are readily discoverable upon examination of the patient by the physician.

Human beings assailed by the forces of a severe mental conflict defend themselves as best they can. Naturally, they use those psychological weapons—mechanisms of defense—best adapted for each particular personality under assault. Each one of us utilizes some of them in miniature, in meeting the everyday problems of life and it is entirely normal for us to employ them in moderate amounts. For instance, some of us are given to a bit of rationalizing and use it expertly. A neighbor calls up inviting to an evening of bridge. We decline regretfully, pleading "a mean headache." We like bridge but the head does ache—and we *can't stand that particular neighbor.*" Fifteen minutes later, a friend we do like phones and we enthusiastically agree to go to the movies. The headache disappears. These mild self-deceptions or rationalizations are comparatively harmless. They even lubricate the wheels of complicated personal and social living.

On the other hand, a patient complains of abdominal pain, headache, nausea, vomiting, dizziness and colitis. As far as the sick woman is concerned, the illness *must be* within the framework of the symptoms. She makes the rounds of physicians seeking confirmation of her strong belief that she had some disease of her stomach or intestines—perhaps "a growth." In two of many such patients I have treated, the symptoms in one were a rationalization of the frustration and hostility resulting from lack of affection during childhood and practically rejection by her mother. In the other patient, the symptoms rationalized dissatisfaction with her husband and rebellion against sexual intercourse with him.

Rationalization and other mental mechanisms not only help shape the symptoms but effectively disguise them. In this way, the material of the mental conflict, the real reason for the symptoms, is excluded from the area of consciousness, where its recognition would belittle and shame the ego. Perhaps this simple diagram will illustrate the operation of the mechanism of rationalization:

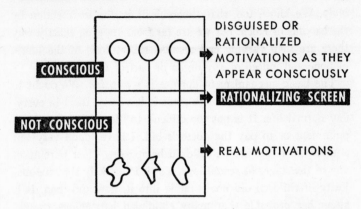

DISGUISED OR RATIONALIZED MOTIVATIONS AS THEY APPEAR CONSCIOUSLY

RATIONALIZING SCREEN

REAL MOTIVATIONS

We would all like to know just how these transformations of mental conflicts into physical symptoms are accomplished. We do know how emotions influence the function of body tissues. We do know some of the passageways, the autonomic and ductless gland systems, certain parts of the brain and, indeed, we know that every tissue and cell of the body and notably the organs that bear the burden of the emotional conflict participate in the process.* A recent theory describes an "assemblage" of nerve brain cells, acting together by repeated, habitual behavior and becoming through frequent usage readily stimulated and capable of exciting the entire central nervous system into action, producing various forms of behavior.

As time goes on, we will acquire more accurate information. Incidentally, in passing it might be noted that even in the more concrete field of so-called physical disease, our knowledge is far from complete. For instance, we know only imperfectly the stages that occur between infection by the spirochete of syphilis and the end result which might be arteriosclerosis or locomotor ataxia or syphilis of any part of the

---

* *Organization of Behavior,* by D. O. Hebb. (John Wiley & Sons, Inc. New York, 1949.)

body. We know, too, that tuberculosis is due to infection by the bacillus of Koch, but we are far from knowing exactly why there are such varying end results: tuberculosis of the lungs, of bone and indeed of any organ or part of the body.

The basic mechanism of defense is *repression*. We ought to understand it readily enough since it has large areas in everyday normal life. It is not too difficult to "forget" a dental appointment or to pay the doctor's bill. I have found very few adults who remember as children having seen their parents in any of the stages of sexual love. Yet it is unlikely that the majority of children did not stumble into it, now and then. It is altogether probable that many childhood happenings fraught with deep emotional import would have confused and frightened our small egos. So they were repressed.

The repression which is a requisite in the production of functional illness is a much more serious consideration. It deals with conflict material which for the time being cannot be even remotely faced. Its mere approach to the periphery of consciousness is sufficient markedly to increase the patient's tension and anxiety. If it were suddenly illuminated by the floodlight of consciousness, there would be psychological panic and chaos. Such sensitive emotional material often dates back to childhood, perhaps early sexual trauma or the severe and damaging insult of being an unwanted and rejected child. Or a strong latent homosexuality. Or, as in war, the terrific emotional experiences of seeing scattered fragments of what a few moments before were whole, breathing, moving, talking, laughing fellow soldiers and friends. Or in civilian life, the sudden death of a beloved mother, the inconstancy of a lover, the sight of the infidelity of a husband or wife.

At first glance, repression would seem to be a psychological blessing. If things that are painful, belittling and shaming to remember can be wiped out of memory, relegated to the Nirvana of the forgotten, then they can no longer trouble us. Unfortunately, they do continue to trouble, often to the point of being instrumental in provoking illness. Emotionally highly charged material that is repressed because we cannot face it openly is not annihilated. It is merely submerged below the surface of consciousness. There it remains, an isolated sensitized focus of psychic unrest. The remembrance of the actual experience has been dislocated from the emotional matrix in which it was embedded. The molecule has been split and the emotional atom is sometimes spoken of as "free floating anxiety." It is inevitable that it should form attachments which often are symbolic representations of the original experience.

A young woman was markedly allergic to alcohol. The smell of any spiritous liquor like whiskey nauseated her, made her "catch" her breath, and the taste of liquor made her sick to her stomach with violent retching, long-continued vomiting, asthma-like gasping for air and feelings of suffocation. She avoided alcohol, which was simple enough, but she could scarcely avoid seeing people drink socially. And usually this made her feel very "uneasy" and tense. She knew of no reason why this should be so. She had no feeling about people drinking socially, and indeed she often envied their enjoyment and wished she could participate.

To cut a few corners, analytical probing of her psyche and removal of inhibition by sodium pentothal revealed that at about the age of six at least three times she had seen her mother in a drunken stupor, quite unconscious and breathing heavily and irregularly.

The case is nicely illustrative of repression. The child could not understand the dreadful situation intellectually. Therefore the psychic insult was all the more severe and damaging. She was desperate and terror-stricken because her frantic efforts to arouse her mother were unavailing. The experience could not be tolerated in conscious memory. It had to be repressed. The emotion which it had engendered became attached in consciousness to the "allergy" to alcohol and the whole train of symptoms, including asthmatic attacks.

The dissociation of thought and feeling produced by repression is scarcely conducive to mental health. Indeed, repression is a dangerous mental mechanism which paves the way for much functional sickness. It provides the favorable setting for the operation of other mechanisms of defense.

For instance, there is the very simple device of *regression*. Regression means to step backward, to utilize the weapons of childhood in attempting to meet and solve adult situations and problems. This is the area of sullenness, sulking and tears, of door slamming and fist pounding on tables, of temper tantrums, even of staged and artificial suicidal attempts. A few days ago I read in the public press the account of a husband who, sitting in an automobile, grew tired of waiting for his wife and expressed his frustration by crashing his fist through the windshield. He had to be taken to a hospital for treatment of severe lacerations. It did not solve his problem.

It is not adult behavior, even though a minimum of it is understandable and permissible in the life of every human being. It is said that a former President of the United States, when his will was thwarted, threw himself on the floor of one of the White House rooms and screamed and kicked like a child. True, his provocation was great, but the kicking and screaming did not accomplish his political objective. The patterns of these regressive techniques are laid down in childhood. Then they are much more logical. After all, a child's range of protest against the environment for what it considers unfair treatment is quite limited. In adult life the same childlike behavior is exhibited but it serves an unconscious complex. It may be an unconscious protest on the part of an immature husband that his wife is unwilling to be his mother, or by a child-wife that her husband is different from the father figure remaining in her psyche from her childhood. The angry vehemence and door-slamming of the husband "because" the breakfast eggs are overdone or the tears of the wife because her husband insists she return a hat which they cannot afford are merely the surface eruptions of emotional volcanoes whose real activities are deeply buried.

In some forms of "nervous" illness, the psychiatrist has difficulty in preventing the patient from putting him in the position of complete authority. The patient wants to be praised and petted, scolded and spanked. Least of all, unconsciously, does the patient want to grow up emotionally. Sometimes the physical symptoms of the neurosis are pitifully transparent— an assortment of discomforts and aches about which the patient unconsciously wants the doctor to show great concern, to rub them psychologically and make them well.

Projection and introjection or identification, its opposite number, are two interesting albeit somewhat dangerous mental mechanisms, commonly employed to escape the reality struggle of inner mental conflicts. They both have large and even mildly useful segments in average everyday life.

Projection removes the blame for things that go wrong, or "are not right," from our inner selves, where it belongs, and places it upon the environment. It does no great harm to blame the "fidgeting" of the caddy for a golf drive that foozled; the "poor" post-war materials for the paint that peeled off a few days after it was applied; the failure of the party upon the stupidity of the guests. We all do this sort of thing from time to time.

Classically, there is the automobile driver, often not too skillful, whose numerous accidents are always due to the "negligence" and even "homicidal mania" of the other drivers.

But there are deeper unconscious levels from which emerge less innocent behavior, behavior pressured by bias, prejudice and even bloody intolerance. And there are cesspools of projection. In one of John Steinbeck's short stories, a "poor white," is one of the ringleaders in the brutal lynching of a Negro. On his way home he ponders on his feeling of satisfaction, pleasant satiation as though he had eaten a fine, large meal. As he enters his cabin, his slatternly wife looks into his face and accuses him of having "had" a woman. In his room, he stares long and reflectively into a broken bit of mirror and concludes, "By God, I look as if I had a woman."

In sickness, both psychotic and psychoneurotic, projection is frequently unconsciously employed as a defense mechanism. In a sense, it flings the "blame" as far as possible away from the inner core of real motivations into the outer world. Thus, the ego is not sullied.

As has been cited in the instance of a strong latent homosexual complex, the personality may accept, unconsciously, definite mental symptoms, hearing of defaming voices and fantastic "persecutions" in order to push out as far as possible the ego-shaming recognition of sexual love for the same sex.

I had a patient, now well, who had a whole host of psychosomatic symptoms referable to the genito-urinary area of the body. There was frequent urination, usually with discomfort, shooting pains in the sexual organs, sometimes "swelling" (which I was never able to verify), headache, fatigue. All these symptoms became markedly worse whenever he felt that his wife expected sex relations with him. At these times, he claimed, she was so "nervous" that she "worried" him. In the course of treatment, it became quite clear that the symptoms were the physical expressions of a defense mechanism, projection foci for a hidden-from-conscious-self, latent homosexuality.

If I may be permitted to indulge myself in another drawing, perhaps motivated by an erroneous belief that I have a talent for making ideas clear by diagrams, I would illustrate projection in this way:

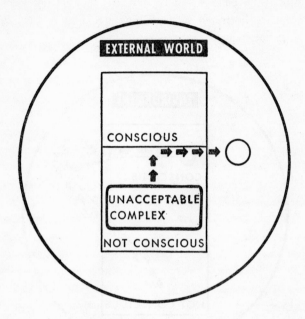

The unacceptable complex cannot face conscious recognition and is detoured into the environment, where it finds ego-saving, but false, explanations.

While I am at it, I might as well perpetrate another diagram, this time attempting to illustrate the workings of introjection or identification, which travels a path opposite from projection. In projection, when the ego is unable to face certain complexes, the personality disowns them, attempts to dislocate them and cast them into the environment, thus escaping self-blame. In identification, the personality, feeling the need of the strength of certain characteristics and qualities it does not possess, but prizes highly, attempts to seize them from the environment and incorporate them into self. That particular personality may then think and act as though the admired qualities really belonged to it. Actually, they do not belong; therefore the borrowed strength they are given is often false and does not endure.

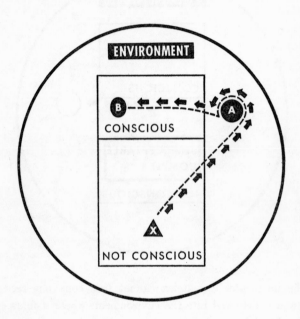

(X) represents some much desired quality for which the particular personality feels a great need, but does not possess, perhaps firmness and decisiveness.

(A) represents a strong expression of such qualities in some person in the environment. It need not be an actual living personage and often is a historical figure or even a fictional character.

The dotted line and arrows illustrate the mechanism of identifying and attempting to take over, as belonging to self. But (B) is not (A), and all too often in its ineffectual expression, it is revealed as a spurious psychological coin.

In its proper place, and kept within reasonable bounds, identification is extremely constructive. In childhood, the identification of the child with the parents, and the imitation that it stimulates, is the single most potent force for the development of personality and the building of emotional maturity. Always provided, of course, that the parents do not have feet of clay. Adolescent hero-worship, too, if not too mistakenly directed, helps to build sound personalities. In adult life we ally ourselves with various movements. Often our selection is unconsciously directed. The particular movement represents an ideal which alone we are too weak to accomplish. So, we identify ourselves with the purposive strength of leaders and numbers and gain personal strength in the identification.

In everyday living, identification enhances our pleasures and satisfactions. When we are really absorbed in a book or play, it is because we identify ourselves with one of the characters. We are so thrilled because it is "we" who do such brave and fine things. We would like to do them in real life.

The test of identification is the kind of action it produces. If it leads to behavior which, even though it be only very slightly, still does make us better and more effective in the right direction, capable of more satisfactory personal and social adjustments, then the identification is well worth-while. If it leads to inaction, if it is merely an escape from reality, then it is useless or worse. It is then much like the identification of a mental patient with Jesus Christ. He does nothing about it and merely sits in a corner of a mental hospital delusionally dreaming away his life.

It is not only a question with whom an identification is made but what in that figure is imitated. Is it the strengths or the weaknesses? The significant things or the trivia? Too frequently one sees rare opportunities to attain personality growth neglected. Among the official family and friends of a great President, a number of men and women profited psychologically by their contact with him. They imbibed of his strengths and of the sincerity of his desire to help the oppressed. They were not tempted by the President's flaws and faults. But then there were the others who identified with and imitated not the greatness of the man, but the manner and mannerisms of his speech and gestures—and the length of his cigarette holder. It was an unprofitable identification—imitation gone to seed. From the identification some of the weaklings gained false strength and confidence and a front of great importance, built on the sands of unconscious inferiority. One is reminded of the fly in Aesop's fable, perched on the wheel of the thundering chariot, observing the huge cloud of dust and remarking, "Lo, see what a cloud of dust *I* am raising."

Sometimes in the treatment of functional sickness, immature identifications occasion considerable difficulty. The psychiatrist in going over the life history has to help the patient topple over a long procession of figures, usually surrogates for the parents, with whom the patient has over-identified, and in weak and ineffectual ways. From them he has not borrowed strength but weakness. They serve to make it exceedingly difficult for him to understand the real meaning of his symptoms. Until they are cleared away, there is a stubborn barrier which blocks that necessary condition of recovery, growing up emotionally and adjusting to life as it is—"Know thyself."

In some degree, in each one of us, there are certain inconsistencies and contradictions in our everyday behavior. Often, our mental right hands do not know what our mental left hands are doing. Conduct quite opposed in character seems to flow from tightly insulated, logic-tight compartments in the unconscious. And never do the twain meet, except perhaps with psychiatric help. If we realized how paradoxical was our behavior it would be hypocrisy. Since we do not realize it at all consciously, and indeed become "hurt" or "angry" when someone calls attention to the inconsistency, it is *segregation,* one of the mechanisms of psychological defense. In its "normal" areas, but, too, in the shaping of a psychoneurosis, or even a psychosis, it is used freely to soften or evade the realities of mental conflict and to save the ego from belittling self-revealment.

Again there is Exhibit A, the "perfect" motor car driver, in reality anything but perfect, who damns and threatens other drivers on the road for the faults which he, himself, freely commits. And then there is the chap who campaigns earnestly for the closing of saloons on Sunday, but sips a cocktail at his club with evident enjoyment on the Sabbath. I am amused at several men I know who scrutinize candidates for membership in the somewhat exclusive club to which they belong with the utmost strictness. To pass their rigid tests, a man has to have a record rather better than Caesar demanded of his wife. It is amusing because their own records were not at all free from blots and they were lucky to get by the Entrance Committee. More seriously, there is the Sunday and Monday man. On Sunday, moved by the church services and a fine sermon, his heart really does overflow with love and mercy for his less fortunate fellow men. But on Monday, he is an aggressive, sharp and ruthless man, not dishonest, but certainly exacting the last ounce of each pound of a business deal. Or, the wealthy woman, wearing herself out in her earnest work in behalf of an organization devoted to improving the personal and social lot of domestic servants. Arriving home from the club meetings, she treats her own servants like dogs. At least she did in that remote area when there were still servants who could be treated like dogs.

There is the story of a Russian Countess, passionately devoted to grand opera. She suffered with the tragic figures and wept at their stage sufferings and distress. With her coachman and footman, she imperiously insisted that they remain at attention at their posts until the opera was over. One bitterly cold winter night, when she returned to the droshky, after having been racked with grief at the sad fate of the heroine of the opera, she found the servants at their posts in the correct postures—frozen to death.

Literature abounds in examples of segregation. Probably the most classical is Dr. Jekyll and Mr. Hyde.

In psychiatry, segregation is strikingly illustrated by the double personality sometimes seen in hysteria. For instance, in Janice X, personality "A" was quiet, gentle, neat, modest and altogether led an exemplary life. But, personality "B" was a noisy, coarse and flamboyant character, smeared over thickly with rouge and lipstick, given to participation in risqué situations and occasionally behaving on a level rather lower than that of the average prostitute. Of course, personalities "A" and "B" did not have even a bowing acquaintance with each other. No doubt "A" would have been shamed beyond expression at "B's" outrageous conduct and "B" would have labeled "A" as a psalm-singing, sniveling old maid.

A few years ago a man about forty years old came to me complaining of backache, headache, difficulty in concentration and great fatigue. No sufficient organic reason was found for the symptoms. In the course of a series of interviews, he said repeatedly and evidently believed that he was happily

married to a "fine, good wife." Again and again he repeated
that he loved his wife and two children very much. As the
story of his life unfolded, another character appeared—a
woman "friend." Again, with evident sincerity, he described
this relationship as "a fine, platonic friendship." This woman,
a widow, was a college graduate, Phi Beta Kappa, with a well-
developed and able mind. Their intellectual interests were
closely akin. Incidentally, she was thirty-seven years old to
his forty, quite feminine in her manner and very attractive
physically. Several times he let slip that she was not so capable and businesslike about "ordinary" things as was his
wife. Even though my patient did not realize it for a long time,
it soon became clear to me that the friendship was far from being solely on a platonic level. For one thing, by actual count,
he spent more of the hours of the day with the widow than he
did with his wife or anyone else. Love-making? Of course *not*—
well, a little kissing and now and then "fondling." (My patient had some trouble with the selection of this word.) After
all, they *were* close friends. Briefly, my patient was in love
with the widow. Largely through his own increased understanding of self, he came to realize this. In all conscious honesty he had not realized it before. He had employed the ego-
saving device of psychological segregation. It is a rather
dangerous psychic fiction.

Often in treatment it is necessary to break down the dykes
which shut off one conscious stream of segregated thinking
from another that runs countercurrent. Observing and particularly feeling the incongruity, the patient arrives at a more
mature evaluation and sounder adjustment.

Now for another diagram, this one to illustrate the workings
of segregation. The conscious behavior does not express a satisfactory compromise between the demands of opposed com-

plexes. They enter the conscious stream of thought and conduct separately and are acted out separately without recognition of their incompatibility.

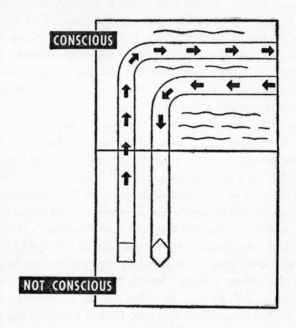

CONSCIOUS

NOT CONSCIOUS

These, then, are some of the psychological stratagems and devices employed by the human psyche.

It is to be repeated that:

1. They are used in small amounts by even the most "normal" of us in the everyday business of personal and social life.

2. When beset by mental conflicts, strong opposing drives which cannot be effectively compromised, we fall back upon the second line of defense and evolve a psychoneurosis. The particular mechanisms of defense used are those which are peculiar to each given personality and have been tried out in everyday life. Each case of "nervous" illness differs from any

other. One may contain a prominent area of regression or projection. Another, rationalization or identification or perhaps segregation, and so on. They all contain repressions. The clinical structure the psychiatrist sees, before he has opened up its hidden cellars and passageways, is largely determined by the markings of the personality which has built the structure.

3. The objective of the defense mechanism is to conceal motivations from conscious self and thus spare the ego from personal and social humiliation. The immediate gain is heavily offset by the penalty which must be paid in terms of functional sickness.

At best all these stratagems and devices are psychological crutches. Often, they are useful and serviceable for a time, but we would not choose to go through life on crutches.

What happens as a result of successful psychiatric treatment? I think it can be best expressed by saying that the patient attains some degree of *sublimation*. Sublimation means to purify or refine. In a psychic sense, it means the direction of the energy away from certain instincts, desires and tendencies into approved personal and social channels—rather than permitting them to flow unrestrictedly and harmfully into wasteful and even harmful and debasing channels.

Always, the patient who has secured fairly satisfactory adjustments as a result of treatment has accomplished something more than the mere disappearance of the neurotic symptoms. There is increased self-understanding. And there is some degree of sublimation. Probably not a great deal, but still some. Perhaps only an appreciation of the need for postponing immediate gratifications and a willingness to modify neurotic demands. A neurosis, though it is unconscious, and not deliberate, nevertheless is selfish in that it tends to sacrifice those in the environment—the family and others who are in close contact with the patient. If the treatment produces enough self-knowledge so that the person becomes more considerate of others, taking less and giving more, in other words, less selfish in behavior, then there is worthwhile sublimation. If treatment gives only relief from the neurotic symptoms, then it falls short of its proper goal. In my mind, it is axiomatic that unless the patient emerges from the treatment a better person than he or she was before, then the treatment has failed.

In history, both profane and sacred, there are innumerable examples of well-nigh complete and perfect sublimations. The prophets and saints, the great humanitarians, the unselfish benefactors of humanity, were men and women of flesh and blood. They, too, had drives which, unrestrained, would have led to selfish and even base conduct. The theologians would call them temptations. In any event, they subdued them and submerged them in the overwhelming love for their fellow men and their desire to help them. I am not suggesting that patients should expect anything similar from psychiatric treatment, or even strive for it. However, the study of the lives of these unselfishly great men and women does furnish good examples of the power of sublimation.

The various symptoms of functional sickness gather themselves into groups and are given separate names. These names are of interest chiefly to psychiatrists, and even psychiatrists have come to recognize that names are relatively unimportant. All the many signs and symptoms, psychosomatic, tensions, anxiety, fatigue, difficulty with concentration, fixation of interest on body sensations, obsessions, phobias and many others, are generously distributed throughout all the psychoneuroses. At most, the names indicate a preponderance of certain kinds of symptoms in this or that neurosis. And psychiatrists themselves do not wholly agree on classification. There are a number of lists and each one has some merit. Much more signifi-

cant and valuable for treatment than the mere giving of a
name to an illness is the thorough understanding of the personality of the person who is sick and a knowledge and appreciation of the important events in his life history.

> "Sticks and stones can break my bones,
> But names can never hurt me."

It is the environmental sticks and stones, the insults to the
ego and the inner reactions to them which break the "bones"
of the psyche—not the designation "anxiety neurosis" or
"neurasthenia."

Personally, I think the simpler the classification, the better.
If I cared to give names, the bulk of the functional illness I
have seen could be grouped under one of the following designations:

A. Conversion Hysteria
B. Neurasthenia
C. Anxiety Neuroses
D. Obsessive-Compulsive Reactions

Conversion Hysteria is a very simple, childlike device.
The patient escapes his mental conflict by the simple expe-
dient of exchanging it (of course, unconsciously) for certain
ego-protective symptoms, usually very gross symptoms, an-
nihilation of whole functions, like paralysis, blindness, deafness, aphonia (loss of speech). Not very flatteringly, I have
compared the mechanism of conversion hysteria to the habit
of the trade rat. He takes something, often of value, like a
watch or a piece of jewelry and leaves in its place something
of no value, perhaps a pebble or a scrap of paper. The hysteric
exchanges the mental conflict which he does not want, and
which indeed would be a burden and trouble to his ego if he
faced it consciously, for some symptom, perhaps hysterical

blindness, deafness, paralysis, which, strange as it may seem, is of value to him, since he can and does regard it with satisfaction as the explanation of his illness. In this way, conversion hysteria does differ markedly from the other psychoneuroses. Once the conversion of the mental conflict into hysterical signs and symptoms is accomplished, the patient washes his psychological hands of the conflict, and regards his symptoms with amazing emotional complacency—even when the symptom is calamitous, like total blindness. In the other psychoneuroses, there is much unrest and anxiety from the inner psychic turmoil of unconscious, unsolved emotional conflicts.

Incidentally, soon in the history of his repeated attacks, the hysteric rarely fools anyone but himself—and almost never the psychiatrist. He or she has become blind or deaf or paralyzed and recovered sight, hearing or the function of walking too often—and too quickly. Nevertheless, it must be clearly understood, it is not faking or deliberate pretense. Hysteria is as definite and actual an illness as pneumonia.

World War I was replete with classical examples of conversion hysteria—the so-called "shell-shock" of the newspapers. As has been stated, they represented the unconscious psychological victory of the behavior demands of self-preservation over the duties, dangers and ideals of being a soldier. In my experience, often the symptoms were strikingly protective. Sometimes paralysis of both legs at the height of the charge against the enemy, deafness after being left in "no man's land" and listening for hours to the cries and groans of the wounded, blindness after seeing horrible death inflicted upon other soldiers by enemy fire. Frequently, the deafness and blindness were fortified by the wiping out of memory (amnesia) so that not only could the cries of the suffering wounded no longer be heard or mutilating destruction be seen, but no longer could they be remembered. Of course, not all the clinical examples of war conversion hysteria were so simple. For instance, in one group of soldiers, we were puzzled for a time by twisting, writhing, convulsive movements of their abdominal muscles. Later we learned that sometimes this followed the bayoneting of an enemy soldier through the belly.

While conversion hysteria is less common than formerly, yet there are still many examples to be found in civilian life.

A woman of middle age mistakenly suspected her husband of infidelity and particularly of an affair with a hypothetical "other woman." In her childhood she had had acute rheumatic fever which had left her heart very slightly impaired. Otherwise, she was a strong, healthy woman. One night, when her husband returned from a business conference, he found his wife in bed, gasping for breath and clutching wildly at her chest. He was frightened. It was a "heart attack." He summoned a physician, who examined the patient briefly, left some medicine, and said everything would be "all right." However, there were many more attacks, in fact, practically every time the husband had to go out at night. A noted heart specialist made thorough examinations and pronounced the heart in very satisfactory condition—"not the least thing to worry about." He suggested a psychiatrist. After a dozen interviews, the situation became quite clear to both psychiatrist and patient. In no wise were the "heart attacks" consciously planned. The patient was not aware of their underlying motivation. However, this motivation, the fear and unjustified suspicion that her husband was having an affair with another woman, leading to the hysterical subconscious wish to keep him closely tied to her side, was close enough to consciousness so that it was brought into the field of the patient's conscious appreciation without great difficulty. With the understanding of the situation, there came quite an emotional outburst with tears and a feeling of shame. Within the next few weeks there were several very minor attacks and then they disappeared. For several years there has not been any difficulty and the patient is definitely better adjusted and happier.

A sales engineer in a large exporting company did not get on well with his superior officer. He disliked him. Despised him would be more appropriate. At the same time he was a bit afraid of him. (During subsequent treatment, he realized that unconsciously J. reminded him of his father who had treated him very harshly during his childhood.) He disagreed thoroughly with J.'s business policies and often planned and even prepared "logical" arguments which would show J. his "mistakes." However, in the interviews with his superior, he acquitted himself very badly. His arguments were awkwardly phrased and ineffectively delivered. Always these conferences made him feel angry and humiliated. One day a rather important matter, about which he felt very strongly, was on the agenda for discussion the following morning. He spent most of the night in his apartment carefully preparing and marshaling his arguments. He awakened the next morning with a "sore" throat, and by the time he got to the office, he could not speak above an indistinct whisper. A laryngologist who examined him the same day said the minor degree of inflammation he found was not sufficient to account for the almost complete loss of speech. Normal, distinct speech did not return for almost three weeks.

A young divorcee, whose marriage had lasted less than a year, chiefly because she contributed so little to it, fell "madly" in love with a man she had met in Reno and married him. After six months of "ideal happiness" she was no longer happy; in fact, she was very "miserable" and "nervous." I was called to see her by the family physician, who had been hurriedly summoned by the frightened husband because as they were retiring for the night, "Estelle screamed and fell to the floor paralyzed, just as she was getting into bed."

I examined the young woman about a week later. She was not able to walk a single step. Her legs were twisted in a grotesque position, crossed above the knees, rigid as though held in a vise. Clearly the condition was not explainable on the basis of any disease of the brain, spinal cord or nerves. Her general condition was excellent—good color, no fever, normal heart action. She did not seem at all upset emotionally and chatted amiably while I examined her. It was hysteria. Furthermore, it seemed fairly obvious that the "paralysis" was not only a symbolic, but an actual defense against sexual intercourse.

Even though the "paralysis" was removed readily enough by suggestion, and although I tried to fortify the "cure" by explanation derived from the material obtained from eight treatment periods (the patient was unwilling to continue) I did not feel I had accomplished much. True enough, she assured me I was a "wonderful" doctor, but then everything in her life was either "wonderful" or "ghastly."

Some years later, I learned that she had divorced her husband, married twice subsequently and that the fourth marriage was "on the rocks."

From the few interviews I had with the patient, including two pentothal interviews, came these few things: Estelle had been a "nervous child" given to hysterical "fits" when she could not have her own way. She loved her father and hated her mother. Why? "Mother punished me" (quite mildly, it proved) "but Daddy was wonderful, so gentle and considerate, and he never even scolded me"—"Probably it was a mistake to break off my first marriage. Jack was nice in many ways and in *one* way we were well suited" (this very coyly). "Bill" (her second husband) "was inconsiderate, rough and demand-ing"—"Well, yes, I might as well say so, I mean about sex." In a pentothal interview, she screamed, "I hate you, Bill, don't you dare touch me." And, so on.

In the brief case histories, I have given, may be found the warp and woof of hysteria.

Neurasthenia, and the anxiety reactions, are basically dif-ferent from conversion hysteria. For one thing, the formation of the symptoms is much more intricate; the use of the mech-anisms of defense is psychologically more skillful and far less obvious. Often the psychiatrist wanders through an uncon-sciously very cunningly contrived maze before he can find a way out for the patient. For instance, who at first glance would suspect that deep overconcern and anxiety on the part of a wife about her husband, frantic with real fear that a dread-ful accident has occurred if he is ten minutes late in returning home, may consciously mask guilt feelings, which overlie an unconscious wish for his death? Or a husband's unconscious desire to be rid of a wife, perhaps because in his emotionally immature perspective she falls far short of his mother ideal with which he is still closely identified. Many conscious and unconscious layers of psychological insulation have to be peeled off before the truth, of which the patient is not even dimly aware, is revealed. Some interesting studies would seem to show that some mothers who constantly overfeed their chil-dren, not in the way of good mothers the world over, but liter-ally stuffing them until the seams of their clothes are strained and their eyes begin to bulge—in reality are consciously com-pensating for inner guilt feelings, for not really wanting the child and not loving it sufficiently.

Another difference is that unlike conversion hysteria which emotionally tends to be a complacent, laissez-faire affair, there is in neurasthenia and the anxiety states marked emotional turmoil, often expressed as tormenting feelings of anxiety and experienced physically as tension. Known dangers, if they are severe enough, may drain our courage and strength, but it is the unknown that really grips our souls.

The psychosomatic signs and symptoms in neurasthenia and the anxiety neuroses tend to be less finished, less complete than in conversion hysteria. Usually total function, like walking or talking, seeing or hearing, are not abolished. More usual are partial symptoms, "muscular weakness," "spots" before the eyes, feelings of fullness in the ears, distressing heart sensations, shortness of breath, skin rashes and a host of others.

Studding the area of anxiety, arising out of unsolved emotional conflicts, and the psychological necessity of keeping them from breaking into consciousness, there are many and varied symptoms. In neurasthenia, fatigue, impaired concentration (which often patients in great alarm interpret falsely as memory failure), self-conscious and inferiority feelings, irritability, depression, phobias, etc. Many of these symptoms are repeated in the anxiety reactions, with perhaps more clearly defined segments or phobias. These fears are tied in consciousness to almost anything one can think of—open places, glass, dirt, fur, feathers. Painful as they are to the patient, they serve to distract him from even more painful experiences, the recognition of the real nature and meaning of the phobias. They remind me of the trailing of the pretended broken wing by the mother bird as she tries to lead the chance observer away from the vicinity of her helpless young. Excepting that in the instance of the phobia, it is the sufferer who tries desperately to divert himself from the hidden nest of emotional conflict by some surface fear, perhaps claustrophobia.

In both neurasthenia and the anxiety states, innumerable psychosomatic symptoms appear, involving functional disturbances in every organ and part of the body. In the anxiety reactions startling anxiety crises may occur, sometimes with blanching pallor terrifically overacting heart and a sense of impending death. Or there may be nausea, vomiting, diarrhea, sweating, feelings of suffocation, dizziness and violent trembling. There could scarcely be plainer evidence of the bodily mirroring of disturbed inner emotions.

Neurasthenia, anxiety states and, indeed, all the psychoneuroses are compromises. Escapes? Yes. Retreats? Yes, but only to a line of defense, somewhere between everyday reality and a psychosis. Carefully they avoid the complete reality abandonment of a psychosis, with its extravagant and fantastic delusions, often spoken of as "insane." The psychoneuroses, all in all, represent the best compromise that a particular personality, besieged by mental conflict, can effect at any given time. The symptoms, I repeat, are the symbols of hidden conflict. To the ego and of the ego, they are the saving justification for being sick. The ego is able to point to the "heart," "stomach," and other symptoms and proclaim, "See, this is why and how I am sick."

The symptoms of a psychoneurosis are more than that. They represent, too, the battle being waged by the personality against the acceptance of the disabling illness.

There is a long antecedent interval of struggle inside the psyche, an attempt to adjust the differences between sharply divergent behavior demands. Then usually there is an insult from the environment, as in one of my patients who suddenly learned the sordid details of his wife's repeated infidelities. It was his Achilles' heel. I am inclined to think that all of us have a vulnerable spot, a psychological Achilles' heel. Usually these sensitive, more or less defenseless psychic areas can be traced back to deficits in the early child-mother, child-parent relationships. In any event, when this vulnerable place is wounded, frequently one may expect the appearance of symptoms. In the patient mentioned above, the first symptom was severe and frightening heart palpitation. So often the bodily symptoms in neurasthenia and anxiety states are the profiles of the physical pattern for "flight" or "fight" seen in frightened or infuriated animals.

Look at a cat, experimentally frightened in the laboratory by a fierce dog! It is obvious at once to anyone that something very moving is happening to the cat. Probably the consensus would be that the cat is desperately frightened and fighting mad. It is. There is every evidence of it. The back is arched, hair standing on end, pupils dilated. The cat is furiously spitting. Examinations show heart and blood vessels at the very peak of energetic functioning. Blood pressure is raised. Muscle metabolism is increased. Not only are the body organs and muscles receiving more blood, but the brain where quick decisions must be made is being richly supplied. Certain of the ductless glands and notably the adrenals share in the production of blood activity and pressure, probably even shortening the clotting time of the blood. If it is to be a fight to the finish, profuse bleeding might mean the difference between life and death. The liver stimulates the discharge of more sugar into the blood stream so that the muscles are adequately fueled for the mobilization of energy. Respiration is rapid. On the other hand, stomach and intestinal movements are decreased. Their functional activity would impede flight or fight.

With certain allowances and reservations, I think all this is somewhat akin to the situation in the body of the patient at certain stages of neurasthenic and anxiety reactions, the fighting stages. The allowances and reservations are largely in favor of the cat. For one thing, human beings *remember*. All too vividly, they remember the symptoms, the heart palpitation or what not, and remembering, the anxiety is increased.

The way is paved for frequent recurrence of the symptoms. A vicious psychosomatic circle is set into operation. Furthermore, the problem of the cat is concrete—the menace of the fierce dog, the fear and anger, the necessity of escaping or fighting it out to a finish, the mobilization of the body forces and defenses best to accomplish this objective. But in the human being, with neurasthenia and anxiety states, the symptoms are so often the reanimation of childhood patterns, serious emotional trauma to the ego, repressed and dropped into the not-conscious mind.

There has been a long period of futile attempts to solve a problem, the origin of which is hidden from consciousness and the nature of which is not understood by the patient. The individual in the grip of a mental conflict senses that there is a psychological threat and more or less blindly fights against it. The symptoms appear and reappear with varying intensity.

Eventually, sooner or later, timed by the resistance of each particular personality, the tide of battle begins to go against the patient. There is fatigue—not muscular tiredness, but the fatigue of emotional wear and tear. The reflex reactions and sensations continue but the patient loses his aggressive attitude. His outer world shrinks and his inner world consists more and more of anxiety and residual sensations. The potential anxiety neurotic, and particularly the potential neurasthenic becomes increasingly introspective about his somatic sensations and brings into focus even normal sensations, usually disregarded, like the beat of the heart or the peristaltic waves of the stomach. He broods and ruminates over them, worries about them, ponders them. Often he endows them with dire significance, heart disease, an impending stroke, diabetes, cancer! It is at about this cross-section of his illness that he seeks medical help.

The analogy I have made might be objected to on the

grounds that there are no fierce dogs in the world of humans. But there are. Even though they do not snarl and bite, yet they are fiercer and more dangerous than laboratory animals. And we are not so remote from the physiology of the cat but that on one level we respond in much the same way to fear.

From the pages of my records here are a few of many situations. They occur frequently in spite of the culture, refinements, material comforts and protections of modern life. These veneers are often stripped, exposing ugly, raw sores. The happiness and security of a woman, married and with two children, is in jeopardy, because a blackmailer threatens to reveal a serious mistake of her past to her husband. A young woman has real reason to fear that she is illegitimately pregnant and by a man of a different race and color. A wife in love with her husband, and for herself and her three children absolutely dependent upon him economically, has every reason to believe that her husband has attempted incestuous relations with a twelve-year-old daughter. An old couple, powerless to stay the increasingly serious delinquencies of an only son of seventeen, seemingly headed for a career in crime, prison and disgrace. These psychological dogs are fierce enough!

There are serious psychological threats within the framework of difficult home problems, sickness, particularly when chronic and hopeless, operations, and accidents and deprivations by death, all sorts of marital problems and sexual maladjustments, illicit relationships, insurmountable obstacles and frustrations in the love life.

Not that a serious insult from the environment is needed to precipitate a neurasthenic, anxiety or other neurosis. There may be merely something quite trivial or, indeed, nothing at all. The amour propre, the pride of the ego in maintaining psychological appearance may not be very great or the surface resistance may have been sapped by the severe and long·continued conflict behind the curtains of consciousness, a conflict more and more insistent upon some relief of inner pressure, demanding a compromise, even though it be a neurotic one. If at all possible, the ego "prefers" the saving grace of some face-saving occurrence. In this connection, it is interesting how often anxiety or neurasthenic symptoms follow close upon the heels of an uncomplicated illness like pneumonia, a simple fracture of a bone or a physiological process like normal childbirth.

Sometimes patients think their psychiatrists are not enough impressed by their symptoms, do not pay enough attention to them. The psychiatrist is impressed by the headache or backache or nausea or dizziness, but he is even more impressed by the necessity of discovering why the patient has these complaints. The answers are to be found in the long life history of the patient, and often in the area of childhood. Many of the answers are shrouded in the fogs of repression.

Obsessional thinking is "must" thinking, thinking which at least until its underlying sources have been uncovered is beyond the control of the person. However much he may consciously strive *not* to think of suicide or murder or serried rows of pine trees or what not, the thought persists and continues to dominate a large area of his thinking. Part, but only a small part, of the reason is simple enough. The very effort *not* to think of "it" defeats its own purpose. Often, if we make up our minds not to think of something, then that something is apt to knock all the more frequently and loudly at the door of memory. In pathological obsessional thinking, the reasons are deeper and more intricate.

Compulsive behavior is "must" behavior. It is behavior which, until its unconscious mainsprings have been revealed, must be carried out, even though the compulsive patient strives mightily to overcome the overmastering urge to do or not to do something. It may involve some simple act, to touch something or perhaps to refrain from touching it. Compulsions may be more serious, such as stealing (kleptomania) or setting fires (pyromania). In compulsive behavior, long and unbelievably involved and complicated rituals may be developed so that it may take the patient hours to get to bed at night or get up in the morning. Sometimes things which should be routine, like taking off the shoes or shaving or brushing the teeth, become the subject of endless pro and con inner psychic arguments. This is called "morbid indecision" and sometimes it may result literally in paralysis of action. I knew a man, who until he recovered, had to resort to the barber for shaving, since frequently for as much as a whole hour he would stand transfixed before his mirror, lathered shaving brush in hand, but unable to decide whether or not to apply it to his face.

Rarely is obsessional thinking directly translated into compulsive behavior. Indeed, sometimes it would seem as though the obsessional train of thought is a protection against carrying out the act. I have never known a true obsessive-compulsive patient, his mind occupied with fears of suicide, who actually took his own life.

On the other hand, unquestionably compulsive behavior is connected with various obsessions, which in turn are the cover-up or camouflage of repressed conflicts. Kleptomania often probably is the compulsive behavior expression of hidden sexual complexes. In the intelligent, middle-aged patient I cited, who was so obsessed by the number "13" that he was compelled to resort constantly to humiliating and ridiculous behavior, such as counting his steps and hopping over every thirteenth one—the real reason was the repressed complex of having been seduced in his boyhood by an ignorant, superstitious serving maid. In the woman who was made intensely sick to her stomach by the sight or odor of flowers, particularly roses, and who was compelled to walk long distances out of her way in order to avoid passing florist shops—the hidden reason was the repressed remembrance of her seduction and jilting by a faithless lover, who under promise to marry her, seduced her the last time he saw her, at which time he brought her a beautiful bunch of red roses.

Obsessions and compulsions are liberally distributed throughout the psychoses and psychoneuroses, but it is in the obsessive-compulsive neuroses that they come to their full flowering.

In this psychoneurosis, the psyche makes use of an ingenious combination of defensive mechanisms—displacement, substitution and symbolism.

A simple physical analogy is worth repeating. If into a tumbler flush filled with water, a stone is dropped, some of the water is displaced. The displaced water represents the emotional mental material which can no longer be contained in consciousness and must be displaced into the area of the "not remembered." The stone becomes the substitute for the displaced water and represents it. It is its symbol. Psychologically, it may be compared to the obsessions and compulsions which appear in consciousness as the symbols of repressed material.

Perhaps this diagram will be of some use in explaining the mechanisms at work in the production of an obsessive-compulsive psychoneurosis. The diagram will be used to illustrate the case of an interesting patient I treated.

$\boxed{\text{E}\ \text{Em}}$: Something which happened in the life of the individual, the experience and the emotional reaction it produced, once joined in consciousness. $\boxed{\text{E}}$ = The remembrance of the experiences displaced (repressed) into the "not conscious" mind.

$\boxed{\text{Em}}\!\frown\!\text{S}$: $\boxed{\text{Em}}$ the unattached emotion (anxiety) becomes attached to S the substitution for and the symbol of the dis-

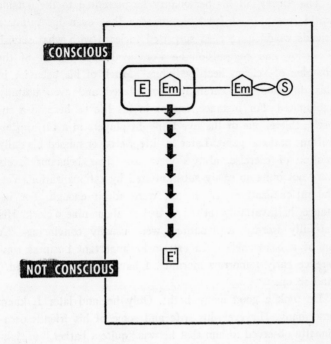

placed experience. It is often symbolized as obsessive thinking and compulsive behavior.

A.B., just turned forty-five, is a very successful man, but until recently he was very unhappy. He is married to a nice, intelligent, mature wife, and they have one child, a lovely little daughter. At one time in the course of treatment, he confided to me that he was "afraid" of the little girl, in fact, that he was afraid of all children. He felt ill-at-ease and somewhat insecure with them.

"But why should you feel that way?"—"Oh," he replied rather vaguely, "I don't think I really know. Sometimes I have a sort of feeling they can see through me."

The "front" of his personality he presented to the outside world was a good front. I am sure that even his intimate friends would have been surprised to learn with what slavish obsession and compulsion he worshiped at the altar of the complex of "clean, healthy living." Much of his behavior in this direction was carefully camouflaged and even usefully sublimated. For instance, earlier in his life he became a superb athlete, one of the five topflight players in a certain important national game. Later in life, he never missed his daily routine of exercise, always vigorous. Other behavior facets were not quite so easily substantiated by rationalization. Yet, the rationalizations, all in all, were adroit enough. For instance, he invariably retired to bed at about nine o'clock. His carefully worded explanations were usually convincing—"A bit of a headache"—"An extremely important business conference early tomorrow morning. I have to be clear-headed." And so on.

He took a good many baths. Only he, and later I, knew how many. However, his wife and some of his friends occasionally observed to him that he was "quite a bather," or, jokingly, "There is such a thing as being too clean." Always he had a fairly adequate explanation: "Got myself pretty sweaty today," or "Messing around the warehouse. Grimy place. Dust and dirt of centuries."

The lower level of the "clean, healthy living" complex was secretive and ritualistic. It was the inner sanctum of obsession and compulsion. Actually, he often took as many as fifteen baths a day—tub baths, showers, sponges, alcohol rubs— most of them surreptitiously and hastily. Ruefully, he admitted to me that probably some days he did wash his hands a hundred times. Taking a drink of water was an opportunity for a furtive mouth-rinsing and, if no one was about, a throat gargling. (Incidentally, he never drank alcohol or used tobacco in any form.) There were many long rituals. The one which had to do with getting ready for bed at night was the most complicated. Its details were almost endless. It would require more pages than the publisher has available to describe the ritual. It was an orgy of cleanliness. Some of the high points were: 1) After bathing, a careful examination of the body surface with the aid of a mirror, and the rubbing of any "dirt" spots with a pledget of cotton dipped in alcohol. 2) The meticulous examination of the clothing to be worn the next day and a rubbing with cleansing fluid of those parts of the clothing which might come into contact with the body, particularly under the arms and the "crotch" (A.B. always emphasized "the crotch"). 3) The careful fashioning of two pieces of cotton, each about five inches long, which were soaked in Listerine, inserted into the inner folds of the groin and left there for five minutes. 4) The meticulous scrutiny of the top and bottom bed-sheets with a few drops of Listerine judiciously applied to any place that "didn't look quite clean." And so on.

The patient, badgered as he was, still retained a sense of humor and once smilingly told me how he had worked vigorously for several minutes on a bedclothes "spot" only to discover that it was a shadow cast by the edge of the bedlamp. Incidentally, A.B. had good insight. He understood that his thinking and behavior were "illogical, ridiculous and fantastic," but at that cross-section he was powerless to inhibit it.

What repressions were there, so serious that it was necessary to keep the lid of obsessions, compulsions and elaborate ritual tightly clamped down to prevent their appearance in consciousness? Of course, there were many repressions, but one seemed to be directly determining. When A.B. was eight years old, an older brother (whom A.B. always feared and disliked) discovered him in the act of masturbation. The older brother took full advantage of the situation. There was quite a dramatic scene. The brother stigmatized A.B. as "unhealthy," "unclean," "filthy," "dirty," etc., etc., and threatened to expose him to the family. He made the little fellow get down on his knees and swear never to do "*it*" again and to promise to lead a "clean, healthy life." There are not enough adjectives to describe A.B.'s emotional state—fear, humiliation, shame, degradation.

Turning to the diagram, we are now at the cross-section when there was an actual experience, vividly and closely associated with a deep, emotional reaction.

$$\boxed{\text{E} \; \boxed{\text{Em}}}$$

For two years following the experience, the older brother, in the words of A.B. "continued to hold it over my head"— "never let me forget it," "made me promise again and again," "kept me terrorized by intimating that after all he might have to tell my father and mother."

CONSCIOUS

$$\boxed{\text{E}}$$

$$\downarrow$$
$$\downarrow$$
$$\downarrow$$

$$\downarrow$$

$$\boxed{\text{E}'}$$

NOT CONSCIOUS

Then the brother went away from home to college. Soon after, A.B. managed to "forget" the experience. He could no longer tolerate the belittlement and shame of living with it in consciousness, so he repressed it. In the above diagram, the remembrance of the happening was displaced into the "not-conscious."

This then left suspended in consciousness the emotional reaction provoked by the original happening as so-called free floating anxiety.

It was psychologically mandatory that this emotionally sensitive material should become attached to something symbolic of what had been repressed. And so it did become attached to the complex Ⓢ of "clean, healthy living" which could be tolerated in consciousness, even though it led to extreme obsessional thinking and bizarre compulsive behavior.

CONSCIOUS

$$\boxed{Em}\!\!\diamond\!\!-\!\!Ⓢ$$

NOT CONSCIOUS

I have sketched the psychological geography of the terrain upon which are erected the houses of "functional" sickness. Each house is built of and furnished with varying and carefully selected materials. In each instance, material and furnishings, the decor is that which the particular personality is familiar with and has found most useful in the small evasions of reality in so-called normal life. When faced with psychological crisis, the "functional" compromise to which we resort must be as secure and protective as possible.

Incidentally, the psychoneurosis has been called the great American disease. I do not know about that, but I do know that each year hundreds of thousands of people are rendered far less effective, in fact, partially disabled and made unhappy, by functional illness.

7 | MANIC-DEPRESSIVE AND
SCHIZOPHRENIA PSYCHOSES

MANIC-DEPRESSIVE and schizophrenia, two common forms of mental disease, represent deep penetrations into the land of unreality and phantasy—journeys sometimes so long and over so many uncharted paths that the traveler never finds his way back to the land of reality. By and large, the schizophrenic tends to cut himself off more completely from the mainland of reality and sanity. The manic-depressive is apt to keep a finger or two on the facts of everyday life. Usually the door to his reality is kept, at least sightly, ajar.

Statistically, these two psychoses account for an extremely large segment of mental sickness. On the basis of returns from public mental hospitals alone, there are about 40,000 manic-depressive patients in the hospitals, and each year 11,000 more are admitted. Schizophrenia makes up the bulk of both the residents in and admissions to public mental hospitals, approximately 30,000 patients being admitted annually. It is conservative to multiply these figures by three in order to arrive at the overall incidence.

About twelve years ago, the Supreme Council of the $33°$ Masons, after thorough study, arrived at the very intelligent conclusion that schizophrenia was the greatest disease menace of our time. In my opinion, it is. While modern treatment saves many, yet it is still true that each year thousands of young men and women are cut off from life as we know it, even before they can really love and savor it, and are condemned by schizophrenia to spend the remainder of their lives, fifty, sixty, seventy and even more years hidden in the back wards of mental hospitals.

The Masonic benevolence made available each year a considerable sum of money for the first concerted scientific investigation of the many problems of schizophrenia. Already the various projects have yielded much valuable information.

I believe that manic-depressive and schizophrenia should be viewed together because they stand out in such striking contrast to each other. This is true, though early even the expert psychiatrist, in certain instances, may have great difficulty in distinguishing manic-depressive from schizophrenia. Nothing is so unusual about this. In many diseases of the body, the first symptoms are much the same, perhaps a little fever, a sore throat, headache, nausea and so forth. Until the rash comes out or there is distinctive pain, it may be hard to know whether the illness is measles, appendicitis, pneumonia or something else.

In the chapter on military neuropsychiatry, I shall again make the analogy between the natural weapons animals use when their lives are threatened and the psychological defenses of human beings when they are faced with the danger of psychological destruction. But the analogy is useful here, too. The poundage animals, huge beasts like the elephant, meet the life threat by a head-on charge, attempting to demolish it. And so on in the scale of human life, each creature uses those weapons which are natural for it, and trustworthy, even to the lowly insects which frequently save their lives by grace of their camouflage, merging imperceptibly into a twig or a crumb of dirt. Incidentally, from the standpoint not only of surviving but increasing in number, in the midst of the constant dangers of the jungle, the sloth is the most interesting of mammals. It is almost devoid of natural protections. It is so dim-visioned, dim-witted and hard of hearing that if one of its babies drops from the body to which it clings, the chances are against the mother-sloth finding it, even though she may pass within a foot of where it lies. The sloth moves so slowly that it consumes several days in crossing two miles. It is so slothful in its courtship that it often stops at "passionate" periods, seemingly forgetting the business at hand. It subsists on a variety of leaves, easily obtainable and disregarded by other creatures. Yet, chiefly by virtue of the inconspicuousness it achieves by hanging from its toes, almost immovable in the midst of the foliage of trees, the sloth frequently escapes destruction. There is a psychiatric lesson contained in the behavior of the sloth.

The manic-depressive patient, certainly in the excited phase, acts rather like the poundage animals, putting out a heavy barrage of words, emotions and physical activity. Often so intense is this display that it is impossible to detour the patient from the head-on charge which, in effect, expresses defiance of reality, its criteria and its inhibitions.

But, behold the schizophrenic patient! If advanced in the psychosis, he rivals the insect or the sloth in achieving inconspicuousness. And deftly and deviously he places the outposts of his defenses against intrusion into the privacy of his phantasy. Indeed, if too hard pressed, like the opossum he can and does feign death (catatonic stupor). He may become mute and almost motionless, has to be fed through a tube and seems quite insensible to pain, as from the sharp thrust of a needle.

Psychiatrists, at this cross-section of our knowledge, think of manic-depressive and schizophrenia as functional psychoses. This means merely that thus far there has not been uncovered enough constant pathology in the body or enough clinical evidence of poisoning in either psychosis to justify the designation of "organic" or "toxic." * This certainly does not mean that there are no body symptoms in these two conditions. Actually, there are many, appearing far too frequently to be explained away by that much overused word, coincidence. Many of these physical signs are too technical to be more than mentioned—such things as the content of the blood, particularly of its less familiar constituents, the bromide barrier in the spinal fluid, the pattern of the gastrointestinal tract, many symptoms referable to the ductless-gland system, signs of disturbances in what are known as the vasomotor, sympathetic and vegetative systems and many others.

Aside from these hard-won technical and scientific contributions, there is fairly plain evidence of bodily involvement in these two psychoses, sometimes so plain that he who runs may read. By and large, notably in the active or manic phase of the psychosis, the metabolism or general energy of the bodily functions is at a high level. Literally everything, the heart and circulation, the breathing, the appetite, digestion and bowel function, the muscles, the skin, all are stepped up and working at the peak. Perhaps in twenty-four hours this same patient may pass into the contrasting or depressed phase. Once, I showed a very intelligent lay person the same patient, first in the excited phase and then ten days later when the patient had become melancholy. He said, "It is hard for me to

---

* The designations, "organic," "toxic" and "functional" should not be taken too literally. All disease involves disturbance of function. However, the terms "organic," "toxic" and "functional" are useful in describing the preponderant level of the disturbance.

believe that this is the same woman I saw ten days ago. Then she was so vivacious, rosy-cheeked, active, bursting with physical health and vigor. You say this is the same woman. But she is dejected, inactive, sluggish, scarcely speaking, more dead than alive."

While I have seen it many, many times, I am still amazed at the physical transformation, almost transmutation, that takes place in patients who pass into the manic from the depressed phase. The sallow skin, the bent-over carriage, the dull eyes, the seeming physical weakness, almost decrepitude of muscles, are swept away and replaced by a healthy, glowing skin, erect, energetic carriage and gait, bright, sparkling eyes, muscular strength and energy. As if by magic, ten years or more seem to have been shed by the patient.

These observations lead me to suspect a total "functional" explanation of manic-depressive. Indeed, a magic, the scientific magic of bodily chemistry, may be a factor. How else explain this passage from one phase of the disease to its direct contrast, sometimes in a few hours? I knew a lady who had at least fifty brief attacks of acute, violent mania. Frequently she would come to the hospital in a cab, seek me out and, with complete control of her thinking and behavior, say, "Doctor, take me in at once, have me sign the necessary papers, put me on the acute ward, for tomorrow I will be in a terrible condition." "How do you know?" "I feel it. I am sure." Always did her prediction come true. The next day found her in "terrible condition," often homicidal.

Another factor that makes me somewhat suspicious of a complete "functional" explanation of manic-depressive is the inheritance factor. The inheritance factor is present, though at this time no one can be sure how heavy it is. I have the record of the wife of a very intelligent and prominent executive, who after the birth of each one of her three children had to be

treated in a mental hospital for severe attacks of manic-
depressive. Each of her three children, throughout their lives,
had a malignant form of manic-depressive, so-called "circular
insanity" in which there are practically no symptom-free intervals. Such a prominent inheritance pattern is unusual, but
it is not unusual for a manic-depressive patient to have a history of the psychosis in one or the other parent. Incidentally,
each patient with manic-depressive tends to establish an individual pattern of frequency and duration of attacks. One of
the more disheartening aspects of the psychosis is the almost
fatal tendency for attacks to recur. On the other hand, a person
may have only one or perhaps two or three depressive or manic
episodes, perhaps less than a year's total illness in a lifetime,
and still be truly manic-depressive. I knew an engineer who
had two typical but brief depressions, one as a young man,
the other at the age of fifty, nothing more. Otherwise his life
was fine and constructive. Among other inventions he worked
out a chemical process without which it would not be possible
to carry on one of the nation's basic industries. Perhaps the
average picture consists of cycles, depression followed by
excitement, with varying periods, months to several years, of
mental health between the cycles.

Not without many exceptions, but still preponderantly, the
manic-depressive patient tends to have a certain type of body
formation called pyknic. Briefly, he is prominent in his girth
measurements, short, thick-necked, powerful muscularly. Inside that big-chested, strong, energetic body, there is the driving engine of a powerful heart and adequate blood vessels.
The glands of internal secretion (ductless glands), the thyroid, pituitary, sex glands, are dynamic. The body exudes
driving force.

As years go on, the pyknic is more liable to fall victim to
certain diseases than to others. He may suffer an apoplectic

stroke or he may succumb to heart and blood-vessel disease. In a way, it seems appropriate that the powerful machinery of the heart, so heavily used, eventually should break. He is somewhat more prone to ductless-gland pathology, and prostate-gland disease is fairly common.

The schizophrenic is far less inclined to tilt with the windmills of reality. For one thing, usually he is not physically equipped to join battle with the environment. In striking contrast to the bodily activity and energy of the manic patient, the metabolic function of the schizophrenic patient is at a low ebb. He seems torpid, sluggish and may have long periods of seemingly apathetic inactivity that are almost suggestive of hibernation. This has led to the unfair designation of "cold-blooded."

The inheritance factor seems less clear in schizophrenia than in manic-depressive, though certainly there is scientific evidence for it that cannot be disregarded. Franz Kallman, who knows more about identical twins than any man of my acquaintance, states that if one of identical twins develops schizophrenia, the other twin has only a 15 per cent chance of escaping the psychosis. If the twins were separated early in life and lived in different environments, then the chances are increased to 25 per cent.

If the bodily characteristics of the manic-depressive are preponderantly pyknic, then the schizophrenic is chiefly "leptic" or perhaps "non-athletic," "dysplastic." He is more likely to be a string bean of a fellow, prominent in his bony measurements, wanting in girth, probably with weak muscles and a stringy neck, an embarrassingly prominent Adam's apple. Usually, not in him the strong, driving heart with large, generous blood vessels to receive and distribute the energetic flow of blood. Rather there is likely to be a small heart and blood vessels, not built for long and sustained physical activity. Usually, too, not in the schizophrenia the dynamos of ductless-gland energy, the thyroid, pituitary and the sex glands. Efficient enough, of course, but functioning on a low, less turbulent level. And when the schizophrenic's body machinery gives way, it is more likely to be because of some condition associated with functional inactivity, like tuberculosis, to which a considerable number of schizophrenic patients fall victim.

In a rough, general way, personality traits seem to be associated with certain physical characteristics. For instance, the pyknic is fairly likely to be an extrovert. The pronounced extrovert is a doer, an eager and bustling "go-getter." At his worst he is "the life of the party," his tongue is multiple-jointed and his conversation runs on endlessly. Physically, he is never quiet. He is the joiner, the conventionaire, the handshaker and back-slapper, the overenthusiastic Rotarian, who above all things loves to wear a dinner-plate-size badge which implores his friends to call him "Sam" or "Buck." In him, all too often, thought is tantamount to action. His shibboleth is energy, and his battle cry is, "Come on, fellows, get going, let's do something exciting." I have seen the introvert unhappily and hopelessly flounder about socially in the maelstrom of the extrovert's energy, almost praying to be able to escape being noticed by him.

At his best, and it is a very good best, the extrovert is efficient, competent, often dynamically inspiring to others, as an executive and even in humbler roles. Our intricate and complex modern commercial and professional world could not get on without him. Mentally and physically, he rolls up his sleeves, clears the decks for action and day after day gets an enormous amount of important work done.

I think the pronounced introvert would almost die if he were compelled to slap his fellows on the back, wring their hands vigorously and wear a badge, entreating them to call him "Sam" or "Buck." Often he does envy the extrovert who performs these rites so facilely, but he could never bring himself to do likewise. In a small group of friends with whom he feels secure, the introvert can be a most entertaining, well-informed and perhaps brilliant conversationalist. A party, particularly a loud and noisy one, locks his tongue. On his way home he may mentally "kick" himself for failing to seize the opportunity to say the clever things he might have said. The shibboleth of the introvert is "instrospection" and his plea is, "Please, not so much noise. Let us not act too hastily. We ought to think things over carefully first." This whether the consideration is a family picnic or a million-dollar business deal.

At his worst, the introvert is the inactive, utterly impractical and visionary dreamer, whose daydreams are made of the useless stuff of unadulterated phantasy. At his best, which is a splendid best, the introvert is the thoughtful thinker and planner for the future. He sees visions which often some day come true. Frequently he is among the great benefactors of humanity.

Almost never does extroversion or introversion occur in pure culture. Fortunately, in the personalities of the vast majority of all human beings, there are varying proportions of outgoing and ingrowing qualities, one or the other being preponderant, perhaps only slightly so. Total and unrelieved extroverted or introverted traits in any person would be mental sickness. There is a story told of a very introverted wife married to an extremely extroverted husband. It was the morning of their twentieth wedding anniversary and they were at breakfast. For twenty years she had endured with resignation and as much of a smile as she could muster her husband's bustling activity, and particularly his unfailing habit at breakfast, just before eating his eggs, of flapping his arms and crowing an imitation of a rooster. When he did this on the morning of their anniversary she did not smile. The iron of twenty years had entered her soul. She got up, went to the kitchen, selected a meat cleaver from the implements, came back and neatly split her husband's skull. She was tried and acquitted on the defense of "justifiable homicide."

There is a serious lesson in this fanciful tale. The typical extrovert is apt to react quickly, emotionally, perhaps with angry or even violent outbursts, but the reaction usually is not prolonged. The behavior has relieved the outraged feelings. The emotional decks have been cleared. Not so the typical introvert. On the surface there is seemingly only a slight and shallow reaction. But it is only seemingly. Annoyance, frustration, hostility are being stored up. The storm clouds are gathering. Then, upon the heels of some trivial incident, weak breakfast coffee, the repetition of a detested mannerism of speech or gesture, almost anything, the storm breaks, thunder rolls, lightning flashes and the pent-up emotional flood breaks through the dykes of inhibition. One introverted wife came to me vainly hoping to be advised to seek a divorce from her extroverted husband—"I can't stand the noise he makes sucking his teeth any longer. He does it on purpose to devil me."

So that I may be entirely cleared of contributing to the ancient error that there is something mentally abnormal in being either an extrovert or an introvert, I repeat there is nothing in the least abnormal. If the problem of manic-depressive or schizophrenia were simply a matter of the presence of one or the other of these two personality types, then long since the whole world would have been insane. For all people in their personalities, in innumerable dilutions, must be predominantly either extroverted or introverted. Both personality types are useful and much needed in our world.

It is true, in my opinion, that the majority of candidates for manic-depressive come from the ranks of the extroverts; the schizophrenics from the introverts. But before the equation is completed, long before the portals of either of the two psychoses swing open, several "x" quantities must be added. The behavior may become so pronounced either in the direction of overactive, somewhat uncontrolled conduct, moodiness, depression or increasingly frequent and longer continued withdrawals from everyday life and its activities, that the psychiatrist, fairly enough, may envision the danger of mental illness. The characteristics in the extrovert called "syntonic," in the introvert "schizoid" are not necessarily mental disease. They may go no further, and the threat may be even turned back. In any event, before the final break from reality occurs, another little-understood ingredient must be added to the personality mixture.

What are the manic-depressive patients in the tremendous emotional-verbal-motor activity of the excited phase or in the contrasting depressions, and the schizophrenic patients in their retreat from reality, trying to accomplish? What is the interpretation?

Sometimes in acute mania, seemingly the explanation is simple, a compensation for unconscious inner inferiorities, sharply pointed by rebuffs from the environment.

A big-brained, but physically weak, puny, non-muscular college professor had frequently brief attacks of mania during which he tumbled about awkwardly, turning pitifully ungraceful somersaults and loudly proclaimed himself, "The world's strongest man and greatest acrobat." He had had only one love affair in his life, a deep and serious one for him, which

came to an inglorious anticlimax. The young woman broke off
the engagement, no doubt because she could not face mating
with a man so inadequate physically.

Another patient, in her manic attacks, was always the
"world's greatest soprano," singing away hour after hour, in
a mental hospital, in her psychosis holding thousands en-
thralled by the "liquid magic" of her voice. This young
woman's voice had shown much promise. She had spent all her
savings and all she could borrow in having it trained. Then
came the public recital. She was a complete failure. Her
teacher advised her to abandon her ambition of a professional
career.

Manic-depressive, in its manic exhibitions, is much more
intricate than merely acting out consciously unattainable wish
fulfillments. It would seem that the purpose of the pyrotech-
nical display of word and act, with the rapid-fire emotional
accompaniments, is to throw a camouflaging smoke screen,
not only between the patient and his environment, but also
between the ego of the patient and the hidden mental conflicts deep in his psyche, which he cannot face. Obviously he
is running away from something frightening and the manic
phase has been called "the flight into reality." At the same
time, the patient can reanimate the ashes of the dead wishes
and hopes of the past. The behavior of the patient, often in
high good humor, may seem "funny" but it is tragedy and not
farce.

Perhaps one sees something similar, but very much reduced
in size, when sometimes in a social conversation an apparently
casual remark probes some hidden sore place in the psyche
of one of the group and he or she initiates a rapid-fire conversation about a totally different subject, an almost desperate
attempt to throw a diverting red herring in the conversational
pathway.

What about the depressive phases of the psychosis? Freud made an interesting comparison with normal grief and mourning. But in normal sorrowing, perhaps for a beloved one removed by death, eventually new love attachments are made or old ones are strengthened. The severed reality threads are gathered together and re-tied. But in the pathological depression of manic-depressive, the binding threads remain severed.

Another explanation of the depression is that the superego, roughly corresponding to the conscience, turns on the ego, punishes it and flagellates it for the "sins" of the id, which is not only the source of energy, but also the fount of strong instinctual behavior demands, often not socially acceptable. Suppose, as is quite often true, a person has in the depths of his unconscious a death wish for husband or wife, or a parent, or someone else. The remainder of the personality, particularly the superego, cannot accept such a debasing wish. Of course, it is repressed. And, therefore, there is depression, feelings of guilt and terrible self-blame. It is pathological atonement.

What steps does the schizophrenic patient take in his retreat from reality? If the manic patient tries to escape his mental conflicts by a flight into reality, the schizophrenic seeks refuge in phantasy. It is likely that even in childhood he was a certain kind of person. In the early history of schizophrenics such adjectives as "quiet," "good," "shy," "reserved," "diffident," "secretive," "unfriendly," "unsociable," "seclusive," often recur. It is likely, too, that even as a child he was more of a daydreamer than is usual. This does not mean that daydreaming is not common and psychologically necessary in childhood and, indeed, throughout life. It is. However, these children succumb more readily and more deeply to the pleasing unreality of "castles in Spain." The strongest weapon of the introvert is thought, the capacity to make thoughts, however fantastic, seem real. The world does not seem such a pleasant place. His sensitive nature shrinks from the hard and sweaty demands of reality. He does admire success and would like to eat its fruits, but even the survey of the grueling competition needed to obtain the rewards is very distasteful. Sex, for instance, is beautiful and fascinating, but chiefly in the abstract. The physical processes involved, perhaps sexual intercourse or having a baby, are—well—too physical, too earthy (later on, if a psychosis develops, female patients may have "thought" babies, as satisfactory to them as real ones and far less trouble and responsibility).

Sooner or later, the individual comes to a psychic crossroads. Which path shall he take? Some kind of unconscious decision is made. There is some sort of an unconscious realization, occasionally partly conscious, perhaps vague and shadowy, but still some appreciation. Slowly but invitingly the door of the psychosis begins to open. Beyond it is refuge. Perhaps at this stage one may picture the potential schizophrenic courting unreality in fantastic daydreams but at the same time realizing that he is listening with dangerous attentiveness to the siren's song. If the psychosis is to be the solution, then each day there is some small yielding of the territory of reality. Before complete surrender, it is still psychologically necessary to "square" things with the ego and the world in which he lives. Otherwise, he would be compelled to believe that he could not live successfully in the everyday world because he was not adequate for the effort. To believe this would be a psychological catastrophe.

Interestingly, quite often the first outspoken and definite mental symptoms are examples of such rationalizations, which absolve the ego from blame.

A patient of mine, a young bank clerk, who had become increasingly moody and seclusive, suddenly in the dead of night screamed out at the "voices"—"All right, I quit. It's a damn lie, but I can't stand this torture from you any longer." Subsequently, he explained to me that the "voices" derided and mocked him as a "sex-crazy fairy."

Of course, the iron screen does not at once descend all the way and shut out the everyday world completely. Often segments of the personality strive desperately to hold on to some shreds of reality. This is the stage of active symptoms—excitements, suicidal attempts, panics, sometimes with a homosexual content. Frequently, at this stage, the psychosis is halted by energetic treatment and the patient brought back to the land of reality.

If, however, the psychosis is malignant, it proceeds, sometimes slowly, sometimes rapidly to a hopeless stage. Even feeble attempts to participate in real life largely cease. Phantasy engulfs the patient. The struggle is over. Unreality is no longer a pleasant, compensating diversion. The unreal has become real. Much has been written describing various stages of schizophrenia. It is largely theoretical. Actually, there are just two stages. The first is the stage of active symptoms. It indicates that some part of the personality is resisting the complete encroachment of phantasy life and its acceptance. This stage may last as little as a few months, but I have seen many patients with one mental foot firmly planted in reality continue to struggle for many years, striving to attain some sort of a working compromise. The second stage is the stage in which all hold on reality is abandoned. The retreat into the ivory tower of phantasy is complete and final and its exits are strongly barred against intrusion from the outside world. This is why chronic schizophrenic patients, stranded on the back wards of a public mental hospital, where the food may be unappetizing, the care indifferent, the surroundings drab and hopelessly monotonous, nevertheless are undisturbed and seemingly content. They are secure in their unreality. No matter how sordid the conditions under which they live, schizophrenic patients still may be and indeed "are" the "Heavenly Queen" or the "Divinely Appointed Greatest Potentate." They can see no incongruity between their majesty and retrieving a cast off half-smoked cigarette.

There is a philosophy of the advantages of unreality, a pseudo and dangerous philosophy but still interesting. In effect, the deteriorated schizophrenic patient unconsciously says, "I place no trust in the things you prize so highly—luxurious food, fine clothing, palatial houses, powerful motor cars. The chattels and mortgages, bonds and stocks, the power of your life, are passing and insecure. I have something much more permanent. I have the real power. I can do anything. I can think pleasing thoughts, dream beautiful dreams and transmute them into realities in which and by which I live. No one and no conditions of life can take them away from me." True enough, a dangerous pseudo-philosophy of nihilism and inaction, but perhaps it does serve to indict some of the defects and injustices of the world in which we live.

The final stage of schizophrenia is often called dementia. It is not an appropriate designation. It is not an eclipse of memory and other symptoms, of mental deterioration, as one sees in dementia due to destruction of brain cells and tissue. It is, perhaps a dementia of the emotional reactions and judgment. The emotions judged by the criteria of everyday life in our world are no longer adequate and appropriate. It is the gross substitution of the unreal for the real.

I have a patient with schizophrenia whom I see a few times a year. As a beautiful young girl she broke down mentally in France during World War I, while serving the French wounded as a Red Cross ambulance driver. She is now about fifty-four years old. By some strange alchemy of her bodily chemistry (which many women would give much to possess) her hair, which has never been tinted, is as beautifully golden and as free of gray as when she was a girl of eighteen. Otherwise, she is quite fat and pleasantly ugly. She receives my visits with a gracious smile and gesture but rarely speaks. She indicates that she prefers me to stand in her presence. After a few minutes, she raises her right hand in pleasant dismissal. The audience is over. I gather that the "golden princess" wishes to return to her prince consort, her ardent and constant lover.

Psychiatrists have not yet penetrated the inner core of schizophrenia, either chemically or psychologically. We have explored the periphery and here and there made some fairly deep inroads into the underlying factors. If I may venture an opinion, very possibly wrong, I would say that rejection of the child in infancy by the mother may be a highly significant factor. It might even produce a psychosomatic injury, that is, the rejection might actually harm the developing brain and nervous system. It must be remembered that in his own concept of his body image, the young child is still a part of, attached to, the mother. Physically, he is frail and the need of emotional support is tremendous. The greatest and most damaging blow to his tiny sensitive ego is to be rejected, denied love and support from the mother of whom he is a part.

I shall not dwell overlong on the symptoms of these two psychoses. Their outlines have been indicated and presently I shall sketch the clinical profiles of actual patients. At this place, some comparative comment might be helpful. All in all, the manic-depressive keeps closer to reality and its ways than the schizophrenic. He may be and often is very sick mentally, sometimes fulfilling the traditional concept of the raving lunatic, but his emotions, thoughts and physical activity are kept fairly well strung together. In other words, if his thoughts are pleasant or angry, he acts them out emotionally in facial and bodily expressions of pleasure or rage. Should his thinking be melancholy, he is apt to show plainly sadness, dejection, remorse for his "sins" and is often suicidal. On the other hand, the schizophrenic is likely to be the original "poker-face." As a novitiate in psychiatry, I was being shown through a mental hospital. On one of the halls I heard a terrific noise. Investigating, I found a schizophrenic patient rhythmically banging his head against the solid oak door of his room. On his face I expected to see suffering and deep anguish. Instead, it was wooden, expressionless. In advanced schizophrenia, there is not only an insufficiency of available emotion to activate the thoughts, but thought and emotion are often contradictory. A schizophrenic patient told me his enemies were going to bind him and kill him by having a single drop of water fall on his head every hour. It was going to take 8972 years to complete his destruction. Yet, he spoke of his suffering and sad fate with a silly simper on his face. That is what we mean by *schizophrenia,* the split between thought and feeling—splitting of the personality.

Perhaps some of these concepts, the parallelism between thought and emotion in manic-depressive and the inadequacy of emotion to thought and their discord in schizophrenia may be illustrated by two simple diagrams:

The manic-depressive embraces the environment, is stimulated by it, draws it into his psychosis and utilizes it in acting it out. The schizophrenic crawls into the shell of his phantasy. And yet, even after many years, he can still briefly re-establish contact with reality.

A patient who had a schizophrenia for ten years would for many months at a time refuse to eat, in obedience to something she vaguely called a "vow" and had to be kept alive by tube feeding. From time to time, occasionally at mealtime, she would awake from her torpor, dash into the dining room, grab a tray of food in each hand, dart to a corner, sit on the floor and cram food by the fistfuls into her mouth. Another patient, a lady in her seventies, who had come down with schizophrenia at the age of twenty, and who year after year sat in a quiet corner of the hospital dreaming her life away, scarcely ever speaking, would now and then wander into the sitting room, join the card players and for an hour or more play an excellent game of bridge. Incongruity of behavior is one of the hallmarks of schizophrenia.

Often the schizophrenic patient gives the impression of being in a daze or stupor, totally unconscious of the surroundings. This is not the usual situation. As far as the external world is concerned, perhaps "boredom" comes closest to expressing the attitude of the schizophrenic. He is much like a man who goes to the theater to witness a play. Soon after the curtain rises, and the first few lines are spoken, he finds the play totally uninteresting. He is in the middle of the row and cannot leave the theater without attracting attention, which he dislikes. So, he finds relief and even satisfaction in idle, errant pleasing thoughts. If he wishes he can turn his attention to the stage. Occasionally he does. But he finds it is still stupid, the actors strutting about, struggling for things which do not seem worthwhile. So he returns to his much more interesting daydreams. Substitute "life" for the play of the stage and you have an idea of the attitude of the schizophrenic toward his environment.

Hallucinations, hearing voices, seeing visions, etc., are almost universal in schizophrenia, but much rarer in manic-depressive. Likewise ideas of reference and delusions of persecution find a much more usual habitat in schizophrenic soil, although they do appear in manic-depressive. These distrusts, suspicions and paranoid symptoms are so usual in one large group of schizophrenic patients that it is called *paranoid schizophrenia*. However, not too much attention need be paid to the various types of schizophrenia. It is true that there may be a preponderance of certain symptoms. For instance, in the simple form the personality splitting occurs rapidly, with deterioration of the emotional life. In hebephrenia, there is a great deal of silliness, the expression of insufficient and inappropriate emotional reactions. Both simple and hebephrenic schizophrenia are likely to appear early in life, usually in the teens. The catatonic form appears somewhat later. It is distinguished by such symptoms as catalepsy, cerea, stupors, muscular resistance, negativism, etc. In fact, catatonia means "to stretch tightly." Paranoid delusions mark the paranoid form which is likely to come to clinical flowering later in life than the other forms, in the thirties or even after. However, these various types do not designate tightly fenced-in compartments. The symptoms overflow the names and usually traces of the symptoms of all the forms may be found in a typical patient. Furthermore, age distinctions are rather artificial. Contrary to earlier beliefs, intensive studies have uncovered schizophrenia at practically any age period.

By far and away, the most interesting manic-depressive patient I ever knew was Elizabeth T., whose illness began with depression at the age of eighteen and continued without interruption until her death at the age of fifty-four. It was a beautiful case for study, since once the pattern of the psychosis was established, excitement and depression followed one upon the heels of the other, each phase lasting almost exactly twenty-eight days. Furthermore, I shall always remember Elizabeth because she almost killed me. Because of an old kidney impairment, the patient had a blood pressure of about 160, continuing at that level during the depressive phase. I noted that during the excited months the systolic pressure was constantly above 200, and often as high as 250 or higher. I posed myself this question: "Does the blood pressure go up first or only after the symptoms of the excitement have appeared?" To find the answer, I sat up with Elizabeth one of the nights when she was due to change from depression to mania, taking the blood pressure every fifteen minutes. The patient was quiet, felt "miserable and unhappy," answered questions slowly, with few words, but intelligently enough. The blood pressure remained evenly between 163-165. Suddenly at about three A.M. the pressure jumped to 255. I removed the apparatus, and looked at Elizabeth. Still quiet, she looked at me, perhaps a bit fixedly. But in less than five minutes she had the fingers of both hands around my throat and was vigorously choking me. I protested, but I doubt that Elizabeth even heard me. My head began to swim, but I managed to hook one foot around the only piece of movable furniture in the room, a metal bedstand, and succeed in overturning it. The crash attracted the attention of a nurse. She took one look and then came back with reinforcements. The nurses, three of them, managed to unhook Elizabeth's fingers from my throat, but not before my face was livid and my eyeballs starting from their sockets.

During her depressions, Elizabeth felt "miserable and unhappy," answered questions in the simplest language, usually in monosyllables, and day after day sat slumped in a chair, scarcely moving, dejected, with deep-furrowed brow and drooping mouth—"I don't want to move"—"Can't do things" —"Can't be interested"—"My head is clouded"—"Thick"— "Stoppage in thinking"—"Brain lacks nourishment"—"Bowels feel horrid"—"I think they are closed, etc." Unlike many depressed patients, Elizabeth was not filled with self-blame for "terrible" and, often, "unpardonable" sins.

As excitement supplanted depression, Elizabeth could be scarcely recognized as the same woman. The change always came quickly—"It drops like a curtain and rises like a curtain." In an hour she looked ten years younger, rosy-cheeked, healthy-looking, active, but a very hurricane of misdirected energy. Constantly talking, screaming, dancing, singing, profane, obscene (when asked to give her thought associations with the word "love," she replied, "If 'X' would come up here tonight, I'd uncover quickly enough" *). In behavior, she was unpredictable, excepting that she was certain to misbehave.

A favorite pastime was to smear her face and body with lipstick, adorn herself with a headdress made of grapefruit rinds and bits of cloth, tie red rags around her arms, legs, bust and pelvis and shout and sing at the top of her lungs—"I'm a copper-colored maiden." She usually disdained clothing and was generally untidy, preferring to void urine upon the floor of her room rather than go to the toilet. Her attention and speech were like rapidly shifting quicksilver. In less than five minutes she touched on eighteen divergent topics and, at the end, was farther away than ever from the subject she began to discuss. Sometimes so great was the pressure of thought and speech that it was a jumble of hoarse-voiced incoherence, resembling delirium. By dint of careful attention once I distinguished the

* During a depressive phase, her association with "love" was "my family."

following: "Sweetheart and *lieber schatz,* also your old fuzzy son of a yard, I mean field, come to me, a violent lunatic calls, balls, she is suffering from lunatic or chronic, crazy, catitus. Will you come to a Hallowe'en dinner and dance . . . at least 100 crazy loons and 100 nurses, also your friends from the east, also your former enemies. B. has fallen. Louis will bring a zither player, a glass of wine, some angel cake and you— music that I heard from you was more than music, bread that I broke with you was more than bread. . . . Meta." And so on. Hour after hour, a cascade of overstimulated, disorganized thought and speech.

The emotional reactions changed with incredible speed, like one color merging into another on a mixing screen. Often beginning with good nature, there rapidly followed one upon the heels of the other, exhilaration, exaltation, boastfulness, pride, irritability, anger, hate or murderous rage. Often a chance and casual remark from a nurse served to turn a good-tempered, laughing woman into an infuriated animal—trying to scratch, kick and bite the nurses, in the meantime hurling a verbal spate of coarse abuse and threats of violence. If thwarted in her desire to injure the nurses, she vented her destructiveness upon the furniture, dishes, panes of glass, anything she could break. In the depressive phase, overmodest, constantly trying to pull her dress down to her shoetops; during the excitement, filled with erotic thoughts, making gross sexual advances to any man who entered the ward. "There are snakes in the room, the hospital doctors force her to take aphrodisiacs, strange and handsome men enter her room in the dead of night and seduce her." She found time to write voluminously page after page, lines running this way and that, underscored, capitalized, crudely illustrated.

During the periods of depression she could not remember

what happened during the excited periods, but from excitement to excitement she clearly recalled her behavior and boasted of it.

There was at least some vague appreciation of the fact that she was in the grip of a mental illness. Once, when particularly coarse, profane and obscene in her language, pouring out a torrent of filth, I chided her gently, pointing out that she was of gentle birth and rearing, a college graduate, etc. Quick as a flash, she replied, "What the hell's the use of being crazy, if I can't say and do what I want to say and do?" During the depression, she said, "I am sick, very sick, my head, all over."

These are a few of the facets of the psychotic life of Elizabeth T. She taught me much psychiatry. I am sorry I could not do more for her.

Naturally, not every manic-depressive patient is as severely sick as was Elizabeth. The majority are not. There are innumerable gradations, from mild depression easily mistaken for a normal "blue spell" to the depths of agonized mental suffering; from slight overactivity in thought and word which might lead to the opinion, "He is certainly a lively fellow, interested in everything" to uncontrolled, unmistakable mania.

Clarence R. was a bright but odd boy. At school he did well in his studies, usually leading the class, but he did not get on with the other children. They teased him a great deal, calling him "specs," "professor" and "sissie pants." He had to wear glasses because of a considerable visual defect, liked to read "heavy" books and was afraid of rough games and athletics. He was very shy with girls and avoided them whenever possible. His parents, particularly his mother, doted on him. Unfortunately, with the idea that Clarence was a genius, she treated him "very special" (her own words), encouraged his non-athletic tendencies, on one pretext or another had him excused from the usual school group activities, was very proud of his interest in abstruse philosophical books far beyond his years, and beamed with approval when he recited long passages from Shakespeare. Disappointed and frustrated in her emotional relations with her husband, she possessed Clarence emotionally (later when the boy was schizophrenic, she complained bitterly, "He was so dear to me. I loved him so much, I even thought for him. Why has he done this to me?"). She decided, lovingly but firmly, not only the kind of haircut Clarence should have, or the clothes he should wear, but also she shaped his opinions and attitudes.

Nevertheless, Clarence did have an excellent mind, and, in spite of his mother, he developed intellectual independence and even originality in thinking. In his freshman college year, he wrote a brilliant thesis on the "Dangerous Political Disregard of Saving Philosophies" which won the undergraduate award. Academically, his first two years of college were distinguished. About the middle of the third year, when Clarence was eighteen years old, his work began to slip so rapidly that he was "warned" by the Dean. He became moody, silent and relinquished even the small amount of fellow-student companionship which he had made with a few "intellectuals." It was discovered that, about this time, Clarence had his first and only love affair, with a nice, intelligent, healthy-minded co-ed. She, in her own words, "liked Clarence a lot," and following the ancient biological urge of women mixed her liking with a great deal of mothering. Apparently Clarence talked rather more foolishly and wildly than the usual undergrad and acted strangely enough so that the young lady diplomatically disentangled herself from the affair and took up with a current campus hero—a football star. Soon after this, Clarence left college and, although he had sufficient money for train fare, walked and hitch-hiked more than three hundred miles to his home in a Southern city. Arriving home late at night, he surprised and frightened his parents by "wild and threatening talk." Among other things, he gazed fixedly into his mother's eyes, and said, "Of course, Mother, you will have to die before I can marry Helen." Then he retired to his room and locked the door. In about half an hour, while his parents were talking over the situation, Clarence burst into the room with blood streaming from wounds in his wrists, where he had cut himself rather deeply with a razor blade. Of course, this decided the issue. The family doctor was called and within a few hours, Clarence was in a mental hospital.

In the hospital, Clarence was quiet and reasonably co-operative. His attitude toward the staff physicians is best described as "cagey." He would initiate conversations about "extrasensory perception," often concluding something like this: "Of course, as you know, Doctor, many scientists do believe in extra-sensory perception. I suppose that if thoughts can be transmitted without spoken words, then they will find a way of controlling them, maybe by a machine. Such machines, I suppose, could be used for evil purposes, maybe to make innocent people think bad thoughts—sexual thoughts. I suppose they might even make a machine to broadcast thoughts against your will. Of course, it's all very fantastic."

There was no doubt that Clarence heard "voices." Several times the nurses overheard him, speaking to "someone" in low but threatening tones, when alone in his room.

Several times I caught Clarence off guard. I found him in his room, cursing and making threatening gestures. When he saw me, he stopped abruptly and said it was nothing; he just felt irritable. But in a few minutes, he remarked, "I suppose a good many male nurses are homosexuals."

Once he met me with an angry, threatening mien and exclaimed, "You know, Doctor, Helen is here and wants to come to me. Those bruisers are preventing her." "Who are the bruisers, Clarence?" "Oh, you know, the footballers. Forget it." And he would not say another word.

Usually the patient's emotional reactions were strong and in keeping with his expressed thoughts, but several times, in the midst of earnest emphatic remarks, he grimaced and giggled in a silly fashion. When questioned he said, "Oh, nothing important. Just thought of something."

Once I came upon him in the grounds of the hospital. I called to him, but received no reply. As I approached, I noted he was staring off into faraway space, his face immobile and the tip of his index finger pressed tightly against his lips. I was unable to get his attention, even by calling his name loudly. I encountered considerable resistance when I attempted to move his finger from his lips, but finally I was able to raise his hand above his head. It remained as I had placed it, and I could move it about and mold it into awkward positions as though the arm were made of wax rather than flesh and blood. Sharply pinching his skin and sticking him with a pin did not elicit even the flicker of an eyelid. Clarence was in a cataleptic stupor. He remained in it for ten days, almost motionless, mute and artificially fed. He emerged from the stupor suddenly, exclaiming, "I have been born again."

Following his "awakening," the patient improved rapidly. Soon it was possible to carry out simple psychotherapy, which reviewed his life history step by step and provided explanations for many of the symptoms. In addition, he was given modified insulin-shock therapy. He has remained well for two years and is working in a plant nursery, doing his job conscientiously and, in addition, is carrying out some interesting experiments in plant cross-breeding. He hopes to return to college in another year.

What is the outlook for the patient who has schizophrenia? In the first place, it has always been interpreted too pessimistically. In the old days, not more than a few decades ago, when a mental hospital superintendent came to write his annual report and found that a number of patients who had been diagnosed dementia praecox (schizophrenia) had recovered, he was likely to change the diagnosis to manic-depressive. At about this time, I reported on a large, unselected group of schizophrenic patients, of whom 22 per cent recovered with ordinary treatment and not one relapsed. Nor is the prognostic situation fairly expressed by the gloomy remark of a friend of mine, an able psychiatrist: "I never knew a schizophrenic patient who could not get well, and yet I never knew one who did." With modern treatment, chemical (insulin) and electrical (electric shock therapy) and psychotherapy, the chances of remission and adjustment have been greatly increased. And yet a considerable number of schizophrenic patients do not succeed in pushing away the shadows and getting back to reality. Not all the factors governing remission are tangible. In a general way, I believe it is dependent upon the amount of the potentiality for emotional growth and maturity in each patient. Apparently some individuals are too inadequate from childhood, too sensitized in their personalities, perhaps even too immature in their physical make-ups, to meet the demands of the kind of world in which we live.* This is, in part at least, an indictment of the superficiality, artificiality and materialism of our culture and mores.

Better understanding and modern treatment have made manic-depressive a far less inflexible psychosis. Electroshock and skillful psychotherapy have a good chance of breaking into the recurring pattern of excitements and depression. It is

---

* Very interesting experimental work with the newly discovered adrenal cortical hormone, cortisone, would seem to indicate that some schizophrenic patients do not have the physiological equipment to respond to its stimulus.

particularly effective in depression. My researches would seem to indicate, among other things: a) that a larger number of Jewish and Irish patients recover; b) that when the onset occurs before the age of thirty, the outlook is better than if later in life (excepting in involutional melancholia); c) that the sounder the ancestry and the more normal the personality markings before the psychosis appeared, the better the likelihood of adjustment; d) that serious heart, blood-vessel and kidney complications may interfere with recovery.

In the section on treatment, the importance and value of drastic treatments, such as electroshock, insulin, brain operations, techniques of psychotherapy and the significance of occupational therapy will be considered. However, at this place, I cannot resist reiterating the value of simple psychotherapy. The psychiatrist knows that almost always at least some odds and ends of the reassurance, suggestion and support he gives, to even the very delusional patient, day after day, are likely to stick. As one patient said to me after recovery from a very serious and prolonged psychosis, "Of course, I didn't believe what you said. I thought you were trying to fool me. Yet, sometimes I wasn't so sure. I think it weakened my strange beliefs a little. Sometimes I hated what you said, but I would have been terribly disappointed if you had not said it."

In this connection, the so-called Rosen technique in the treatment of schizophrenia at least deserves to be mentioned. It involves the attempt to bring the patient by a very direct technique back to his childhood, and particularly to the places at which emotional development apparently had been halted. The therapist attempts to have the patient relive these phases of his childhood, and actively participates with the patient in their reliving. For instance, the patient may be given a nursing bottle. In effect, there is an effort on the part of the therapist to have the patient grow up by actually reliving his child-hood and the hope is that with such a therapeutic experience the regressive, immature symptoms will be relinquished.

In addition to the target therapy, chemical, electrical and psychotherapy, there is for each patient a daily round of chores to be done in the details of treatment. In carrying out these details of treatment and rehabilitation, the main arms of execution for the psychiatrist are the nurse, the social worker and the occupational teacher.

Every patient is a problem in internal medicine. Intercur-rent illness, perhaps serious anemia, or a tumor growth may have its presence masked by mental symptoms and establish dangerous beachheads upon the patient's body before being recognized. Even if no improvement in the mental picture is to be anticipated from such measures, yet every competent psychiatrist strives to bring the bodies of his patients to their optimum. Perhaps the skin and gastrointestinal tract merit particular vigilance. For instance, obstinate constipation may readily occur in manic patients, far too busy with interesting and important matters to visit the toilet, the depressed pa-tients too miserable to care, and the schizophrenics too absorbed in phantasies to heed the mundane calls of nature. Furthermore, catatonic, negativistic patients may retain the contents of bladder and bowel for long periods of time. It takes much effort and endless patience to keep patients clean and to attempt to establish even a skeletonized habit routine of general, oral, skin and bladder and bowel routine. It is well worth the time and effort expended.

"Keep up the nutrition of your mental patients." Glibly said by teachers to students, but not so easy to attain. The excited patient is usually far too busy to want to stop for food or else often he may consume it in enormous quantities and at such express-train speed as to defy every dictum of digestion. The really deeply depressed patient never wants to eat. Perhaps he may be too unhappy and slowed up to make the smallest effort. Or he may feel too unworthy to partake of food as "less sinful" people do. Or, and frequently, he may be attempting suicide. Or his food rejection may be immediately activated by the delusion that his stomach is sealed. The schizophrenic patient, too, with pseudo logic may disclaim against putting food into the stomach, simply to have "it remain there and rot." Or, the food refusal may be at the behest of fear of poisoning by the persecutors or even the fulfillment of "vows" vaguely associated with "purification by fasting." Frequently at some cross-section of these major psychoses it is necessary to resort to tube feeding. Even though the nutrition may be satisfactorily maintained, the psychiatrist does not accept this artificial situation willingly. For one thing, it is too much a debasement of a normal function—eating. And for another, it is too far afield from the return to the reality objective. So the psychiatrist and his aides accept the non-eating situation unwillingly, as temporary. From time to time there are invitations to resume eating by bringing in trays with small portions of temptingly arranged food. There are auxiliary treatment factors which not only may help nutrition, but also influence the mental reactions—occupation, calisthenics, walks, outdoor and indoor games, amateur theatricals, group singing, dancing, the theater, cinema, etc. These are healthy symbols of activity and perhaps they diminish the distance between the unreality of mental illness and the realities of everyday life. These adjuncts may and often do serve to turn the destructive activity of the manic patient into useful and acceptable channels, win the depressed patients (even if only briefly) from the lethargy induced by the melancholia and, for the schizophrenic, keep open (albeit only slightly) the vista of participation in everyday living.

In everyday practice, insomnia certainly is among the five most common symptoms which the psychiatrist has to combat. In manic-depressive patients, particularly in the depressive phase and in many cross-sections of schizophrenia, sleeplessness is a frequent problem. Sometimes relatives of patients do not understand why the psychiatrist does not give more sleeping medicine, enough to give the patient a peaceful night—"At least he ought to have that much. He suffers enough during the day." But it is not quite so simple. Even mild hypnotic drugs are not entirely harmless. They are toxic. And they may exact a toll of a "hangover" the next morning so that, for instance, the depression is perceptibly deepened. And, too, there is some risk of habit formation.

The psychiatrist weighs each insomnia situation carefully. He, too, wants his patients to sleep, but he is not willing to purchase sleep at too high a price. He remembers, too, that many patients are apt to overestimate the periods of wakefulness and that relaxation in bed is about half as good as sleep. In a given case, the psychiatrist may decide that for a few nights the patient should be given rather large doses of sleep-inducing medicine, but generally he is apt to rely on exercise, massage, physiotherapy, hydrotherapy and particularly long-continued baths, at neutral temperature, with the patient lying comfortably in a hammock fixed to the rim of the tub.

If Freud was correct in his death-wish theory, and it does seem reasonable to assume that in human beings, coexistent with the wish to live there is also the wish to die, then this desire often reaches its peak in depression and sometimes in schizophrenia. Granted, by and large, but of course with exceptions, that suicide is an emotionally immature, exhibitionistic, somewhat narcissistic and childish retaliatory act, still one may understand that often this exit from life is very inviting to a depressed patient beset by agony of mind and overwhelmed by self-blame. Or to the schizophrenic patient whose reality horizons are fading and yet are still distinct enough so that he experiences the desperate panic of deep mental conflicts threatening to emerge into consciousness.

All the measures mentioned, which attempt to keep the patient active, interested, perhaps diverted, making a display of the more attractive goods of reality, are helpful as obstacles in the path of self-destructive drives. Non-intrusive nursing vigilance is valuable. If, however, it is too intrusive, too obvious, then it defeats its purpose. It keeps alive the suicidal thought, rather than quieting it. And the patient may make a macabre game of trying to outwit the keeper-like nurse. Theoretically, suicide is preventable by constant and open, never-relaxing watchfulness. Practically, it is not always preventable, since no competent psychiatrist is willing to make prisoners of his patients, denying them all treatment involving even the slightest risk and keeping them constantly at a non-decisive, non-assertive level, without the encouraging symbol of progress—fewer restrictions. Many years ago, my first preceptor in psychiatry said to me, "An institution that never has a suicide is badly and inhumanly run. It is a prison, not a hospital."

The psychiatrist, particularly the hospital psychiatrist, has the responsibility not only of coping with but of foreseeing a thousand and one emergencies. In their uninhibited activity, manic patients are likely to bruise, abrade and lacerate themselves. Manic patients, too, mischievously and depressed patients, often with suicidal intent, try and sometimes succeed in swallowing all manner of things. I have the photograph of a collection of thirty-two articles removed by operation from the stomach of a depressed patient—pins, needles, screws, nails, hairpins, corset stays, etc. Strange behavior may emerge from the sick psyche of manic, depressed and schizophrenic patients. All sorts of objects may be inserted into the body orifices—ears, nose, vagina, penis, rectum. Schizophrenics, at the command of "voices," may injure or occasionally kill others or mutilate themselves in horrible fashion. One patient "heard" the Biblical injunction and tried to obey it literally, by attempting to pluck out his eyes and cut off his right hand. Another did succeed in amputating his penis with a knife and died of hemorrhage.

Schizophrenic patients may suddenly react to their delusions of persecution by homicidal behavior. Recently, a young war veteran suffering from schizophrenia shocked the nation by responding to his delusions by the mass murder of thirteen people, including several children.

Having been, earlier in my career, for many years a staff physician in a mental hospital, my sympathies are with the overworked hospital doctor. His problems are endless. Relatives of patients, frightened and worried by the spectacle of mental illness in those they love, sometimes think that the psychiatrist sits in his office bemused with vague theories, neglecting the patients, *their* wives, husbands, mothers, daughters, fathers and sons. I have indicated only a few of the many chores which the doctor must do (or see that they are done) for each patient. Usually hospital physicians are willing to listen to any reasonable suggestion or request, but some of the ideas of relatives, to say the least, are a bit odd. One devoted mother wanted to be secreted in an adjoining room, so that she could listen to every word her schizophrenic son uttered. A wife asked if she could be disguised as a nurse and care for her depressed husband. A mother felt sure that if she could be permitted to prepare all the food for her son and feed it to him personally, he would be soon well. When the hospital physician insists on less frequent visits to the patient or interdicts them altogether, relatives so often feel that they are being discriminated against or even that the doctor does not like the patient and wants to punish him. Of course, one visitor more or less does not make much difference, but certain visitors, particularly those who "understand the situation thoroughly" often complicate already difficult problems by arguing with patients or "cheering them" with Pollyanna bromides. Sometimes I think that the deepest hell of Dante's inferno should be reserved for those who say to a deeply depressed patient, "You look as though you had lost your last friend. For heaven's sake, forget your troubles. Smile. Laugh and the world will laugh with you."

We have scarcely scratched the surface of the area of prevention of these two great psychoses. If we subtract the influence of inheritance, there still remain large and attractive preventive potentialities. Childhood presents the golden opportunity. I firmly believe that the amount of manic-depressive and schizophrenic psychoses would be materially decreased if every child could have its rightful heritage—the emotional security of being wanted and loved by its parents, loved with that unselfish and complete love that makes a proper balance between holding and releasing, possessing and emancipating.

A very important facet of such a parent-child relationship is that it should provide for the inculcation into the young growing personalities the ingredients from which may be developed a reasonable fund of correct information and helpful attitudes about sex. Not complete revealment, of course, but enough so that there is not too much room left for the extravagances of sexual phantasies, which so often dominate the mental decor of these two psychoses and notably of schizophrenia.

Can a child who early in life shows extreme extroverted and impulsive traits be helped to a better balance of personality? I should say, "Yes." I believe that a reasonable amount of safeguarding forethought and reflection can be taught to children, not by sermonizing precept and admonition, but by parents providing good examples to imitate. A little girl who scurried about my office like a restless sprite said, "Mommy and Daddy are jittery," and, proudly, "So am I."

Conversely, I am convinced that much can be done for the withdrawn, dangerously introverted children, but not by too much pressure from the environment. The home should be reasonably peaceful and harmonious. There should be neither harsh non-explanatory discipline or, its reverse, spoiling. "Playing favorites," centering parental attention upon a brother or sister more socially favored, is destructive, as, too, are attempts to shame the introverted child into copying the social or athletic assets of the other children. Some children become enmeshed in phantasy because they are too much alone. Children need plenty of companionship with other children of both sexes. Introverted children are usually avid readers. Without being dictatorial, it is wise to see that their reading interests contain some antidotes to vividly fantastic literature. Religion may supply an important need if it is beautiful and inspiring (not grimly fear-producing) and, at the same time, social and contributing to inner security. The schooling of these children should be scanned and the tendency to study too many abstruse and obscure subjects tactfully minimized. Rather should socializing subjects be encouraged, so that youth may be kept fairly close to facts and friendly personal contacts be maintained. Ruthless competition for intellectual primacy is not mentally healthy.

In the earlier days of psychiatry any mental illness that appeared at the so-called "change of life," particularly in women, was very likely to be called "involutional psychosis." Now it is clear that many of these hitherto misnamed psychoses belong to groups which also occur at much earlier life spans, for instance, schizophrenia.

Perhaps there is one psychosis which is somewhat influenced in its expression in both women and men by the "change of life" and deserves to be called involutional—"involutional melancholia." This psychosis is about three times as frequent in women as in men and occurs rather loosely around the time of the menopause. "Loosely," advisedly, since the menopause can come on a changeably physiological date. I know one family in which three generations on the distaff side have "changed" before the age of thirty. However, the average age is the early fifties in women and the middle sixties in men.

There must remain some doubt as to the exact clinical nature of involutional melancholia. Some authorities feel that while its expression is unusual, yet basically it is a manic-depressive psychosis. Others believe it is a more or less independent mental disease which can develop only in a certain cast of personality, in a mold of rigidity, meticulousness, slavery to detail, overscrupulousness. This is the man (or woman) who, even early in life, cannot unbend and forget himself, even with himself. His superego seems to be overdeveloped. He tends to judge himself not only harshly, but sometimes with almost cruel exactitude. In his own mind he falls far shorter of his inner self-ideal than does the average man. Small faults and transgressions worry him enormously. Constantly he places himself at the searching and unrelenting bar of his own self-critique and usually he finds a true bill of indictment. He looks after his daily affairs and the business of others entrusted to his care faithfully but with almost painful attention to detail. He tries to sign every letter. His desk is neat as a pin, with every desk accessory and every letter and paper in its proper place, with the exact nicety of "just so." Not for him the happy clutter of more casual men. Occasionally, I ask a patient who has this rigid type of personality and is beginning to bend mentally under its lashings to take a look at my office.

I can always count on a certain amount of disarray, at least a few papers, reprints and books scattered about on the desk, perhaps on the couch and window sills, and even one or two on the floor, when my aim at the waste-paper basket was not so good. (In my own defense, I may say I know where everything is, even though occasionally I cannot find it.) I say to the patient, "When you can look at an office like this one without flinching you will be a lot better than you are now."

In any event, I have briefly described the markings of the personality, particularly in men, in which an involutional psychosis may occur. If it does occur in serious form, then there is a wide departure from reality. The depression may bring severe, indescribable mental suffering. The belittlement and self-blame may amount to abasement and torture: "I'm so loathsome that even a filthy animal would shrink from me." Sometimes the delusional ideas of sinfulness are embroidered by a rich association of thought. Rather more often there is a poverty of ideas, the patient repeating endlessly some phrase like, "Oh, my God." Or, there may be no verbal expressions, merely rocking the body back and forth, moaning piteously. Quite often instead of the retardation or slowing up of physical motion, there is activity varying from restlessness to frenzied agitation. In many patients, there are gross delusions pertaining to the body, diseases like syphilis or other diseases "too loathsome and horrible" to be named by the patient. One patient said, "Everything gone—everything out of me, no stomach, no lungs, no insides, just a shell. All my organs have passed out of my rectum. There is nothing left in between. There is nothing but hands, feet and eyes. This is a miracle —no breath—or anything— Oh, God!—not an earthly thing left."

Briefly, this is the picture of involutional melancholia. Before the day of modern treatment, the outlook was not very good. About 25 to 32 per cent of the patients remained chronic —a sad life sentence. About 20 per cent died from intercurrent disease and suicide. The recovery rate was less than 40 per cent.

With better understanding of the psychopathology of the underlying mental conflicts and of the role of the upset in the balance of the ductless glands due to failing secretion of the sex glands, the outlook is much more hopeful. It is true, however, that though the administration of ovarian, testicular and other endocrine products sometimes produces brilliant results in the usual physical menopausal symptoms, such as "hot flashes," they have not yet accomplished much in combating the mental symptoms. On the other hand electroshock therapy has not only shortened the psychosis and made it much more bearable, but has almost doubled the number of recoveries. This form of treatment and others, including operations on the frontal lobe of the brain, will be discussed in the section on treatment.

That vague and somewhat imponderable condition described as "mental health" involves, among other things, a reasonably close and satisfactory contact of each individual with the realities of the environment in which he lives. Of course, it goes without saying that no one lives in constant and complete contact with his situation in life and certainly not with its unsatisfactory, painful and difficult segments. Everyone is permitted a bit of daydreaming or the use of other reality softeners. But manic-depressive psychosis and schizophrenia are long and perilous journeys into the land of unreality.

8 | PARANOIA AND PARANOID
CONDITIONS

A BACKWASH from the flood of popular psychiatric writings in the press and magazines is the loose way in which important psychiatric terms are used in social conversations. "Homosexual" is one example. From some after-dinner talks I have heard, I get the impression that any man who is seen looking with interest into the windows of an interior decorator's shop is in danger of being discussed as a sexual deviate.

"Paranoid" is another word which is likely to be treated very casually conversationally. The fact that a person insists on going over the details of a proposition very carefully, whether it be a business deal or a wager, does not mean that he is paranoid. Nor does he merit this designation because he questions statements made in conversation, asking for more proof before he agrees. Usually such attitudes merely mean that some people have been more or less hard-bitten by experience and have learned not to be too naïve, compliant and credulous. Paranoia is something much more serious than that.

Before behavior can be labeled paranoid, it should contain

considerable evidence of serious distrust and suspicion, usually with ideas of persecution. And it should be continued for
a fairly long time. An occasional flash of suspicion, as when a
husband now and then accuses his wife of deliberately hiding
the sports section of the newspaper, is not sufficient. Finally,
paranoid means like or resembling paranoia. And it must be
more than a passing resemblance. In mumps, there is swelling
of the face, but by no means does everyone with a swollen face
have mumps. What is paranoia?

A definition given more than thirty years ago has stood
the test of time: "A fixed type of disease, due exclusively to
internal causes and characterized by persistent systematized
delusions, the retention of clear and orderly thinking and acting, and by the absence of hallucinations (hearing of voices,
seeing visions, etc.)."

The definition needs some explanation and amplification.

True paranoia is amazingly rare. In many years I have seen
not more than six paranoiacs.

What does "the retention of clear and orderly thinking and
acting" mean? It means a great deal. For one thing it means
that paranoia is the intellectual aristocrat among all mental
diseases. The paranoiac does have fixed delusions. Perhaps his
delusional conclusion is that some powerful religious organization or even the government is conspiring to destroy him.
Nevertheless, however erroneous the conclusion may be, the
development of the argument is practically flawless. Each link
of the argument fits perfectly into the next, until the chain is
completed. It has been said that if one is willing to accept the
delusional conclusion of the paranoiac, for instance, "the government is persecuting me and plotting to have me killed"
then every "proof" that the paranoiac sets forth is clear, logical and must be accepted.

Some years ago I accomplished something very difficult. I

made friends with a paranoiac. He trusted me; of course, with certain mental reservations. He even consented to let me present him at a clinic before my students. He told his story clearly and with deadly seriousness. (I do not believe that a real sense of humor can co-exist with paranoia, although there may be bitter, sardonic wit.) My paranoiac friend's delusion concerned a certain trust company which he claimed was conspiring with one of his relatives to defraud him of a large legacy. It all sounded very reasonable and logical, even though it happened not to be true. In fact, it sounded so reasonable and logical that after the patient left the clinical amphitheater, a student from one of the back rows, in a very tense voice, called out, "Professor, how dare you say there is anything wrong with that man's mind?"

Sometimes paranoiacs may become leaders of religious and other movements. They may become killers. A considerable percentage of assassins of rulers and other prominent persons have been paranoiacs.

The delusional structure of the paranoiac is not hastily planned and built. It is mulled over for a long time and then is erected with the utmost care and precision. It usually makes its outward appearance in the third decade of life, sometimes later, more commonly in men than women. Then it is meticulously elaborated and perfected during the remainder of the life span. Furthermore, the mind of the paranoiac does not deteriorate. Even though they are employed in the service of a false goal, yet the mental processes are never slipshod or intellectually inferior. They remain true in their close-knit and logical reasoning. Paranoia is, indeed, a psychiatric paradox.

The paranoiac disdains such feeble props as hallucinations to shore up the structure of his false beliefs. Such supports are freely used in lesser paranoid states. If I asked a patient with paranoid schizophrenia why he could be so sure that the night before his enemies had tried to overcome him with a deadly gas, he might very well reply, "Why, of course I am sure. I smelled the gas. And I heard their voices plotting to do it." Once I said to a paranoiac, "What would you think if I told you I heard voices talking about me when there was no one around?" He smiled in cynical fashion and said, "Don't be silly, Doctor. You haven't lost your mind yet, I hope."

Both in mental health and illness, it is the emotions that give substance, strength and purpose to our thinking. So, as one might expect, in paranoia, the delusional ideas are coupled with appropriate and strong emotional reactions. The paranoiac is in deadly earnest. Verbally he strikes out against his persecutors and their machinations with outraged feelings, satire, resentment, bitter anger and hostility.

I have been at some pains to describe the house of paranoia, so that less elaborate psychotic structures are not mistaken for it. The path of the paranoid traverses all psychotic territory and, indeed, some traces of it may be discerned in many so-called normal personalities. Sometimes the paranoid path markings are merely narrow and poorly defined lanes. Sometimes they are fairly broad and solid roads.

In the toxic psychoses, for instance, delirious states, paranoid symptoms do not amount to much, since they are fleeting. True enough, a delirious patient, like a colleague of mine who had pneumonia, may murderously attack the nurse or someone at the bedside, shrieking, "You're trying to poison me." But, like as not, such pictures will soon fade out in the ever-changing panorama emerging from the delirious psyche.

In the organic forms of mental disease, like the senile psychoses, paranoid symptoms when they occur are somewhat more constant. Yet, all in all, they are only details of the whole picture, rather than dominating motifs.

Sometimes, but in rather less than half the patients, there are well-defined paranoid trends in manic-depressive psychosis. They may be strongly maintained with moving emotional accompaniments. Again, they are apt to be the smaller and not the larger and more dynamic part of the mental illness.

Now one takes a long step into territory in which paranoid terrain is much more frequent and well defined.

In the area of schizophrenia, there are carefully designed and fairly closely woven intellectual paranoid patterns. The emotional component of the psychotic pattern is strong and proportionate enough, at least for a number of years, sometimes five or more. It is true that the weave is neither as lasting nor as exact as in paranoia. There are gaps and rents in the intellectual pattern of the delusions of persecution which have been filled in crudely and loosely brought together by hallucinations, ideas of reference, etc.—"I know 'they' are trying to get me. I listen in on the 'voices'," or, "Did you see how that man took out his handkerchief just as I passed? That was a signal to the gang to move in on me." And, as the years pass, the intellectual design of the delusions becomes less and less distinct. The emotional colors begin to fade. Now and again the patient may simper in silly fashion, even when he is discussing the most dramatic phases of the psychotic spectacle.

Finally, the structure of the delusions and the personality of the patients begin to crumble. I knew a paranoid schizophrenic who once had a most elaborate system of delusions. It was a cleverly contrived and rather logical tale of delusions of persecution by a powerful organization of his enemies who feared the power which he was destined to gain and which he would use for the deliverance of suffering mankind. Its telling consumed hours. After ten years the patient became less and less vocal and, finally, mute. He began to walk in a stiff, ungainly manner. Sometimes he would stand in one position for hours. Often he smiled and grimaced. When I questioned him about his delusions, once so rich in idea content, he would merely point to a bit of dirty, frayed ribbon pinned to his coat. It meant that he was the "Emperor of the World and of all the Terrestrial Planets." What a degradation of the symbol!

There is another rung on the paranoid ladder. It is the so-called Paranoid Condition. In the paranoid conditions, the paranoid symptoms are well defined. The delusions of persecution are solidly put together and closely systematized. Usually the patient presents them with intelligence, although there are some flaws in the premises of the delusional argument. The emotional reactions are strong and adequate—fear, resentment, anger, threats of violence. Nevertheless, here and there are weak spots with insufficiency of the emotional responses to the delusional conceptions. Also, while hallucinations are not common, they usually do occur. Eventually, though sometimes not until many years have elapsed, discrepancies and flaws appear in the logic of the delusions and the consistency of the emotional reactions.

The Paranoid Conditions bring us to the portals of paranoia, the content of which has been described.

In order to give an idea of the distribution of paranoid trends in various psychotic groups, a schematic diagram follows. The shaded lines indicate paranoid content.

Unquestionably, there are still many factors operating in the production of paranoia and the serious paranoid conditions which have not yet come under the focus of our knowledge. I am convinced that an important determining factor which shapes the paranoid symptoms is a strong, *latent* homosexual trend in the personality. Not in any personality, but in those which are so constituted that the existence of homosexual drives and desires cannot be faced consciously. To be aware of them, indeed even only to suspect their presence, would be the ultimate psychic catastrophe. Yet the homosexuality, although hidden, is there in all its stark realism and demanding

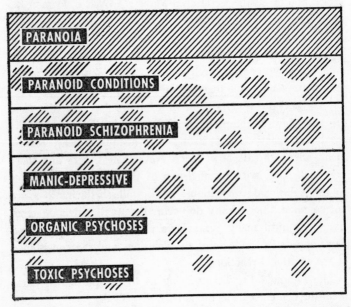

an outlet. It will not remain quiescent even though rigidly repressed. There is tension and nagging unexplained feelings of inferiority and guilt. It is a dangerous psychic dilemma, from which, for certain personalities, there is only one escape. It leads to a dubious haven. Yet a paranoid psychosis is the only choice, the lesser of two evils, more acceptable than the facing of the inner sexual deviation. So this complex is, indeed must be, literally and completely disowned and dispossessed. It is pushed out of the person and into the environment. This mechanism is called *projection*. The psychological advantage is obvious. Now the environment can be blamed. "They whisper dirty things about me"; "They are trying to ruin me by spreading the rumor that I am one of those awful people"; "I hear their lying voices"; "They are terrible sex degenerates and they hate me because I am normal." The more loudly and vehemently "they" can be blamed, the less likelihood there is of hearing the faint inner voice, which might whisper, "Perhaps you are . . ."

Rarely do psychiatrists have the privilege of having the mechanism of the workings of a sick mind revealed in one interview, revealed so plainly that he who runs may read. When I saw Joseph B. on my service at the city psychopathic hospital, he was in a state of intense agitation, pacing up and down, desperate. "For God's sake, Doctor, help me. Protect me from 'them.' 'They' are torturing me every minute. Driving me out of my senses."

"Who are 'they,' Joseph?"

"I don't know, Doctor, I never saw them. But they never give me a second's peace. They are at me, day and night."

"What do 'they' do?"

"What do 'they' do; my God, Doctor, what don't they do? They scream at me day and night. They call me stinking names. You know what I mean. They say I am one of those creatures, sex perverts I think they are called.

"And, they don't stop at calling names. They torture me. They have instruments with which they work on my brain. I call them 'pincers and pullers.' They pinch and pull my brain. The pain is excruciating."

"Joseph, why do they do these things to you?"

"Well, Doctor, I didn't know until the other day. Then, 'they' practically told me. They don't want me to have sex relations with my wife ever again. In fact, they want me to leave her. My God, Doctor, isn't that terrible? You know how dearly I love my wife. My God, what am I going to do?"

"What *are* you going to do, Joseph?"

"Well, Doctor, at first, I refused even to listen to 'their' vile suggestions. I cursed them and demanded that they let me alone. But 'they' just torture me more and worse. And, 'they' said to me if I don't do as they say, leave my wife, then what they are doing to me now is nothing compared to what they will do to me. They say they will torture me as no human being has ever been tortured in this world."

"You don't want to leave your wife, do you, Joseph?"

"Good heavens, no. I love her with all my heart. Life would be terrible without her. But what can I do? I can't stand any more torture. No human being could. I am so weak from it. And so frightened. It will be terrible to be away from my wife. But what can I do? I am helpless. Please explain it to her, Doctor. Tell her that, though it breaks my heart, I don't dare live with her any more."

The patient went on in this vein for a long time. He was filled with paranoid delusions. Always they returned to the central theme. His enemies would bedevil him ruthlessly and unmercifully unless he left his wife. Outside of his hallucinations and delusions, he was clear enough and in contact with his surroundings.

An interview with his wife was revealing. She felt that Joseph disliked sexual relations. For this reason she herself never suggested intercourse, but "they had it," from time to time. Joseph never made love to her and she felt he "had sex with her" from a sense of duty. She was very unhappy about their married life.

And she was even more worried by the way Joseph acted when he had too much to drink at a party. "It worries me."

"Why does it worry you?"

"Well, he gets too friendly with the men. Almost affectionate. I don't know much about such things, but I have heard people talk about it. It's kind of unnatural. I have wondered whether Joseph is that way."

In Joseph, the strong, latent homosexuality came very definitely to the surface. Not openly as such. His ego could not have faced that. So a psychosis was unconsciously accepted. It was the exhibition of projection. The more "they" could be blamed, the less likely it was that he would suspect himself. Furthermore, the hallucinatory-delusional system which was evolved, not only protected Joseph from self-revealment, but also provided a path of escape from heterosexual life which his personality could no longer tolerate.

Not too much can be hoped for from treatment. When the paranoid symptoms are part of a toxic picture or of some other benign form of mental illness, then they disappear with the skillful treatment of the psychosis. In well-developed paranoid conditions, particularly those with relative mental clearness and where the patient is in close contact with the environment, the outlook is not very promising. Sometimes when the patient trusts the psychiatrist, a fairly satisfactory adjustment may be obtained on a semi-logical basis. While the patient is not able to accept the psychiatrist's explanation of his symptoms, yet he may come to an understanding of the desirability and advisability of not reacting socially to his symptoms. I have had a number of patients, including a sea captain, a stockbroker, several business men, a physician and a minister, who made such compromises with behavior. While inwardly they retained their delusions and believed they were being persecuted, yet they learned not to translate their false beliefs into overt behavior and, all in all, conducted their lives successfully.

If the patient's paranoid condition activates too difficult or anti-social and dangerous behavior, then commitment to a mental hospital becomes imperative.

9 | PSYCHOSOMATICS

PSYCHIATRISTS are still chuckling because many of their fellow practitioners in other fields of medicine think of psychosomatics as something new. The word is comparatively recent, but the thought is very ancient. The introduction of "psychosomatic" not so many years ago sounded like the announcement of the nuptials of the body and mind. Along with medicine, presumably psychiatry was in the bridal party.

If the union of body and mind has been consummated only recently, then for a long time psychiatry has brazenly sanctioned an illicit relationship. Long before the word psychosomatic was compounded, psychiatry had insistently taught that man was a total and indivisible unit, and therefore, in health and disease, every physical process at once reverberated in all of the man and notably in his emotions. Conversely, that every emotional reaction, whether it was strong and violent like rage or hate, or merely a feeling tone like mild satisfaction or slight chagrin, immediately has repercussions in every part, tissue and cell of the body.

The basic idea of psychosomatic medicine is very ancient. At least 2500 years ago the wise and observant Socrates, returning from the second Thracian campaign, chided the Athenian physicians for not realizing, as did the Thracians, that the body could not be cured without favorably influencing the mind. "This," he said, "is the reason why the cure of many diseases is unknown to the physicians of Hellas, because they are ignorant of the whole."

Even before the time of Socrates, the obvious body-mind union and its daily demonstration should have been perceived. It is truly amazing that for such a long time physicians should have failed to note and interpret the medical significance of the time-immemorial experiences of our species, so common that they have become part of the language of all people. From primitive man to homo sapiens, human beings have been trying to explain to their medicine men, and later to their doctors, that under stress of emotion they felt lumps in their throats, that their hearts pounded or jumped, that stomachs turned over or dropped or that they had "no guts" (courage) or "too much guts," that they were paralyzed with fear, so angry that they could not see straight or blinded with rage. The great poet noted there were those who viewed the world with jaundiced eyes.

A woman who had had a serious quarrel with her husband complained to me that she felt as though she "had been pulled through a wringer."

In China, so often a food-deprived country, the stomach has been elevated to a sentimental plane. Two lovers, separated from each other, might write in this vein, "My stomach is hungry for you," instead of "My heart yearns for you." There is a psychosomatic note in this ancient and beautiful Chinese wish: "May Joy sing in the topmost boughs of your heart."

And yet physicians for centuries averted their gaze from what was constantly happening in the bodies of their patients. Only recently did they begin to think psychosomatically.

That the body should profile the inner, hidden emotions of man is not at all remarkable to psychiatrists. They encounter it frequently in their patients. Sometimes patients are cataleptic, that is, their limbs may be placed in awkward, strained positions which often are retained beyond the time limits of even an athlete's muscular endurance. Other patients without evidence of organic disease may become stuporous, not responding to pain, even from a sharp needle thrust. The bodies of these patients are mirroring profound happenings within the psyche. Naturally, psychiatrists can understand readily enough that headache, backache, nausea, vomiting, rapidly beating heart and a host of other common symptoms often may represent the bodily expression of unconscious emotional conflicts which could not be settled otherwise.

There are many erroneous ideas concerning what happens when a psychosomatic symptom is produced. At first glance, it appears as though the organ or part is actually diseased. If the structure of the stomach is normal, why should there be nausea and vomiting? Or, if nothing is wrong with the heart why should it beat so fast, sometimes twice as fast as the usual rate? The structure of the stomach or heart or other organs is quite all right. They are merely responding by increased tempo of function to the stimuli of various emotional drives. They have to do this. If a rubber ball is dropped gently to the floor, it bounces slightly. But if it is thrown down with some force, the area of rebound is much greater.

All sorts of psychosomatic manifestations occur in the daily lives of all of us. We do not think of them as symptoms. Indeed we notice them only infrequently. Yet, every part—organ, blood vessel, tissue and cell of the body—is reacting at the behest of inner and environmental emotional forces. It is as though the various parts of the body were like the instruments in an orchestra, each instrument playing the notes it is designed to play, sometimes playing loudly, sometimes softly, all in obedience to the movements of the baton of the conductor.

It is only when the psychosomatic symptoms are marked and persistent enough to obtrude themselves into consciousness that they become the subject of medical attention. Even then, the many and varied functional displays in themselves do not indicate any structural disease of the human body. They do indicate somewhat serious inner emotional conflicts which are at an impasse. No solution has been found. The appearance of functional psychosomatic symptoms represents an effort to work out a compromise.

A forty-nine-year-old man was married to a wife thirty-five years old. There were two healthy children. He described himself as desperate because he was sexually impotent. He had tried every kind of treatment in order to regain sexual potency and happiness: various instrumental treatments of his genito-urinary tract, general massage and massage of his prostate gland, hydrotherapeutic, electrical and ultraviolet therapy. He had a long list of ductless-gland and vitamin medicines, all of which he had taken faithfully. His impotence was no better. Indeed, to it there had been added annoying sensations and sharp pains in his sex organs, burning when he urinated, nocturnal emissions, headaches, loss of energy and concentration. Repeated careful examinations did not reveal any organic disease.

Even with a few interviews, the outlines of the emotional conflict began to emerge. Far into his manhood he had been dominated by a positive, aggressive mother. His Jehovah-like father had not given him much affection. He was particularly remembered for the frightening family sermons he delivered about punishment for sexual discrepancies. The patient's own sex desires had never been very strong. His wife was fourteen years younger and she was "highly sexed."

The psychosomatic symptoms appeared after an unsuccessful attempt at sexual intercourse. He said his wife was irritated and impatient at his failure.

A married woman, forty-two years old, complained of severe nausea, "sick stomach," vomiting, complete loss of appetite, headache, backache, dizziness. She had had two rest cures, numerous x-ray examinations of the gastrointestinal organs, special corsets to hold up a sagging stomach and weekly drainages of the gall-bladder. None of these helped more than very temporarily.

In the psychiatric interviews it soon developed that this woman had lost "all desire for sex." Worse than that, sexual relations had become very unpleasant and painful. The patient confessed that "sex never meant very much to me." By various subterfuges, she had decreased the frequency of sexual intercourse but was filled with anxiety, lest her husband should tire of her and leave her.

It soon became apparent that the most important figure in her memory life was her father. Her mother died when she was seven years old. She frequently repeated that her father "blew hot or cold." Sometimes he was very strict and whipped her for the smallest disobedience. But, often he became very indulgent and "covered me with love and kisses. I adored my father. He was my ideal of a man." What she knew about sex she "picked up here and there."

After her father's death, she married a pleasant, rather matter-of-fact young fellow. There were no children. As the treatment proceeded she came to understand clearly that unconsciously she had rejected her husband in her love life because he was so different from the father-figure love object. The husband could not displace him.

A twenty-two-year-old student wanted to leave college since he felt he was too sick to go on. He said, "I would rather quit than flunk. It's no use trying. I can't concentrate."

Tuberculosis had been suspected but careful examinations had definitely ruled it out. There were a great many psychosomatic symptoms—"head colds," headache, "stuffy feelings," shortness of breath, pain in the chest, "stitches" in the side, nose bleeds, loss of weight, fatigue.

Nose and throat treatments helped only briefly. Dietary regimes and rest treatments did little good. Psychotherapy did help a great deal.

The student, at the first interview, was enormously relieved at the opportunity of easing his troubled and remorseful "conscience" about masturbation. During much of his life he had been tightly tied to the apron strings of an emotionally possessive mother. She had warned him excessively about "girls" and their "tricks" and "lures." The masturbation had not been continuous from childhood, but had been resumed soon after entering college, upon the heels of three heterosexual experiences occurring in a setting conducive to embarrassment, feelings of inferiority and fears of discovery.

In these three patients, all of whom were relieved of their psychosomatic symptoms, the symptoms represented an exaggeration in the functioning of the genito-urinary and gastrointestinal systems, the nose, throat and respiratory apparatus. They were responding to pressure from unsolved emotional conflicts. This does not mean that they were the seat of the disease. They were bearing the burden of the emotional conflicts.

Organs of the body in their functioning are elastic but they cannot bear a peak load of pressure for an indefinite time.

Something must give. If function is distorted overlong, then the tissue of organs does succumb and the result may be organic disease due to unconscious emotional conflicts.

George H. is an important business executive. After a long period of treatment, medical and psychiatric, he is back at work, more effective than ever, and with a much better perspective on life.

Mr. H. was an illegitimate son of a mother who abandoned him when he was an infant. He never knew his father. He was raised in an orphan asylum. He was treated kindly enough, but in an impersonal fashion. He is remembered as a solemn, silent, rather unhappy little fellow. He had one friend among the orphans, to whom he frequently confided, "Some day I'll show them. You wait and see."

Under the lash of inner belittlement and ego-shame, he accomplished the almost impossible. Rapidly he climbed the ladder of business success and became president of a great advertising corporation. It was another Horatio Alger story. In treatment, as the lid of his unconscious mind lifted and the history unfolded, the shamed, defiant boy merged into a stern, determined, aggressive but still unhappy man. His material success was very great but he was usually tense and anxious. As he looked backward, he now realized that unconsciously he feared his success could not last. He would crash and again be at the mercy of the cruel world as he was when his mother abandoned him.

Interestingly, he carried large sums of money in his pockets. His tastes were not expensive, yet "if I found myself with only fifty dollars or so on me, I felt frightened."

He treated his employees fairly but strictly and coldly. He drove himself ruthlessly. He knew the most minute details of the business. He signed every letter. He could not "stand it" unless every paper was neatly placed on his desk.

He is now fifty years old. At forty, he married a woman of thirty, poor but of good family. She was intelligent, pretty, vivacious, pleasure-loving, not a worrier. His wife loved him, but he was not happy. During treatment, it became clear that he felt unconsciously inferior to his wife. Inwardly he resented her talk about her family. He began to nag her because she would not keep better household accounts and was "too easy" with the servants. About this time he began to have indigestion and vague pains in the stomach.

These symptoms became increasingly severe and nausea, occasional vomiting and dizziness were added. Tension and anxiety grew apace. Periodic examinations by competent specialists did not detect any organic disease. One gastroenterologist suggested seeing a psychiatrist. Mr. H. saw him once, but refused to return. "It's all nonsense. It's my stomach, not my head. Besides, he wants to pry into my early life."

Mr. H. had two children, a boy and a girl. He tried in fumbling fashion "to play" with them, to be a pal. But the children seemed to be afraid of him. He felt they preferred their mother. Several times he even wondered fleetingly whether they "knew" about his history.

He had now had "stomach trouble" for almost eight years. The symptoms were present practically all the time. Enormous quantities of alkaline powders were consumed to no avail. At an examination (the eleventh one) there was unmistakable evidence of duodenal ulcer. Tissue had finally broken down under the long-continued impact of distorted function motivated by a deep-seated emotional conflict.

Ten years ago, in collaboration with a dermatologist, I was treating a man, fifty-five years old, who from head to foot was covered with a flaming red, itching dermatitis (skin eruption). From time to time in past years, he had been troubled with small patches of dermatitis, usually trivial and readily cured, but for the first time it became so widespread and serious that there was danger to life.

Our patient was a bachelor, who all through his life was dominated by his mother and was closely attached to her. He was an only child, given every material advantage but denied even a minimum chance of achieving emotional maturity. Three times in his life he thought of marrying. Each time his mother adroitly and successfully intervened. At first he made some show of defying his mother's will. It is interesting to note that at this time there was quite a sharp attack of the skin trouble.

As the years passed, the patient settled into a "pleasant, satisfying life." He devoted an hour or so daily to his business, he played cards with his friends at the club, occasionally a little golf. He saw women socially, enjoyed talking with them, but other than two more passing-thought episodes in which he mildly contemplated matrimony, he had little or no interest in sex. (He was latently homosexual.)

Increasingly, his mother became the central theme of his life. She became more and more dear to him. He loved to do things for her, not only to keep her business affairs in order, but to render many personal services. He "worried terribly" even if she was slightly ill or even only indisposed. At such times the patient canceled all his social obligations. Also, at these times, "my skin trouble flared up and I had to consult a dermatologist."

Six years later, the mother died suddenly of a stroke. Again the dermatitis became threatening but again it subsided.

Our patient now devoted himself to settling his mother's estate. True enough, it was a large estate, but there is no doubt that he unduly prolonged this work. He, himself, said, "I felt she was still with me and I was doing something for her."

Finally, however, it was necessary to sign the last papers and the estate passed into the hands of a trust company. The morning after the day of the final settlement, the patient awoke "itching all over." In forty-eight hours the rash had enveloped his entire body. Soon it became infected.

Mr. H. and the skin patient belong in an important area of psychosomatic medicine. It is the territory in which function has been too hard pressed and for too long a period of time. The organs are no longer able to bear the heavy burden of the emotional conflict. It becomes necessary for some part of the organ to be sacrificed. In the first patient it was tissue in the small intestine that gave way. An ulcer resulted. In the second patient, the integrity of the skin had to be sacrificed. Its functional endurance had been too sorely tried. Finally, so much of its function was lost that kidney impairment was threatened. The skin is a sensitive, emotional barometer. If normally it so readily blushes with shame or blanches with fear, it is easy to understand that it would react with marked sensitivity to inner emotional conflicts.

There is an interesting and significant question which can be only partially answered at this cross-section of our knowledge. What determines the location of the psychosomatic symptoms? Why in the five patients presented were the symptoms in one patient in the genito-urinary system, in another in the respiratory, a third in the skin and two in the stomach and intestines? And, why in many other patients do the heart and blood vessels announce and express the underlying emotional conflicts? Or the ductless glands, muscles, bones and joints or any part of the body and even its appendages, like the hair or nails?

Some years ago, I knew a frightened little rabbity man, quite insecure emotionally, and overwhelmed by a marriage that had netted him a tired, sickly wife and three very energetic and noisy children. Five times, through some mysterious balding process, he lost a luxuriant growth of head hair. Unfortunately, it grew back only four times.

I am told that in many women, nail polish will not hold while they are menstruating. It cracks and peels off. No doubt an intricate chemical reaction, but no doubt, too, there is an emotional factor at work.

In giving the history of the man with the skin eruption, I withheld one item, thinking it might be more informative at this point. As far back as he can remember, his mother had skin rashes frequently, probably due to allergy. I think a factor in fixing the location of psychosomatic symptoms is the strong emotional impress during childhood of illness in some member of the family. This is notably true if there is a close and strong emotional bond between the child and the sick adult. It would almost seem as though a deep unconscious memory picture was etched into the child's personality, to be boldly revealed in adult life. It is emotionally conditioned imitation.

I had a young woman patient in my clinic who had a great variety of severe heart symptoms. There was pain in the heart, radiating down the left arm, shortness of breath with the slightest exertion, inability to lie on the left side, cold hands and feet, pallor, etc. The heart was not only free of disease, but remarkably sound and strong. During her childhood, this young woman was devotedly attached to her mother, who had actual heart disease for a number of years and died suddenly of angina in the presence of the child. Some twenty years later, the mother's symptoms were faithfully reproduced by her daughter.

I regret that the word psychosomatic does not carry any intimation of the enormous influence of the environment in "selecting" the location of the psychosomatic symptoms. The occupation may be influential, as for instance, in "writer's" or "telegrapher's cramp." The effect of environment, personal, social and vocational, is so significant that I once proposed that the word psychosomatic be changed to "psycho-enviro-somatic."

It is the dream of those workers who have spent years in studying psychosomatic symptoms and attempting to interpret their meaning that from various physical and personality patterns one day they will be able to predict the kind of psychosomatic manifestations that are likely to occur in a given individual. It is something more than a dream. Already considerable progress has been made. These studies are reminiscent of the work of the great French clinicians more than a century ago. They described certain distinctive physical types. For instance, the "apoplectic" and the "phthisical." This did not mean that those who belonged to the former group had heart disease, and the latter tuberculosis. It did mean that eventually the one was more likely to suffer a stroke of apoplexy, the other consumption. In a way, these two types were the forerunners of the well known present-day extrovert (pyknic) and introvert (leptic). The extrovert is traditionally the well-muscled, somewhat short-necked, prominent-in-his-girth-measurements, genial, social, backslapping Rotarian. The introvert, a long, spindly, quiet, shy, reserved fellow. Perhaps one day it will be possible to make careful measurements and dispositional studies and be able to tell what kind of psychosomatic symptoms are likely to appear and where they will be located.

Finally, one may reach back into man's dim past and find reasons for the prevalence of certain psychosomatic symptoms. The heart was and is the organ of life and power. Primitive man ate the heart of the enemy he had killed in order to gain more strength and courage. So, too, were the sexual organs symbolic of power in life. They still are. Genital psychosomatic symptoms are often fronts for unconscious fears of diminishing confidence and success.

Naturally, and very anciently, the gastrointestinal organs were very literally the organs of survival. They were enormously significant to our primitive forebears. The amount of food he could get to put into his stomach made the difference between life and death. In our own time, there is an enormous amount of advertising propaganda devoted to the life-sustaining properties of an endless number of patented foods.

It is interesting to recall that in World War I the larger number of psychosomatic symptoms in soldiers were heart and circulatory. In World War II, they were gastrointestinal.

It is one of my cherished hopes that the interest in psychosomatic medicine will leaven the undergraduate teaching of medicine. In my opinion, it is still somewhat too traditional, too static. Many more teaching hours are given to the dissection of the human body and the examination of diseased organs after death than to anything else. True enough, there has been remarkable progress in the teaching of physiology, how the body functions, in chemistry which studies the finer workings of the bodily organs in health and disease and in many other directions. True enough, too, it is scarcely possible to know too much about the physical mechanisms, which later on the student as a physician will be called upon to treat and try to readjust when their workings become disarranged by disease. Nevertheless, the teaching balance is wrong.

In the four-year teaching curriculum schedules in medical schools averaging well above 4000 hours, less than an average of 160 hours is devoted to the teaching of psychiatry. In a few medical schools, practically no psychiatry at all is taught. Even more unfortunate is the fact that the impact of psychiatry is usually far too light in the first two years of medical studies, the time when it is most urgently needed. There is grave danger that the embryo doctor will learn to think too restrictedly of human disease in terms of tissue inflammation and destruction. There is the serious educational hazard that he will become insulated against the teachings of psychological medicine and will somewhat overvalue and seek only those things which can be seen through a microscope or in a test tube. This in the face of the fact that more than 50 per cent of human sickness is largely functional in origin.

Of course, some of the difficulty comes from the dearth of trained psychiatric teaching personnel. But even allowing for this, the teaching balance is still too uneven.

When a physician takes a history, or feels a pulse, or makes any other examination, he should have been so taught and trained, that he has in his mind's eye not only the detection of signs of diseased organs, but also the possibility of covered mental conflicts, so motivating in the production of sickness. If the loaf of medical practice is to be thoroughly leavened, the medical student must be given from the very first week in medical school the opportunity of studying all of man and not only a hypothetical physical half.

THE PSYCHONEUROTICS AND PSYCHOSOMATICS OF PREG-NANCY AND CHILDBIRTH

Pregnancy and childbearing are keen-edged blades. Unerringly they cut through the outer garments of simulated maturity and pitilessly reveal the baby clothes of emotional immaturity.

There is no symptom described in the books of doctors or even in patent-medicine almanacs which cannot occur during pregnancy or after the baby is born. Headache, dizziness, pains in the back, the legs, any part of the body, itching, nausea, vomiting, spots before the eyes, ear noises, indeed any symptoms of which you can think, and a few more. Sometimes these symptoms are expressions of organic disease, perhaps of the kidney, liver or gastrointestinal tract. Then careful medicinal treatment is needed. But, more often than not, they are functional, not founded in actual disease of organs, although the organs are certainly disordered in their workings.

Then, in what are these many functional symptoms founded? Their reason is in unsolved unconscious emotional conflicts. For instance, in neurotic nausea and vomiting, the stomach bears the burden of the emotional conflict, whatever it may be, and expresses it by becoming disturbed in its functioning. Perhaps nothing is more highly individualized than the woman who is going to have a baby, and the functional symptoms, too, are likely to be very personalized. Yet there is a universal coverage for hidden conflicts which have not been satisfactorily compromised.

Three basic things must be understood before attempting to penetrate the maze of the psychoneurotics of pregnancy.

Pregnancy and childbearing should be and in fact are among the most normal of human functions. Menstruation, one of the signs that pregnancy is *not* present, has been described as "the weeping of the disappointed womb." Nevertheless, a long succession of cultures have done much to change and sometimes distort the quality of fine normality inherent in pregnancy and the bearing of children. So, today, sex and everything connected with it is in an unusually contradictory position. More than any other function, even more than eating, it retains and must continue to retain certain primitive characteristics and, at the same time, again more than any other human function, it has become, in the course of ages, heavily veneered with modifications, additions, highly artificialized distortions, concealments, taboos. It has remained for our culture to insult sex in the cheapest commercial fashion, as when we permit and are not ashamed of such advertisements as these: "Apartments to let. Not available for families with young children," or, more tersely, "Apartment for rent. No children."

The second basic consideration is ambivalency, or double weighting. It is a psychological law that in the same thought or feeling or act, positive and negative values are present, the pull for it and tug against it. It is not hard to understand that at one and the same time a woman may both want and not want a pregnancy.

Finally, we are total in our functioning, and the body expresses not only part, but all parts of a feeling and all its shades of meaning. A symptom like vomiting may be a protest against the things pregnancy does to the figure or to the fact that it may be interfering with social life, but by no means need it mean that the oncoming child is not wanted at all and will not be welcome.

There is an ideal of healthy, sound attitude toward pregnancy and having children. It is set firmly in the matrix of strong maternal feeling. Its facets are such considerations as the desire for the security and happiness of the family and home, gratifying the husband, obligation to society. But even in those women whose attitudes are on a very high level, still there may be a few neurotic symptoms expressive of some amount of reservation and hesitancy. They, too, like their emotionally weaker sisters, may give rationalized reasons for not becoming pregnant. But here the similarity ceases. The rationalizations of the emotionally grown-up woman are far less numerous, not nearly so emphatically advanced and contain a much larger segment of truth than do the protests of the child-woman.

Naturally, these child-women present more or less convincing profiles of maturity to their social environments. So, too, often do their rationalizations for not becoming pregnant seem grown-up and sensible. And there may be some truth in them. But not enough. Furthermore, the decidedly immature woman believes her own rationalizations. To her they are very real. They would have to be. Her ego could not survive the shaming realization of "I am too selfish or too afraid to have a baby."

Here are some of the more common rationalizations: "It is too soon to be tied down by a baby. We want to have some fun first. Of course, we want a baby. Maybe in two years, or three, or five," and often, the unspoken "never." Or, "It is too soon after our first baby"; or, "Before we have a baby, we will need more money, much more money." Or, "I must keep on with my job. We need the income for extras and, besides, my boss says he couldn't get along without me."

There may be the high-sounding pleas of social obligations and careers. I know a woman who "could not have a baby—not now anyhow. My teacher tells me my voice shows great promise. He thinks that some day I may make thousands of people happy by my singing." (After all, this is more important than the faint, thin wail of a newly born infant.)

"My husband isn't very anxious to have a baby. He thinks it would take too much of my time. He needs my attention. After all, my first duty is to keep my husband satisfied and happy."

The fear of the dangers of childbirth may be very real. Certainly having a baby is not without risk. Some of the fears of childbirth need and deserve careful psychiatric attention and treatment. However, the pictures of the physical threats, suffering and horrors of labor and the undermining of future health, more often than not, are found in the frame of emotional immaturity. I knew a woman, a college graduate and now married. Her mother died in childbirth. She herself at the age of twenty-five had her uterus and ovaries removed so that she could never have a baby.

Quite often in this day we hear the voice of immaturity raised in loud protest against bringing a child into this terrible world of confusion, doubt, uncertainty and atomic bombs. Sometimes, it is so convincing that one gets the picture of a small atomic bomb placed at the portals of the birth canal, ready to explode at contact and blow the baby into fragments.

Of course, the more serious and lower the level of the emotional immaturity, the more complete and the more firmly fixed are the "reasons" for not becoming pregnant. Far down on the scale are those women who unconsciously have almost completely rejected the feminine role and its biological implications. They need not be in the least masculine. They may be superficially delightfully feminine, charming creatures of frills and fripperies, ribbons and bows.

Mrs. "X" was such a woman, the victim of an unfortunate childhood. She had three brothers, two older, one younger. It was a thoroughly masculine household, dominated by the father. He was the perennial adolescent, fascinated by his sons, and was thoroughly "one of the boys," participating every minute of his spare time in their sports and rough activities. Generally, Betty was allowed to play with "the team"; she was just about tolerated, and not very generously. There were many derisive remarks, beginning, "Gosh, girls—what can you expect!" Dolls were objects of contempt. Soon Betty didn't want any dolls. She became a fairly successful, thorough-going tomboy and continued being a tomboy far beyond the age when it is psychologically safe for a girl. Betty's mother was an ineffectual, rather immature woman, "ailing" much of the time. Her chief contribution to Betty's development seemed to be weak and futile protests that Betty ought to be "nice and ladylike." Certain material from the treatment notes of Mrs. X make it clear that Betty, in her inner thoughts and feelings, was frustrated and miserable, above all things envying the anatomical advantages of being a boy. She did not have them, and, thus deprived, she was halted at the doors of the inner sanctum of the lives of her adored father and brothers. No wonder the psychoanalysts speak of the "castration complex."

Mrs. X, under some protest, came to a psychiatrist because she was "deathly afraid of having a baby and hated the very thought of it or anything connected with it." She confessed that sexual relations were abhorrent. "Yes," she loved her husband, but hated him, too, because he didn't have to put up with the things that made life so "mean" for a woman. "How would he like it if he had to be 'sick' seven days out of each month?"

After a long and difficult period of treatment, Mrs. X finally did gain enough understanding and adjustment so that her marital situation became much better and she did have a baby.

The reasons for wanting pregnancy are not always mature. Pregnancy and motherhood may be used as weapons to accomplish selfish ends. They may constitute escapes from difficult and unpleasant family and social situations. Unconsciously, and even partly consciously, they may be employed to bind the husband closely, to keep him away from "that woman"— the woman who may be and often is entirely mythical. Sometimes such immature women insist on a detailed accounting of every minute of the husband's time. They must know exactly where he is when not at home so that they can reach him instantly. "I am afraid. Something might happen. I might have a miscarriage and die."

Finally, pregnancy may be accepted in order to secure economic support. Or to gain an inheritance.

Apparently some well-adjusted women defeat their desire to have children by being overeager. They do not fear pregnancy or labor. In fact, if they fear anything, it is sterility. It is possible that the very intensity of their wish and fears produces too much tension of the pelvic structures and interferes with physiological function. It may be that the follicles mature too soon and the ova are extruded prematurely. In support of this it is common experience that many women who have tried for years to have a child do successfully conceive after they have adopted a baby. It is at least possible that the security that comes from loving a baby and the performance of yearned-for maternal duties may produce quietude of the pelvic organs, readjusting their physiology, so that pregnancy can occur.

The pregnancy that has the best chance of being reasonably free of psychoneurotic difficulties is the one that is wanted and planned by both wife and husband. Unfortunately, less than 25 per cent of all pregnancies fall into this group. Of course, the ideal situation is one where the couple entering into marriage are mature enough to understand and face all its implications and responsibilities, including the eventual having and raising of a family. So that without "businesslike" planning, they happily and naturally accept and welcome the pregnancy and baby when it comes along.

It must be remembered that even in emotionally mature women some psychological upsets are to be expected. In view of the pressures exerted by our culture and mores, it could not be otherwise. Among the more common functional displays are food idiosyncrasies, nausea and vomiting, many and varied bodily sensations, neurasthenic preoccupations with "feelings" in the pelvis, particularly from fetal movements, weeping, anxiety, marked sensitivity to criticism, irritability, exacting and demanding attitudes often focused on constant claims upon the husband's attention, feelings of embarrassment and self-belittlement. In relatively small amounts and degrees, these manifestations are not much out of line. They seem to be the more or less natural sequels of restrictions and decrease of social and other activities, changes in the relationship to the husband, wounded pride because of the physical deformity. It is said that peasant women have comparatively few psychological disturbances in their pregnancies.

In decidedly immature women, neurotic and definitely not

wanting their pregnancies, all the symptoms are intensified and many more are added. Nausea and vomiting may be very severe, notably during the early months. I understand that obstetricians believe that one-half of all vomiting, especially in the early months of pregnancy, is functional. I understand, too, that Southern Negro women have little of this kind of vomiting. It expresses partial or total rejection of the pregnancy. On the other hand, in so-called phantom pregnancy, in which of course conception has not occurred, it would seem fairly obvious that the sometimes remarkable display of the signs of pregnancy, cessation of the periods, enlargement of the abdomen and breasts, pigmentation of the nipples, morning sickness with vomiting are all expressive of the wish for a baby.

Vomiting may be interestingly selective. I know a woman who when pregnant always vomited copiously when her mother-in-law visited her. With psychiatric help, a patching up of their differences resulted in less vomiting.

Many degrees of frequency and shades of intensity of the symptoms announce the level of the emotional immaturity. Rather low on the scale is the woman in whose childhood there was an overwhelming amount of father-daughter dependency. These women unconsciously marry their own fathers. Such a woman was Dorothy M.

Dorothy M. was the only daughter of a small-town lawyer, only moderately successful in his practice. Her parents did not get on well, though they decided to stick it out together. Probably the important factor in the unsatisfactory marriage was that Dorothy's father, who had been deeply attached to his own mother, constantly demanded from his own wife maternal care, solicitude and "fussing over." He did not want a conjugal partnership. Soon the wife, after a brief maternal response, declined to be her husband's mother, and her behavior plainly said so. By unspoken and mutual agreement, they terminated their sex life.

Thereupon, the father ardently turned to his daughter. She adored him and became his mother. In fact, he referred to Dorothy as his "little mother." Father and daughter became intimate confidants and in effect established a pact which excluded the mother. They agreed that "mother did not understand." Dorothy babied her father and loved it, but no less did her father "love" and baby her. It was his happiness to satisfy her smallest whim. She had from him first expensive toys, then later clothes and parties and trips beyond his financial resources. If there was any hesitancy about giving her what she asked for, Dorothy soon discovered that a little pouting or a few tears put into her lap just what she wanted. Besides it was such fun "making up" with Daddy after a little "tiff."

Dorothy married a nice, reasonably sensible young fellow she met in college. He had his way to make in life. For a short time it was intriguing to coddle and "baby" an attractive young wife. But Bob soon tired of it. Besides, he could not afford to get Dorothy one-tenth of the things she demanded. "I don't see why you can't. Daddy did." Bob was hard hit when he discovered Dorothy did not want a baby. With some idea of getting their marriage back on a working basis, Bob insisted, and finally, Dorothy did become pregnant.

To a psychiatrist who saw her because of "depression" it was obvious that she hated the pregnancy and everything connected with it, including Bob and sex in general and particular. Then followed a long train of severe functional symptoms—headache, nausea, vomiting, "terrible tiredness," pains and aches "all over." Dorothy was only cheerful when she "sadly" expressed the fear that "the doctor would have to take the baby away from me. I am so deathly sick." But the

doctor finally said, "No abortion." Even now, years after, Bob
still winces when he remembers "the hell he went through."

In this instance, psychiatry was not successful. It was not
possible to find any garments of emotional maturity small
enough to fit this child personality.

The baby was born. Of course, there was a divorce. Now,
happily enough, Dorothy is back in the Midwest with her
child, keeping house for her father. Her mother is dead.

The post-partum period is one of varying length of time following the baby's delivery. Among other things, it is the time
during which there is the final sifting of the chaff from the
grain—the grain of the reasonably well-adjusted woman and
the chaff of the immature and deeply neurotic ones. Of course,
the post-partum period brings up many problems for all new
mothers. The baby must be nursed or fed in some way. The
house is somewhat disorganized. A moderate amount of grum-
bling by the husband and a little jealousy because he gets less
attention from his wife than before or somewhat fatuous attempts to look after the baby are all to be anticipated. There
are social hindrances, too.

The emotionally grown-up woman takes these difficulties
in her stride. The child-woman falls by the wayside. Too
often, she takes her revenge upon her husband and the child
she did not want by becoming an immature mother of the
worst stripe. The kind of a pseudo-mother who clings to her
child, absorbing it for her own selfish neurotic satisfaction,
refusing to release and emancipate it and denying it the priceless boon of emotional growth and maturity.

For the woman who is biologically and emotionally complete, the post-partum is a time of great happiness. She has
achieved her goal. Now, with all her heart and mind she turns
to her baby, holding it and loving it and at the same time
planning gradually to prepare it for a life of its own. The hus-

band shares in his wife's happiness. For one thing, the baby provides the newly made father and mother with an inexhaustible conversational fund; anything from finger painting to where Jimmie will take his Ph.D. or whether Mary will marry a business or professional man.

I would like to digress briefly to hold up a torch which I have been carrying for some years. I am unutterably opposed to the rigid separation of mother from child which obtains in many maternity hospitals. Perhaps the plea of the danger of respiratory diseases and other epidemics has some merit, but, in my opinion, not enough to compensate for the psychological loss of depriving a mother of her baby at a time when it is emotionally important for both mother and child and for their futures, together and apart, that they be close to each other physically as much as possible. Never again will there be the same opportunity for mother-child unity. A friend of mine, the wife of a physician, tells with great glee how she thwarted the spinster maternity nurse and managed to keep her baby with her for three hours by concealing it. "It was the only chance I had in the hospital of getting to know my own baby."

The majority of the functional disorders of pregnancy, childbirth and the after-the-birth time can be solved by adequate treatment. However, it is neither a simple nor an easy task. It amounts to a somewhat painful process of growing up. The roots of such disorders usually have to be traced back to childhood and dug out of the soil of emotional immaturity. It would have been so much easier and saving of anxiety for the woman and of concern for everyone involved if the holding, loving and releasing formula of childhood had been reasonably satisfactory and complete. After the lapse of twenty or more years, it is fairly difficult to bridge large gaps in the early child-mother-parent relationship.

A few of the more prominent and specific deficits in the child's earlier relationships should be mentioned. They are heinous offenses against even the barest minimum requirements of the code for the attainment of emotional maturity. First, without going into detail at this time, I would indict that immature mother who, usually in retaliation for the thwartings and frustrations of her own sexual life, by constant repetition inculcates into the personalities of her growing daughter excessive caution, worry, fear and even horror of sexual life.

Next to be blamed is the mother, and frequently the parents, who by their attitudes create an environment in the home which repulses a child's natural curiosity about sex and makes it seem an ugly thing—something about which to feel ashamed and guilty. I knew a child who, denied any information and preparation for her first menstrual period, when she saw the blood attempted suicide feeling she had committed a "terrible sin." Of course, children driven to it by the taboo on sexual curiosity in their own homes, pick up odds and ends of sexual information here, there, anywhere they can get it. This sordid design of ignorance, misinformation and misinterpretation, tinctured with guilt feelings, often stands out in bold relief in the functional symptoms of the child-bearing period. Frequently, it has been so firmly imbedded in the plastic emotional matrix of childhood that it cannot be removed by acquired intellectual criteria. Psychiatric help is needed.

Finally, there is a long and sorry train of reactions, the aftermath of unhappy homes with much disagreement, bitter and often violent quarreling, more often than not followed by separation and divorce. Obviously, it is difficult for a woman whose childhood has been lived in such emotional turmoil to take with confidence and enthusiasm the final step of pregnancy which she has seen lead to so much misery. Incidentally, divorce, which admittedly is shamefully common, probably in itself does less harm than does the attitude of the divorced parents to the child victim about their former marital partners. Of course, there are many fine exceptions, but far too often the attitude is such that the emphasis is placed on the unhappiness of marriage and having children. It is fertile soil for psychoneurotic pregnancies.

Actual mental disease, psychoses, may occur during pregnancy and with more frequency after childbirth. All in all, they are less common than frightening old wives' tales would indicate. Such psychoses are still referred to as "puerperal psychoses," a designation which makes no more sense than "pneumonia psychoses" or "heart-disease psychoses." The name is less unfortunate than the prevalent idea that "puerperal psychoses" all get well. They do not. Too often I have had the unpleasant professional duty of informing a husband and the family that even though the mental illness did appear a few days after delivery, nevertheless it is malignant schizophrenia and recovery is unlikely. A few years ago, I investigated carefully a number of consecutive psychoses appearing during the puerperal period. Roughly, one-third were schizophrenia and one-third manic-depressive. The outlook in these two groups was not too promising. Only in one-third of the women, many of whom had infection with fever, was the recovery rate high.

In a general way, but with exceptions, when the family psychiatric history is badly tainted and with marked personality upsets during pregnancy but with a rather good physical health and pregnancy record, plus an easy labor, a psychosis, if there is one, is more likely to be schizophrenia or manic-depressive, with considerable doubt as to the outcome.

Conversely, if the family tree is reasonably sound mentally, and there have not been any manifestations of severe personal ity deviations during pregnancy, but perhaps the previous physical and pregnancy record has been rather poor, plus a long, difficult labor, possibly with infection, then the resultant psychosis is likely to get well.

All in all, pregnancy and childbearing are more than physical feats. Unfailingly they indicate the measure of a woman's emotional maturity.

II | PATHOLOGICAL DRINKING

THE HISTORY of alcohol is co-existent with the history of the human race. The deciphering of tablets of great antiquity reveals that the Egyptians and other ancient people enjoyed beer. Rome was drunk not only on its military victories, but also on its wines. From cereals and honey the barbarians from the north brewed delectable mead. No doubt seeking to offset the bone-chilling fogs that hung over their moors, the Caledonians contrived Scotch whiskey, now one of our national drinks. Before his white brother bartered beads and "fire-water" for his hunting grounds, the North American Indian concocted and drank an evil but potent beverage, made by exposing to the sun the gall of freshly killed elk and buffalo.

Anything which has persisted through the ages, defying all efforts to eradicate it, either by legislation or moral suasion, must be motivated by a powerful driving force. Alcohol is. It has the quality of blurring rosily the hard, unpleasant and forbidding aspects of reality. If taken in sufficient quantity, it has the magical power of effacing reality altogether. *It is a quick solvent of reality. It is phantasy in a bottle.* To this it may be added that it is readily obtainable, produces its magic quickly and for a long time, escapes too severe social stigma and reprisal. Similar non-alcoholic behavior, as in mental illness, would be likely to land a person in a police station or psychopathic ward. Yet, time and time again, the alcoholic is apt to encounter a kindly Samaritan who tenderly deposits him at the door of his home and rings the bell. Alcoholism is a tremendous economic, social, ethical and spiritual problem. In this country alone, eight billion dollars annually is probably not an overestimate of the economic loss incurred directly and indirectly. In order to get an approximate idea of the alcoholic social, ethical, spiritual and national expense account, think of one drunkard you know, reckon the amount of damage he inflicts upon himself, his family and the community in which he lives. Then multiply that damage by at least two million, a conservative estimate of the number of alcoholics in this country.

Alcohol is always a narcotic. It holds its reputation as a stimulant, since it lets down the bars of ordinary inhibition and, particularly in introverts, produces a too ready flow of shallow thought and speech. In alcoholism there is a loss of inhibition, abolition of self-critique and regressive behavior. The superego is seriously weakened, even annihilated.

In a social gathering, perhaps a New Year's Eve party, which, let us say, is only mildly alcoholic, the rapid descent on the ladder of even minimal mature social behavior may be easily observed. On the basis of the extravagances of their speech and behavior, portly middle-aged dowagers and gentlemen even older, with the infirmities of their years upon them, obviously are re-enacting (albeit not very convincingly) scenes from the remote days when respectively they were beautiful, slim belles and dashing, gallant young beaux. These good people are not alcoholic. On New Year's morning, they will take a few aspirins for their hangovers and firmly resolve never again to make such fools of themselves.

In more serious situations, there is complete shedding of all adult responsibilities. The drunkard becomes as helpless as an infant, with profound loss of control, even involving bladder and bowel. Psychiatric experience makes it clear that alcohol in excessive amounts is the most commonly utilized technique for accomplishing unconsciously an escape from mature obligations.

Not every person who gets drunk is alcoholic. For instance, there is the marked extrovert who, upon frequent occasions, from a fraternity banquet to a successful business deal, celebrates alcoholically. Usually he is not a pathological drinker. Then there is a motley group, often erroneously spoken of as alcoholic, sometimes even by psychiatrists—some paretics in the early stages of the disease, mildly depressed or excited patients, psychopathic inferiors, morons, a few psychoneurotics striving to relieve tension and anxiety and many others. These exhibitions of alcoholism bear about the same relation to the basic condition as does the rash to scarlet fever or a headache to brain tumor. It is merely a symptom and often only a passing symptom.

What is chronic alcoholism? I do not believe it is organic disease. True enough, alcoholics may have cirrhosis of the liver, neuritis and many other morbidities of the body. These conditions may occur, too, in non-alcoholics, and even in chronic drinkers the vitamin deprivation incidental to many alcoholic debauches (debauchees take little food during their sprees) is probably more instrumental than the alcohol.

Is chronic alcoholism a psychosis or mental disease? I think not. The excursions into unreality via the alcohol route are too abrupt, too frequently repeated and the patient clears up too quickly. All this is quite unlike actual mental disease.

Probably, pathological drinking is a psychoneurosis. Further, but of course with many exceptions, it is preponderantly a psychoneurosis of the introvert, that elusive, shy, reserved, diffident fellow who tends to be socially awkward and acquires social facilities and graces only with the greatest difficulty. Yet, above all things, he desires social ease and popularity.

Sooner or later, he discovers the magical potion. A few cocktails or some other alcoholic beverage melts away his reserve. Not only does he feel more secure but he actually begins to enjoy the society of his fellow men. Said one alcoholic to me, "I can't enjoy myself. I can't even say anything worth listening to unless I have lubricated my brain with a few drinks of whiskey."

Alcohol is employed to evade reality much as psychoneurotic symptoms are used for the same purpose. One need merely observe the large segment of rationalization in each condition. The psychoneurotic is "sick" and cannot meet the requirements and chores of everyday life because of headache, ear noises, vertigo, nausea, vomiting, rapidly beating heart and what not. These symptoms are functional, i.e., founded in emotional conflict. The alcoholic when he gives the "reasons" for his excessive drinking, says it is because of financial losses, poor health, his wife nags him, the children disobey and are noisy, the dog barks all through the night, the weather is cold and damp, etc., etc. He believes these "reasons." Of course, they are rationalizations and, like psychoneurotic symptoms, are utilized unconsciously as screens to prevent honest facing of real basic issues.

Finally, if the alcoholism is very severe, the last vestige of even the faintest rationalization disappears. Drinking is now wholly uncontrolled. The only objective is to attain the anaesthesia of complete drunkenness in order to escape the horribly painful mental conflicts which arise to the surface, at the first dawning of sobriety, much like the post-hypnotic behavior which faithfully follows suggestions made during a hypnotic trance. The faint stirring of conscious thoughts acts like an automatic signal to engulf the mind in another tidal wave of alcohol.

Akin to the psychoneuroses, the basis of alcoholism is emotional immaturity and, reminiscent of the psychoneuroses, the roots of the immaturity go back to childhood. The usual pattern is "loving" dominance. Deprived of the right and practice of learning to make decisions, emotional growth lags. When adult years are attained, the individual is ill-equipped for the give and take of personal and social relationships. Nonplused, thwarted, frightened and resentful, he soon discovers temporary but false confidence and security in alcohol. Alcoholism is in the making. It is almost like a retreat back to the feeding bottle of babyhood or even the mother's breast.

I am just beginning to feel mildly hopeful about a pathological drinker, a man twenty-six years old, who has been under treatment for more than two years. His father died when he, an only child, was six years old. The wife was left well supported financially, but poorly equipped to fulfill the complete function of motherhood. Her praiseworthy desire to make up to her son for the loss of his father led her astray. She gave the boy love and much affection, of which, incidentally, a child cannot have too much. But she failed lamentably in helping the youngster grow up emotionally. Readily she fell into the deceptive pattern of loving tyranny. She decided everything for Jack, the style of haircut, his clothes, his sports (no football—too rough and dangerous!), his diversions, his playmates, his reading, his very thoughts. Naturally, Jack did not get on too well with his boyhood companions. His mother repeatedly violated that rigid boyhood code of fighting it out among themselves, by stepping in and "protecting" her "poor, fatherless boy." Jack was bright and got on well in school academically, but not socially. At least sign of any complaint or difficulty, his mother visited the headmaster and in no uncertain terms delivered her opinion of the teachers who were "always discriminating" against her boy. Nevertheless, Jack finished school and entered the college of his mother's choice. She disclaimed vigorously against the rule that the first-year students must live in the dormitories. But, at least she could live in the college town and during the second, third and last year keep house for her boy. She did. Jack, puzzled and a bit anxious because he was such a failure in making and holding satisfactory social contacts with his fellow students, began to drink excessively. This was "duck soup" for the mother. She managed to keep the situation fairly quiet and excused, protected, occasionally punished by giving Jack less spending money. More often she lavishly rewarded him for periods of comparative sobriety. At a strongly alcoholically tinctured party just before his graduation, Jack met and soon after married a young woman. After several terrific hysterical outbursts, his mother finally "forgave" him. So after receiving his degree, Jack took his wife and mother, or, rather, his mother took Jack and his wife to New York, where through influential friends, she had secured a position for her son in a brokerage firm. (Jack wanted to be a commercial artist.) The marriage might have worked, since in spite of the dubious conditions of their meeting, his wife not only loved Jack but she was reasonably intelligent and mature. However, after almost a year of guarding the fortress of their apartment against the constant siege of Jack's mother, who wanted to move in and be with her "dear children"; vainly attempting to mitigate the disturbing effects of innumerable daily telephone calls and visits between Jack and his mother (who was so lonely for her only son); trying to calm Jack's fears, as to what would happen to them if his mother cut off the liberal supply of cash, she finally abandoned the matrimonial ship, sued for and obtained a divorce. Jack's mother immediately moved in with him to "comfort" him. But now Jack began to imbibe with such complete abandon that it became not only psychologically but physically impossible for his mother to look after him. Besides, he became quite threatening in his attitude toward her. So, grudgingly, the help of a psychiatrist was sought. Now, for more than two years, painfully and stumblingly, Jack has been learning a lesson which he could have been taught so easily in childhood—the lesson of growing up emotionally. If his mother does not interfere too much, Jack has at least an even chance of achieving a non-alcoholic adjustment.

Conversely, I know a man who is rapidly drinking himself to death. It is an alcoholic suicide—a pitiful gesture of hostility and revenge upon a father, a total authoritarian, who during his childhood treated him with rigid and cruel discipline, denying him even a minimum of love and affection.

Many psychoanalysts believe that alcoholism is derived from latent homosexuality. Unquestionably, sometimes this is true.

I knew a man, the vice-president of a bank, who at the age of forty-two married an attractive and suitable woman. While he had had pleasant social relations with women, there had not been any close personal affairs. He had never had any sexual relations, feeling, as he said, sex should be reserved for married life. Further, he feared the danger of venereal infection. "Fastidious" best describes his personality. On the marriage night, he suddenly dashed away from the nuptial bed, left the hotel and got roaring drunk. This initiated an alcoholic debauch lasting three months. Then he came under psychiatric treatment. It soon became evident that his personality contained a much larger segment of homosexuality than is usual, of which, of course, he was not conscious. When for the first time in his life he was confronted with a heterosexual situation, he broke psychologically and found temporary escape in alcoholic oblivion.

Nevertheless, I think that more usual than latent homosexuality is latent heterosexuality. This is part and parcel of the emotional immaturity, a casual flitting about sexually, an evasion of mature sexual responsibilities, home building, having and loving children and participating in their training and development.

Because of the insult to the ego, it is exceedingly difficult to accept the fact that one is becoming a pathological drinker, even long after it is quite obvious to everyone else. Pathological drinkers are usually recruited from the ranks of social drinkers. It is important to note the signs of beginning addiction and heed their significance.

Some years ago, at the request of the Pennsylvania Liquor Control Board, I wrote a pamphlet entitled, "Are You a Social Drinker?" In Pennsylvania and a half-dozen other States, it had a huge circulation, hundreds of thousands of copies. The explanation was simple. It was given away free with each purchase in the State liquor stores.

I quote a few pertinent paragraphs:

"When you feel that you must habitually drink in the morning to recruit enough courage to get through the day, then you are in danger. Another time to take stock of yourself is when you find yourself taking drinks with regularity throughout the day. This is not so much a question of the amount of alcohol consumed, but rather that the drinking seems to spring from an imperative demand arising from within the drinker.

"Any decided departure from the pleasant ritual of social

drinking is to be viewed with suspicion. For instance, almost every man who drinks at all occasionally takes a drink before lunching. However, if you find yourself having a drink before luncheon, then perhaps two or three drinks, every single day and feel that without them something very necessary is lacking, then properly you may be concerned. Again, if when you are having a few drinks with friends and as the party is about to break up, you find yourself hastily gulping down a 'couple of quick ones,' then you had better be concerned. Finally, if you find your social drinking becoming less important and your solitary drinking much more prized, then you are in grave danger of becoming an abnormal drinker.

"There is no absolute rule for the best and safest use of alcohol for each person. But if you want to safeguard yourself, review the history of your drinking from these four points:

"1. In your frank judgment, and in the honest opinion of your friends, is your behavior under the influence of alcohol such that it would make you think that you are one of those who should not use alcohol?

"*In vino veritas.* Alcohol lifts the lids from our minds so that latent or hidden things are revealed. Naturally, there are unpleasant and difficult traits in all of us. In those who have a mental allergy to alcohol, such traits are very likely to come quickly to the surface under its influence. This does not mean at all that these people are unpleasant, mean or dangerous in their characters. It simply means that because of the mental allergy, alcohol releases certain types of behavior which, although beneath the surface in most personalities, yet do not appear excepting rarely under great provocation.

"Some people under the influence of even moderate amounts of alcohol become aggressive, pugnacious and dangerous. Without alcohol, these same individuals are often well behaved and even pleasant, but they have such a marked emotional allergy to alcohol that under its influence they act as though everyone in the environment was ill-disposed and hostile toward them. I knew a man who became dangerously aggressive even after imbibing small quantities of alcohol. Finally, one night after two small drinks of whiskey, he shot and killed a policeman.

"Less severe, but still unpleasant, are those drinkers who spoil the party by becoming sullen, rude and insulting.

"Some men even only slightly in their cups retire into a deep and brooding melancholia.

"These are only a few of the behavior reactions indicating psychic incompatibility with alcohol. Its normal, social function is to promote relaxation and a feeling of good fellowship. When anyone strikes too discordant a note in a social gathering, then there is something in the make-up of that person which does not mix with alcohol and he had better leave it alone.

"2. Consider the history of your drinking. Is it at about the same level of moderate controlled drinking as it was in the beginning or has it increased to dangerous proportions?

"3. What do you gain by drinking? Is that 'gain' something upon which you are dependent or could you manage your life satisfactorily without it?

"4. Are you sure you could stop drinking?

"When these departures from the social-drinking pattern become frequent and serious, the drinker is in a fair way of becoming an alcoholic, *the person who cannot face reality without alcohol and whose adequate adjustment to reality as long as he uses alcohol is impossible.*

"It is conceivable that a drug may be discovered which will cure alcoholism. After all, the wonder drug, penicillin, could scarcely have been predicted. However, while the products of pharmacology have an important role in the treatment of the complications of alcoholism, yet it is extremely doubtful that drugs ever will actually cure the condition itself." *

The sickness of pathological drinking is less in the body and much more in the personality of the drinker. The logical and most promising treatment is psychological re-education. For convenience, it may be divided into four categories:

A. Rules

B. Psychological Aspects

C. Re-educational

D. Physical.

Any plan of treatment depending largely upon the patient's co-operation must impose a few conditions, but the fewer the better.

a) On the patient's part there must be at least minimal understanding of the alcoholic situation, some recognition of the need for help and some desire to be helped. Any bullying, overpersuasion or tricking the patient into taking treatment should be discouraged. If the patient "agrees" to accept treatment, solely because his wife has threatened him with divorce or his father promised to kick him out of the house unless he does so, then the re-education plan is doomed to failure.

Blessedly, the technique of organic horrors, attempting to frighten the patient into treatment by showing him pictures of lividly inflamed stomachs and leathery-looking livers, or persuading him to witness the stark terror and fear of delirium tremens, is now buried in the none-too-praiseworthy archives of alcoholic treatments.

A fair query is, "What happens to those patients who are

* Recently a drug called Antabuse has been widely used. It sensitizes to alcohol so that immediately after taking a drink containing only a small amount of alcohol there appears flushing of the face, palpitation, rapid breathing and general uneasiness. It is a potent drug and there are a number of conditions, cirrhosis of the liver, certain heart and kidney conditions in which its use is dangerous. If taken at all, it should be only upon the advice and under the supervision of a physician.

not co-operative?" Perhaps about half of those who cannot honestly accept treatment are apt after some time to reconsider, particularly after further descent on the ladder of alcoholism. For a smaller group, there is nothing to be done, other than hospital commitment, which at least saves them from a hopelessly sordid life and from personal and family degradation and disgrace. Some of these patients emerge from their incarceration and become hopeful treatment prospects. Of course, a relatively brief period of hospital or sanitarium treatment is often very useful. It gives the patient time enough to mobilize his psychological defenses and to get himself into better physical condition. But the intramural stay must not be continued overlong. It is possible for the sanitarium to become a kind of a maternal womb of bricks and mortar, where there is no need of emotional maturity. Further, because the desire for alcohol wanes, there is developed a false sense of security. The main engagement against alcohol must be fought on the terrain of everyday life.

b) An honest willingness to try to remain abstinent. Of course, there must be no attempt to extract promises or pledges to "go on the wagon" for any limited time period. Even if the patient does not break the pledge, he is apt to live for the date when he can return to alcohol.

c) Frankness in all dealings with the therapist.

d) The patient must agree that if a relapse occurs, he will notify the therapist or see that he is notified as soon as possible.

The analysis of a relapse, the conditions under which it occurred and the situation which seemed to precipitate it—all have much treatment value.

In a group of recovered patients, irrespective of the duration of the alcoholism, the relapses averaged less than three per patient.

It is psychologically important that the attitude of the therapist be unemotional, impersonal, objective, not condoning, but still not judgmental or critical. The atmosphere in which the patient has lived was very different. He has been constantly watched, praised and blamed, rewarded and threatened. At first, he is nonplused at the attitude of the doctor. He expected, and unconsciously hoped, to be treated as a child. It is somewhat amusing to note the patient's puzzled disappointment when, after a relapse, he is not verbally spanked. The relapse is merely intelligently and impersonally discussed.

While the alcoholic habit is the bull's-eye of the psychological treatment target, yet as the therapist retraces with the patient his life history, many concentric circles of mental conflict are hit. A pattern of emotional immaturity begins to emerge. Usually, its nucleus is in a parent-child relationship in which sufficient opportunities for developing a design of mature security and decision were wanting.

The "cure" of the alcoholic is incidental to helping him achieve a reasonable amount of emotional maturity. Strictly speaking, there is no cure. The duration and soundness of the recovery depend on the understanding by the patient that the remainder of his life must be lived on a "no alcohol" basis.

At the proper cross-section in the treatment, the therapist begins to inculcate into the personality of the patient, and strengthens by repetition, positive and negative thinking reflexes. The positive, when it has been acquired, leads the patient to respond to the stimulus of alcoholic thoughts, not by attempting to repress them, but by reviewing each time the entire distressing and sordid panorama of events in the past, the sequel of taking a single drink; the negative, consisting of habituating the patient to thinking in terms of the many life satisfactions which are non-alcoholic.

From the very first interview the therapist declines to deal with the patient on anything but a mature basis, even though the mature segment of the personality may be very fractional. The patient must learn to make his own decisions. If, as often happens, he asks whether he should remove all alcohol from his home, stop serving cocktails to guests, keep away from the club, where he enjoys chatting with his friends, or from the taproom where he likes to play darts, the answer is, "Think it over and do whatever you decide is better."

It is psychologically important that the patient come to a true understanding of why he wants to get well. The reason is not, as he so often sincerely but erroneously believes, because of the unhappiness, shame and distress that alcoholism has brought to his wife and children, his old mother, father and his friends. Actually, he wants to get well and *can* get well for only one reason—himself. These emotionalized rationalizations seem genuine to the patient and the remorse is very keen, but they do not bring about recovery. Actually, the self-reproach and guilt are borne until the mental suffering becomes too severe. Then it is drowned out in the tidal wave of a prolonged alcoholic debauch. A professor friend of mine, who is somewhat alcoholic, was so fascinated by my book (*Alcohol—One Man's Meat*) that he sat up until three o'clock in the morning to finish it. He felt it was a true and moving human document. In fact, he felt so saddened by the book that he went out and got very drunk.

As his life history is relived by the patient in his talks with the therapist, he gradually comes to the appreciation and conviction that his future life must be non-alcoholic. Sometimes this belief is ushered in by a series of alcoholic dreams. The patient is an usher at a dear friend's wedding and it would be rude if he did not toast the health of the newly married pair. Or else he is at the annual union picnic. It would look queer and "high hat" if he did not tilt a few beers with the boys. So these patients enjoy a few drinks—in their dreams. In those patients who are destined for recovery, the abstinence conviction becomes very strong. It has been said that should such a person be welcomed by St. Peter at the heavenly gates, proffering a cup of celestial ambrosia, he would decline it on the suspicion that it might contain alcohol.

Many treatment facets are directly re-educational. From the beginning and throughout the treatment, the patient is asked to read authoritative writings on alcoholism. It is suggested that he record his opinions, either in agreement or disagreement. This promotes an independent and detached viewpoint and the notes provide a helpful basis for discussion.

Since the patient makes his own decisions, he is not directed to do this or that, but suggestions are made. Among other things, he is encouraged to make out each night a schedule of the next day's activities. Co-operative patients learn to arrange this schedule so that unoccupied times in which there is danger of relapse are largely avoided. Deviations from the schedule which could have been avoided offer useful topics for consideration.

It is a fallacy to believe that a change of occupation can cure pathological drinking. There are no occupational drydocks. But it may well be that the patient's occupation is not suitable for him, perhaps because it is beyond his capacities and limitations or too far beneath them, or because he dislikes it. Then vocational guidance testing may be valuable. Avocations, too, are important and the patient is likely to be helped if he can develop interesting hobbies, particularly those involving manual craftsmanship.

While again his everyday conduct is not dictated, yet it is a good sign if the patient decides upon an attitude of frankness toward his friends and tells them without evasion why he is no longer drinking. The stomach ulcer excuse is becoming a bit shopworn.

In keeping with the mature level upon which the treatment is being conducted, it is usually necessary to secure the co-operation of wife and family. They should understand and be persuaded to abandon childish attitudes with their methods of entreaty, praise, blame and constant watching. The wife of one of my patients had attempted to cure her husband by doling out sexual relations—permitting it if he had been sober for a week, denying it if he had imbibed. The plan failed. Some good-intentioned women seemingly were born to be "sniffers." It does not help treatment if the patient is met at the door each night and sniffed over by his wife.

There is a physical aspect to every alcoholic situation. Medicines of one kind or another and other forms of treatment are needed in practically every case. The liabilities of the patient are checked by a careful examination and the objective is to raise his body to its physical optimum.

There should be a normal amount of exercise, but it is important to counsel against serious overfatigue. Sometimes a patient unconsciously overtires himself in order to gain a rationalization for drinking—because he is "so worn out."

The eating habits of the alcoholic are atrocious and his nutrition is poor. At best he snatches a bite here and there during the day and is apt to eat a hot, heavy meal late at night. At the crescendo of a debauch, practically no food at all is taken. The patient should be encouraged to eat a well-balanced diet at customary mealtimes.

In a segment of alcoholic patients, blood taken at certain periods during the day shows low blood-sugar levels. These periods more or less coincide with the appearance of a great variety of sensations, headache, empty feelings in the head, dizziness, assorted sensations in the stomach and, indeed, in any part of the body. These feelings stimulate the patient to take large amounts of alcohol, unconsciously meeting a carbohydrate need. This may be used advantageously by suggesting that late in the morning and afternoon the patient eat a bar of chocolate, a few cookies or pieces of candy.

It is important to be sure that the vitamin and other chemical needs are adequately supplied.

The Alcoholics Anonymous movement now has gained great momentum, with organized groups all over the country. It has many chapters and its membership will soon reach 100,000. It utilizes many of the ideas which I have presented. In my experience, those who have been adjusted in the A.A. group spare no amount of time, trouble and patience in attempting to help pathological drinkers at every economic and social level. Often the effort is successful.

I know of no better note with which to close this chapter than to repeat the advice I have so often given my students and others anxious to have the right attitude toward alcoholism. It is contained in the words of the man, who, gazing at a drunkard lying helpless in the gutter, reflected, "There but for the grace of God go I."

12 | MENTAL DEFECTS*

MENTALLY speaking, a psychotic patient is like a person who has had money in the bank but the account has been temporarily or permanently closed. A feeble-minded person has never had any, or at least very little, money in the bank of human intelligence.

Probably there are more than 3,500,000 people in the United States who live in the shadows of low-grade intelligence. For every idiot there are about three and a half imbeciles and eighteen morons. Before we boast too loudly of our superior national intelligence, we might remember that, during World War II, the Army alone discharged almost 140,000 men for mental deficiency or other constitutional deficit. Many more were rejected by Selective Service Boards.

The exact part played by inheritance is not yet determined. It does have a significant role, as may be inferred from the in-breeding of feebleminds in the "piney" districts of New Jersey and other places throughout the world. But, by no

---

* There is a very satisfactory trend in the direction of abolishing old, undesirable and somewhat stigmatizing terms like mental defect, feeble-mindedness, with a classification of idiot, imbecile and moron, and substituting for them the descriptive words "intellectual limitation" which, of course, has many gradations.

means are all the feeble-minded produced by an intelligence-tainted ancestry.

This was about the sum total of our information when I began my study of psychiatry. Since that time there have been increasingly larger encroachments upon the inheritance area as directly causative. The brain may be permanently injured during labor, sometimes by obstetrical forceps. Often the intellectual depreciation is accompanied by paralyses and other neurological handicaps. There may be brain inflammation, sometimes due to syphilis. Hemorrhage inside the brain may be the fault. Mongolism is a low level of mental defect. It would seem that "mongolians" are somewhat more likely to be born of parents thirty-seven to forty years old, and half of them are last in the order of birth. Microcephalics are small-headed and light-brained. Hydrocephalics may have very large heads due to "water on the brain," from blocks in the system of the circulating spinal fluid and its accumulation sometimes in enormous amounts. In cretins, the mental defect is due to insufficient thyroid secretion. If thyroid feeding is begun early enough, a miracle of physical and intellectual restitution may be witnessed. Disorders of the small pituitary gland which rests in the so-called Turkish saddle of bone at the base of the skull may decidedly impair the intelligence, as well as produce various distortions of the body, including the fat and bearded ladies and giants of the circus side-shows. Amaurotic (blindness) family idiocy is distinguished by a bright, cherry-red spot which may be readily seen by looking through an instrument into the depths of the eye. And there are many more conditions to which feeble-mindedness may be traced.

In many of these situations notable progress is being made in the areas of both prevention and active treatment. The value of sterilization is still a moot question. Based on his observation that only one of twenty feeble-minded children has a defective mother or father, Lionel Penrose believes that sterilization would decrease feeble-mindedness by only 5 per cent. Increasing attention, but still far from enough, is being paid to the physical and emotional health of the expectant mother. The diet, particularly sufficient vitamin intake, is important. Lues in both the mother and child should be detected and skillfully treated. Obstetricians are making notable gains in minimizing birth injuries. Later in life, in some of the birth-trauma or head-trauma conditions sustained in childhood, expert neurosurgical and orthopedic operations may greatly reduce the handicaps.

There is no magic drug for mental defect, like penicillin for certain types of infection, yet often much can be done. While there are not many problems like cretinism, in selected cases satisfactorily solved by feeding thyroid extract, yet other endocrine substances sometimes may be useful.

Recently considerable attention has been focused upon a substance called glutamic acid. Several investigators have reported improvements in the mental age and I.Q. and a gain in general mental functioning. The highest level of improvement appears about six months after beginning treatment, but then the improvement rate diminishes. The "ceiling" is reached in about one year.

Of course, it goes without saying that general physical hygiene and body care are extremely important in mental defectives. Without the teaching of habit formation even ordinary cleanliness will not be practiced and many sources of trouble, such as decayed teeth or skin diseases, will develop.

The intelligence tests originally devised by Binet, and other very accurate tests, not only identify the feeble-minded but sort them out at various levels. The normal I.Q. is about 100, but the idiot has an I.Q. of 20 or less; the imbecile scores between 21 and 50; the moron rates above 50 and below 70. Between 70 and average intelligence, there is a sub-normal group.

The behavior readily tells the story. The idiot has little or no sense of physical self-preservation. I have a little idiot friend who does not move away but simply looks blankly at me when I threaten to crash a heavy baseball bat against his head. Imbeciles cannot be taught to manage their own affairs but, at best, if not too low, they may learn to do simple, repetitive, chiefly manual tasks. Morons need supervision and help. Usually they are not able to earn a living under even minimal competitive conditions. They need protection against social dangers. Many morons are prostitutes.

From time to time there are waves of public hysteria because an imbecile has committed a sex crime. Occasionally this does happen, but so do criminals with high I.Q.s commit sex crimes. Idiots do not know enough to commit crimes and there is no reason to believe that imbeciles or morons break the law in much greater proportion than the non-defective population.

Naturally, parents and particularly mothers whose egos have been grievously insulted by having produced mentally defective children are very loath to accept a diagnosis of mental defect. They are apt to point out that their youngsters in certain ways are "very smart." They may give signs of pleasure at the playing of a certain phonograph record. Or, displeasure at hearing another. Or copy "funnies" from the paper. Or hide when it is bedtime. In themselves these things do not mean much. The intelligence graph is usually not an even level. There are peaks and valleys. It is the average that counts.

Occasionally there may be even remarkable capacity in one isolated area—so-called idiot-savants. There was an imbecile who earned an excellent living on the stage by being able to reproduce any piece of classical music he had heard but once. After each performance, he applauded himself vigorously. Another imbecile could add up a long column of figures, four across, without ever making a mistake. Old "Doc" Green, a friend of mine, was a very pleasant imbecile who could scarcely look after his ordinary body needs. Yet he had a memory store of more than 300 dates which were unfailingly accurate. "This is Lafayette's birthday," or, "This is the date on which Washington crossed the Delaware."

On the other hand, it is extremely important not to mistake mental retardation for mental defect. Children may do so poorly in school that they are suspected of being or may be actually diagnosed feeble-minded, because of some correctable physical situation, perhaps anemia, infected tonsils, tapeworm or some other parasite, eyestrain or even only the need for a circumcision. These and many other bodily difficulties may absorb so much of the child's attention and disturb him so much emotionally that the school work suffers seriously.

Environmental situations may be at fault. When she was ten years old, I knew a young woman who now is doing brilliant work in college. Her I.Q. is 140. Ten years ago her teacher in school recommended that she be put in the special school for backward children because she was "hopelessly behind in her studies." The explanation was simple enough, though it was very difficult to uncover. Sadie's parents generally conversed in the "old-country" language and their English was hopelessly broken and confused. Sadie was so ashamed that she always found excuses for not inviting her playmates into the house.

Children may fail seriously in school because of mental conflicts emerging from unhappy home situations, dire poverty, quarreling between parents, divorce, serious illness, death and many other disturbing conditions. In fact, mental retardation, severe enough to give the impression of actual defect, may result when the parent-child relationship fails to meet the minimal needs of the child, on the one hand, for love and demonstrations of affection, and, on the other, for gradual emancipation from the parental emotional apron strings. The engendered unconscious hostility may express itself in the guise of apparent intellectual deficit.

One of my colleagues examined psychologically a group of boys in an institution for the feeble-minded. One of them, a boy of fifteen, was quite unco-operative. He either threw the testing material on the floor or simply held it in his hands, made no response whatsoever, staring blankly at the examiner. He had been in the institution for six months and was classed as a low-grade imbecile.

My colleague was interested enough to investigate. The youngster had been sent to the institution because he did not get on at all in school, and, in a group test, had an I.Q. of only twenty-nine. His home life had been very unhappy. His father was alcoholic, and after some years of ill treatment and abuse of his wife and child, he deserted. The boy's mother, never very adequate emotionally, spent most of her time bewailing her fate. The economic situation was marginal, but some sort of support was derived from sympathetic relatives.

Considerable time was needed to gain the boy's confidence and breach his stubborn resistance. It was his defiance of a world which had treated him so shabbily. But eventually it was broken through. Then tests showed an I.Q. of 120. Now, in suitable surroundings, the youngster is happy and making excellent school progress.

In addition to the intelligence deficiency, the symptoms are about what might be expected in a situation where someone is compelled to take part in something for which he is in no manner equipped to participate. It is like being asked to play a game in which the chips represent intelligence. All the other players have an adequate supply of chips. The feeble-minded player has none, or a few very low in value. The game is the game of life.

Naturally the feeble-minded person who is asked to do something he cannot do becomes puzzled, confused, nonplused. Unless he is too far down on the intellectual ladder, he is very frustrated and unhappy.

As to actual mental symptoms, well-defined psychoses do not occur in the low-grade feeble-minded. There may be episodes of confused hearing of voices (hallucinosis) or periods of aimless activity, dashing about, grimacing, gnashing teeth, twisting, contorting. One would not expect much more than this. In other words, the person who develops a psychosis has a background of information, experience and association of ideas from which he draws and upon which he constructs the symptoms of his psychosis. The person who is intellectually limited does not have such a background and, therefore, can only produce symptoms at a correspondingly simple level. At higher levels, the moronic, fairly well constructed psychoses may appear, but even here the symptoms are usually much more simple than in those who have a normal complement of intelligence. For instance, schizophrenia is very simple, much like its manifestation in primitive people.

If there were enough institutions of the proper kind within the financial reach of the people in the moderate and lower income brackets, probably it would be the most satisfactory answer to the economic and social challenge of three and a half million sufferers of mental defect. In the right kind of institution, not only are the physical needs of the child adequately met, but satisfactory and useful habit patterns are inculcated and the peak of attainable intellectual functioning is secured for each child. For many children, so trained and equipped, particularly for those in the higher grades of feeble-mindedness, there may be found in their adult lives vocational niches within the limits of their capacities in which they may have satisfaction and contentment.

Almost always there is a penalty to be paid for keeping a mentally defective child in the home circle. For the child itself, its parents and its brothers and sisters, it may be a very severe penalty. The following three summarized case records are illustrative of many similar situations I have encountered.

Mary was a pretty moron, nineteen years old. Jean, her bright, attractive and much sought-after sister was two years younger. The parents unwisely insisted that when Jean went to parties or had her friends in the home, she have Mary with her. At first Jean's friends were reasonably considerate and kind. Soon they tired of the one whose sum total of contribution to the festivities was a few inane remarks and almost constant simpering. Furthermore, they resented the fact that Jean, who was very popular, should be embarrassed and shamed at being publicly saddled with a moronic sister. So they began to disregard Mary and even make rather unpleasant remarks about her and even to her. Children are apt to be realists. Poor Mary was confused and vaguely troubled. She was just intelligent enough to sense the situation. She became frustrated, jealous, resentful and hostile. One night she crept softly into Jean's room and attacked her viciously, scratching her face and pounding it with her fists. Now she is in an institution.

A very similar childhood setting had existed in the instance of a woman of forty, whom I treated for an anxiety neurosis. She, too, had had an older, feeble-minded sister. During their teens, and indeed, until my patient married at the age of twenty-five, the parents insisted that the two sisters "go out

together" so that the feeble-minded one would not be "hurt."
There was the same pattern of embarrassment, shame, resentment and stumbling explanations. When I saw her fifteen
years later, even though happily married with two lovely children and an assured position, she suffered severe anxiety reactions, sometimes amounting to emotional panic, in any social
gathering.

When the first-born child is mentally defective, it is a tragedy. Too often it is even more tragic than it need be.

Mrs. R. was a young and very happy wife, one year married. She and her husband were deeply in love with each other.
A much-wanted baby was awaited eagerly by both. A baby
boy arrived. Everything was fine. But even in infancy it became apparent to everyone except the mother that the child
was mentally defective. There was no known reason. The ancestry of both husband and wife was sound enough. There had
been no birth injury. Nor did the child have any serious diseases. Occasionally such unexplained tragedies occur.

Naturally, expert opinion was sought. A half-dozen able
specialists made careful studies and gave their honest verdicts.
The child was an imbecile. Nothing more could be done than
to place the child in a suitable institution at the proper time.

The mother could not or would not accept the insult to her
ego. Consultations were sought far and wide. The financial resources of the husband were strained to the breaking point.
He was filled with worry and anxiety and his work suffered.
Several times he was passed over and fellow workers were pro-
moted. His wife became increasingly bitter, resentful and difficult to live with. Her child could *not* be feeble-minded. Any
remark, even remotely suggesting it, brought forth either angry tirades or tears, sulking and days of silence. She rejected
all social life. All her time was needed to look after her child,

which she did with a slavish devotion worthy of a more hopeful cause. This continued for almost five years. Finally, she agreed to see a psychiatrist, hoping as always that he would "take her side."

It took almost a year of careful and intensive treatment to bring about a change. The patient's attitude and reactions were related to certain unconscious hostility feelings and conflicts derived from a mother-child pattern of insufficient affection. Mrs. R. began to understand this and put the pieces together. Spontaneously, in the last month of treatment, she expressed two saving thoughts. Perhaps, after all, the child would be better off in an institution. Perhaps, too, it would be a good idea to have another baby. A few months before, if either suggestion had been made, it would have unleashed an angry storm of protest. "All the time I have is dedicated to the poor little fellow whom no one understands or loves."

The feeble-minded child was placed in an institution. A year later, a fine, healthy, normal baby was born.

If there is no reason in inheritance or otherwise, and this question has been carefully passed upon by competent physicians, then a good antidote for a mentally defective child is a normal child. It may avert personal and marital catastrophe.

Unfortunately, there are not enough institutions of the right kind where mentally defective children may be sent for training and rehabilitation so that they may have a place in life. There are a number of good private places, but even when they are non-profit-making, the expense is prohibitive and quite out of reach of the majority of the population. Well-trained, skilled personnel is expensive. Not always, but far too often, public hospitals for mental defectives, perforce by reason of inadequate and sometimes niggardly support by the State, are very inadequately staffed and maintained so that the care is largely custodial. So, some thought must be given to extra-mural care and treatment. This, too, is very incomplete.

To be at all satisfactory, it must have many facets—recognition, classification and registration, special training facilities in the public-school system with emphasis on manual training, visiting teachers, nurses, social workers and educational counselors, all with enough tact to deal with parents and secure their co-operation, attention to special disabilities, adequate follow-up work and vocational guidance. All this and much more. Very costly but very worthwhile in a democratic culture. Why is it worthwhile?

If all the feeble-minded were unaided and left to their own devices, they would soon perish from the face of the earth. The idiots would die soon of starvation, accident and disease. The imbeciles would survive a little longer. The morons would keep above the surface for a time, if not too hard pressed. But if the going became more difficult, as in times of economic tightening, and they had to enter the lists of stern competition, then they, too, would go under. This is a simplified, realistic solution which we instantly reject with abhorrence.

If we are to be saved from cultural chaos and spiritual degradation, then the world in which we live, every nation and, indeed, each individual, will have to be measured and assayed not only from the standpoint of material utilitarianism, his kilowatt hours of production, but also from the less tangible but more important criterion of the cultural and spiritual salvation of civilization.

Measured by this bi-faceted rule, it seems to me that the mental defective belongs to the wheat and not to the chaff. Science and civilization owe him a threefold obligation. The mental defective has a three-dimensional perspective. The advancement of science derived from him. His actual and potential value as a piece of physical machinery. His leavening effect upon the nature of the progress of civilization.

In the first place, purely investigative science is deeply in debt to the mental defective. It is a criterion of the development of techniques which unlock the doors of the unknown that one proceeds from the simple to the intricate. The average normal brain is hallmarked by intricacy of design and complexity of structure. The pathways of many of its functions are still to be traced.

Comparatively, the brain of the defective is simple in pattern. The investigation of such brains, checked and helped pave the way for a better understanding of the structures and functions of the brains of those who have normal intellectual endowments.

In the feeble-minded, behavior tends to be simple and naïve and its meaning may be more readily penetrated. Vocabulary is limited but direct. The mental defective does not learn in any great degree how to use speech to mask thought. He escapes the double-edged trickery of words. Unlike the characters in O'Neill's *Strange Interlude* he does not speak twice, once to conceal his thoughts and then again to say to himself what he really thinks and what he would have liked to have said when he spoke aloud. Neither does he become adept in donning the social poker face used to conceal our emotions. Usually the limited emotional life is expressed directly. The study of the feeble-minded in these areas has been fruitful in interpreting so-called normal behavior. It is one of three important sources of information and comparison—the other two being the behavior of children and of the mentally sick.

The field of mental testing has been enlarged and enriched by modifications of testing techniques originally devised for the classification of the feeble-minded. From the humble beginnings of the Binet test, there have been developed a great variety of helpful tests, having far-reaching utilization in the more accurate delineation of personality, in vocational guidance and in many other directions.

In training and teaching, much stimulus has come from the efforts of those who work with the mentally defective. It is a difficult and trying terrain. Infinite patience is needed. Even small lessons must be endlessly repeated and relearned. There are needed, too, on the part of the teacher, faith in the objective sought and enthusiasm about its accomplishment. It is neither the time nor the place for educational cynicism. The goal is the conversion of the utmost potential capacity of each child into actual serviceable usage. It is known in advance that there cannot be a Ph.D. and a brilliant career—or, indeed, any career at all. At the maximum the defective may learn how to earn a living under controlled conditions. Perhaps all that can be accomplished will be to teach the child to do happily a few simple, unremunerative daily chores. Maybe all that can be gained is the inculcation of the habit of physical cleanliness.

Again, is it worthwhile? More than worthwhile. If for no other reason than because it teaches the rest of us who are not handicapped by irremovable limits of intelligence how precious is that supreme organ, the brain, and its function, and yet we are so often casual and almost indifferent to its development and usage. How much may be accomplished by continuous concentrated striving! But we must accept certain limitations imposed by innate and external conditions of life. Too frequently we who are blessed with normal intelligence batter ourselves against those psychological stone walls which exist in the life of every human being. Such ineffective onslaughts are foregone in conclusion and the result is comparable to the plight of the mental defectives if they were forced to try to scale intellectual heights far beyond their endurance.

Is there a place for the mental defective in our industrially keynoted civilization, unbelievably efficient, with an amazing accomplishment of vast quantity standardized production? Of necessity in much of this work simple operations must be endlessly and monotonously repeated, hour after hour, day in and day out. I do not mean to suggest that all or even the bulk of such work could be done by those who are in the higher brackets of mental defect and subnormality. I do think it would be feasible to train many of them for the simple, safeguarded tasks of standardized production. Much of such work would just fill the measures of their mental capacities and not overflow them. No energy would be left over to flow into the fortuitous and dangerous channels of brooding dissatisfaction, envy and antisocial attitudes. And the workers would have satisfaction in their work and there would be that sense of accomplishment, the dividend accruing from contributions to society, irrespective of the amount of the contribution, provided only that it is all one has to give.

After all, the chief contribution of the mental defective is derived neither from what we may win for science by studying him, nor from what we may teach him to give in terms of work hours. His greater value comes from the enormous civilizing and cultural stimulus and the humanizing response, not because of his strength, but because of his weakness. There is nothing stronger than weakness. Man has added many cubits to his cultural and spiritual stature by virtue of what he has gained in protecting the weak. True, progress has been slow and uneven, but history records that significant upward strides came from the momentum acquired when the strong battled for the weak. Thus did our species raise itself by the bootstraps of emotionally activated humanitarianism to higher levels, where inspired intelligence took hold and wrought effectively for human betterment—scientifically, politically, economically, culturally.

Think of the enormous significance of the humanitarian gesture of Philip Pinel when at the Salpêtrière, in the shadow of the guillotine, he struck the chains from the insane! The echoes of that gallant blow have never ceased reverberating. It was from the emotional impetus of the humanitarianism which Pinel inspired that psychiatry eventually became a science. Without the dynamic objective of protecting the weak and defenseless, the scientifically brilliant chapters of psychiatry would never have been written.

Man has become dominant, not because of his muscular strength, but by reason of the emergence of that better-than-self, the superego, and the gradual thickening of this veneer over his primitive core. And each time he thought and fought for those of his species who were weak and needed his protective strength, another layer was laid down and the ethical veneer became a bit thicker and more firmly attached.

This veneer is still but a thin coating. It still rubs off rather easily. Witness our war orgies. The ethical covering is a recent acquisition, not so very many thousands of years old. Obviously the coating must be spread very thin to cover the delineation of man—so huge and ancient that it cannot be covered nor can its age be reckoned by written history or even tradition.

Paradoxically, one might say that man is still far from being strong enough to stand without the ethical support of the weak and defenseless of his species—like the mental defectives, who are not strong enough to stand alone.

13 | CONSTITUTIONAL PSYCHO-
PATHIC INFERIORITY

FOR MANY YEARS, constitutional psychopathic inferiority was the diagnostic scrapbasket of psychiatry. Human behavior deviations which did not seem to fit elsewhere were thrown into the catch-all receptacle. Today, while the diagnosis is still made far too frequently, yet a more sensible and restricted viewpoint obtains and certain minimal criteria are more widely respected.

For a time, during the war, the diagnosis of C.P.I. was made with almost joyous abandon in the Army. Then, upon sober second thought, it was realized that a single or even several examples of malbehavior, even if outstandingly bad, scarcely scientifically justified such a pessimistic opinion. Particularly was this true because the antisocial conduct occurred in the abnormal setting of military life, involving abrupt and often unpleasant dislocations from the everyday customs and manners of the civilian. To be sure, the behavior often indicated personality disorders, but usually not of the gravity of the psychopathic inferior. Now it is increasingly widely accepted that before affixing the C.P.I. label, it is necessary that the behavior not only involve a considerable departure from a minimum of the accepted average, but also that it has been continued over a relatively long period of time.

Furthermore, a somewhat dubious psychiatric custom of calling every alcoholic or drug addict, sexual deviate, liar, kleptomaniac or pyromaniac a C.P.I. is no longer in good repute. Some of these unfortunates unquestionably fit the diagnosis, but by no means all of them do.

Nevertheless, even after all those who do not properly belong are trimmed off, there still remains a considerable group of human beings who inhabit a kind of "no-man's" behavior area, half-way between the countries of the mentally sick and the well. They seem so much a part of and so closely related to everyday reality that it is hard to think of them as having mental disease. Yet their behavior is so bizarre and inexplicable that it is not easy to accept them as sane. Often I have thought of some C.P.I., "Here is a chap who is behaving abnormally in a normal sort of fashion."

What and why is C.P.I.? Viewing the behavior separately, in all its strangeness, some observers have been strongly inclined to believe that there must be a psychosis. I do not think so. The grip upon reality is too tenaciously held. Sometimes it does seem as though phantasy was being "lived out" in contrast to the schizophrenic who largely "thinks out" his phantasy. True enough, psychopathic inferiors may have psychotic episodes, but so may the feeble-minded. And mental defect is not mental disease.

Incidentally, constitutional psychopathy is not due to mental defect. Generally speaking, the intellectual equipment is at least average. Often it is better than average. Indeed, a galaxy of geniuses, who were psychopaths might be presented. By no manner of means is this equivalent to saying that a genius is a C.P.I. Far from it. Some of them **are**. So are some ditch-diggers.

Certain physical conditions, notably encephalitis ("sleeping sickness") and head injury in children may produce behavior which cannot be distinguished from psychopathic behavior. This, plus the fact that the electrical "brain waves" may be abnormal, has led some psychiatrists to conclude that the behavior of the psychopath is due to actual disease of the brain. I do not think so. To me, it seems like mistaking a part for the whole. The vast majority of the patients have not had demonstrable brain diseases, nor do I think their brain waves are out of line.

Interestingly, Franz Alexander has dubbed the condition "destiny neurosis." The C.P.I. child does seem destined by his conduct to get into a long and complicated series of difficulties.

Why do psychopaths behave as they do? I have known many of them. It looks as though they could not help it very much. Their behavior seems to come from inside pressure. It seems to me that "inside" their personalities, there is a drive from strong, unconscious inferiority patterns, probably acquired in childhood, which must be translated into behavior. For all the world, they seem to be forced to act out compensations for inner, unrecognized self-belittlement and inferiorities. This would nicely explain the fantastic, often purposeless lies which the psychopathic inferior not only tells, but acts out in detail.

I am sorry I have lost track of Morton W.* I last saw him a few years after World War I. He was sent to me for study because he had been impersonating a minister and representing himself as the "noted Princeton boy evangelist."

---

* Adapted from *Practical Clinical Psychiatry*, 6th Edition, Strecker, Ebaugh and Ewalt (Blakiston Co., Philadelphia).

Two years before, Morton, in association with another man, began to do street-corner speaking. He told his parents that he was attending a Bible Institute (a lie) and night school (a lie). He embarrassed his family by forging a check for $25.00, and a lenient magistrate placed him on parole.

His schooling was limited to grammar school. He obtained jobs easily, since he had a bright and attractive personality, but he did not hold them very long. Morton was too busy preaching.

His mother died when he was four years old. The father had been a drug addict and the home life was insecure and unhappy. Two uncles were ardent members of a bizarre religious cult. One sister is a trained nurse, a woman of fine intelligence and character, deeply troubled about her brother.

A prominent minister who tried vainly to lead Morton into the ways of truthfulness gave us some interesting information. Morton began to lie and steal as a child. Once, as a gardener's helper, he stole a watch from a fellow worker and presented it to his father.

Morton loved to go to public lectures and meetings of all kinds. He was always in the front row and never missed opportunities of shaking hands with the lecturer and many members of the audience. Morton, himself, spoke whenever given half a chance. He was an accomplished, convincing and interesting liar, telling stories of being a student for the ministry at many Bible schools, Drew Theological Seminary, Franklin and Marshall, Princeton, etc. His technique for securing speaking engagements was often successful. Calling a well-known minister, he would say something like this: "This is Mr. Green of the senior class of Princeton Theological Seminary. I am arranging for a field day in Philadelphia. I wish to send you M.W., the noted boy evangelist." On such a basis,

Morton often did preach eloquently and without ever asking for monetary remunerations.

As one of many examples of acting out lies, Morton went to a department store and asked for an unusual style of clerical collar. The store did not have them, but the clerk offered to order them. "Yes," said Morton, "do that. Please send a dozen to the Rev. 'X' C.O.D." Dr. X, a prominent clergyman, was somewhat mystified when the collars were delivered to him.

In spite of a reasonably high I.Q., Morton did some rather stupid things. For instance, he took a pair of gloves from a man's pocket, placed them in his own pocket, but allowed them to stick halfway out. He stole Bibles with names and addresses in them and presented them to young women upon whom he called. Morton had numerous ardent courtships, none of which went much beyond the verbal stage, although several of them culminated in engagements to marry. To these young women, he told amazing tales of his intensive preparation for the ministry, often adding a moving account of his army service overseas, reaching its crescendo in a terrific battle scene in which "my two dear brothers were killed in action." Morton did have two brothers, but they died in infancy. Needless to add, he had never been in military service nor outside this country for any reason. Once, a friend had to take a trip, and Morton begged him to stop in to see his father, since he had just had word that he was critically ill. To the friend's surprise, Morton's father was as well as usual and working. He had not written to Morton for at least a month.

Very occasionally, Morton did admit to me that he had lied. Usually, when confronted with the evidence of his complete disregard of the truth, he would remain silent. Once he said, "I am sorry, Doctor, you do not believe these things." When

I asked him to stop preaching, he said, "I would like to oblige you, but I can't stop. I have to preach."

I have tried to explain constitutional psychopathic inferiority on the basis of what it is not: not organic disease of the brain or mental defect, not actual mental disease (psychosis) or psychoneurosis. It remains to give an idea of what I think it is. I believe it is a condition of defect. That it is inborn is very doubtful. It would seem more likely that it begins early in life and is the result of the reaction between a certain kind of make-up and environmental circumstances, usually personality-damaging in type.

Looking at the behavior of the psychopathic inferior, there are, of course, varying degrees of severity. Yet the threads of a more or less common design may be readily perceived. There is emotional instability, occupational inadequacy, impulsive conduct with inability to postpone carrying out certain wishes and desires, inability to form mature judgments, absence of ethical and moral appreciation, disregard of truthfulness, decency, social responsiveness and the rights of others. In all, quite an indictment. The conduct threads work out into a pattern of *inability to profit by experience*. In this the psychopath, in spite of his normal intellectual endowment, is like the mental defective.

Early in my career, I learned this lesson. I was on the staff of an out-patient psychiatric clinic. A social agency asked me to study and report on the case of a girl of eighteen, attractive and seemingly very intelligent. Julie was illegitimately pregnant. She seemed to be so genuinely sorry and so understanding, with such excellent insight, that my mind and heart warmed to the task. Julie absorbed the psychotherapy as quickly as I could give it out. I was enthusiastic. At the end of several months she thanked me sincerely. I agreed with her conclusions: "I now understand everything. You have made it very clear and helped me very much. My behavior has been stupid and childish. I will have to pay a heavy penalty for what I have done. But I will live it down. There will be no mistakes in the future. I have learned my lesson."

Her child had been adopted. I reported optimistically to the social agency. Julie would now lead a fine, constructive life.

A year later, I was a little less optimistic when Julie was sent to me, again illegitimately pregnant. Five years later, when she was illegitimately pregnant for the fifth time, I began to understand that the constitutional psychopathic inferior does not profit by experience.

From the rather pessimistic vein in which I have presented this subject, it will be inferred that treatment is not very promising. That is true. Sometimes, with great patience, close supervision and the opportunity to manipulate the environment, some improvement is won. More often not. Perhaps we have been too pessimistic. The assumption has been that little or nothing can be done. Perhaps we have not tried hard enough. In any event, much more investigative research is needed. When we gain clearer concepts as to what produces C.P.I., then we shall begin to move forward in its treatment.

Psychopathic inferiors are frequently antisocial and often come into contact with the law. Generally, the offenses are not in the category of major crimes. Commonly there are minor offenses, petty larceny, quarrels, threats, assaults, many infractions of the motor-vehicle code, prostitution, drug trafficking, etc. Since the psychopathic antisocial record is constantly repetitive, the economic burden is enormous.

Sometimes a major crime is committed by a constitutional psychopathic inferior. At once it brings into focus many legal, medical and social difficulties and opposing viewpoints: for instance, the rigid, legal concept concerning the capacity to distinguish between right and wrong, which cannot be accepted in toto by psychiatrists. On the psychiatric debit side there is the unsatisfactory state of contending expert psychiatric testimony. In young criminals, the question of the culpability of parents is in the courtroom limelight. Finally, what is to be done with the psychopath after he has been found guilty?

Recently, I was appointed by the Court as a member of a Commission to examine a seventeen-year-old murderer. It was the most brutal slaying in the annals of Philadelphia crime, the sadistic sexual murder of a twelve-year-old boy. His body was horribly mutilated with more than forty knife and scissors wounds. One knife thrust was so savage that it severed the great blood vessel (aorta) from the heart. Medical testimony proved beyond doubt that there was a sexual assault. From the nature of the testimony and the examination of the killer, it was obvious that in the legal sense he was able to distinguish between right and wrong, though from his life history he was clearly a psychopathic inferior. The sentence was life imprisonment. Three eminent social-minded judges co-operated in our desire to go beyond the usual agenda of examination and report of the mental condition of the accused. They felt that the public weal might be served by the lessons to be derived from the tragedy.

Incidentally, the determination of being able to distinguish between right and wrong rests on the McNaughton rule, now 108 years old. This rule was the first application of psychiatry in a court of law. It was derived from the ruling of the judge in the trial of the murderer of the Secretary of the Prime Minister of England. It made the test of the admissibility of insanity the capacity to distinguish between right and wrong and the ability to understand the nature and quality of the act. As it is often applied in our courts, it is crude and archaic. Far too often the life or death of the accused is held in the senile and palsied hands of the McNaughton rule. Psychiatry has made much progress in the past 100 years. It is now a science, a science that understands much of the working of the human mind and personality, and its counsel and guidance is urgently needed in assessing the degree of responsibility entering into the commission of crime.

Since our report has some value in medico-legal situations, not only involving psychopathic inferiors, but also certain other criminals, I quote a few pertinent paragraphs:

"While it is not within the province of our authority to determine guilt or innocence or to mete out legal punishment, yet we feel very strongly that we would be remiss in the performance of our duty if we did not recommend that society be completely and permanently protected from his serious antisocial behavior tendencies for the remainder of his life.

"This is particularly important and significant, since by reason of his personality, his previous behavior and by the nature of the crime and its motivations, the accused would be likely to commit similar crimes unless adequately restrained.

"Human behavior, and in this connection certain antisocial and criminal behavior, is the result not only of the impulse to act but also of the amount of inhibition that can be interposed against carrying out such behavior.

"It is obvious that in some individuals the inhibitions against acting antisocially and criminally are less than the average and, in fact, are often definitely weak and ineffectual. This is true in many people, who according to the legal criteria are able to distinguish between right and wrong. It is true in many constitutional psychopathic inferiors in which category the prisoner belongs.

"Among the factors which might be operative in the production of constitutional psychopathic behavior it is likely that one is a serious lack of the ordinary mental hygiene of childhood in an environment which does not contain the ingredients and conditions that favor the attainment of emotional security and maturity.

"Careful, thoughtful and well-advised legislation which would meet the needs of some of the individuals in this group is indicated. Legislation contrived to cover all behavior construed as psychopathic will lead to legal confusion and conceivably might be employed mistakenly or even deliberately to impede the processes of the law, to produce miscarriages of justice and to escape just punishment.

"To make a satisfactory diagnosis of constitutional psychopathic inferiority and to give a helpful legal opinion requires in each case careful study by skilled psychiatrists of the whole life history of the individual with intensive scrutiny of the childhood history, a thorough estimate of the personality markings, of the motivations for the behavior, of the length of time during which the behavior was manifested, of the nature of the behavior, of the settings in which the antisocial behavior appeared and many other considerations. The variation between individual constitutional psychopaths will be considerable and will have great medico-legal import.

"We regard it as particularly important to find some satisfactory method for arriving at valid conclusions, without staging a court battle of psychiatric experts, which, to say the least, is anything but edifying. We believe that this can be avoided without additional legislation.

"We would suggest that the Board of Judges and the Bar Association collaborate with the State and local psychiatric societies in creating a panel of qualified psychiatrists willing to serve as needed. If counsel for the defense and the prosecutor would agree to the selection of psychiatrists from such a panel, the presiding judge could appoint the psychiatrists to examine the accused. The report should be made available to both defense and prosecution."

(The area of disagreement in consultations between qualified psychiatrists in practice is small. Why should it be so large in medico-legal practice? If the plan suggested were followed, I would forecast that a group of psychiatrists usually would agree about the essentials of a given situation. Occasionally, of course, there would be healthy differences of opinion and minority reports. Naturally, the psychiatrists would be subject to direct and cross examination. Eventually the law should be so modified that psychiatrists will be able to function in the area of greatest service. This area is not as a "pro" or "con" witness, helping to determine whether the accused is guilty or not. That is the function of the prosecutor, the counsel for the defense, the judge and the jury. After this has been determined, then the skill and judgment of the psychiatrist are urgently needed in order to assess the degree of responsibility and in deciding the corrective punishment.)

"Nothing in this procedure would abridge the constitutional right of employing as many experts by both the defense and the prosecution as they might desire. However, if they agreed upon the selections of psychiatrists, it would be paradoxical to have others. Furthermore, their testimony would be less weighty, since it would be given against the background of the presumably objective and impartial testimony of the panel of experts.

"We do not believe that it would be intelligent or common-sense thinking to expect parents or those in charge of children to be able to predict future serious antisocial behavior and to be held responsible for its occurrence. Yet we do believe there are situations in which parents or guardians of children do have some measure of responsibility and culpability.

"If there has been repeated, continued and serious anti-social conduct in children, then it is the personal and social duty of parents to utilize every means available to seek such skilled help as may be needed to uncover reasons for the behavior and to arrange for proper treatment. In the kind of serious situations indicated, if parents do not fulfill their personal and social obligations, they are contributing to the delinquency. Naturally, this would apply only when there has been a wanton disregard by parents of their duty to society.

"The true constitutional psychopathic inferior does not fit satisfactorily into prison. He is apt to be disruptive of routine and discipline. Neither does he get on well in mental hospitals. There, too, he upsets the routine care and treatment of other patients.

"It would seem to be necessary in the future for the State to plan for care designed and managed to meet the particular needs of the psychopathic inferior.

"Such care and management should have a tri-partite objective:

"1. To keep them usefully employed.

"2. To afford society adequate protection against their behavior.

"3. To study them scientifically in the hope that better treatment criteria and techniques will be evolved."

I trust that the revival of interest in the constitutional psychopathic inferior will not abate, but rather increase and expand. He has wandered too long alone in the "no-man's land" between mental illness and so-called sanity. If his appearance of sanity is only a mask, let us strip it off and study and treat him as a mental patient. If, as is more likely, this social misfit comes from the reaction between certain personality types and an unsatisfactory environment, then let us scrutinize both carefully and frame more satisfactory concepts of cause and treatment.

14 | TREATMENT

Mention has been made of the uncovering techniques. They are methods designed to uncover the inner core of truth in the unconscious of the patient—to reveal the real nature of the mental conflicts, often encrusted with many layers of symptoms, symptoms constructed and arranged to mislead, to conceal rather than reveal the truth.

The free association of psychoanalysis is aimed directly at uncovering the mental conflicts. In considerable degree, support therapy, which will be described presently, has the same purpose. There are numerous techniques which are used sometimes as shortcuts in finding out what is inside the psyche of the patient—word association tests, hypnosis, the Rorschach and thematic apperception tests, narcosynthesis and many others. Several investigative techniques, perhaps notably the Rorschach and narcosynthesis not only seek to bring to the surface buried emotional conflicts, but also try to furnish the therapist with material which he can use in the treatment of the patient. It is vital that the therapist know the truth so that he may lead the patient to understanding and facing it. However he may derive the information, it is highly important for the therapist to know, for instance, that in one patient there is a strong latent homosexuality perhaps due to the emotional possessiveness of his mother during childhood and perhaps in another a deep well of hostility traceable to insufficient love and consideration from a father who openly preferred a younger brother. And in a third patient, a more recent trauma to the ego—the repressive belief that his wife (or her husband) no longer loves him and is unfaithful. Narcosynthesis and the Rorschach sometimes give valuable clues to disturbing situations and may even clearly reveal them.

In narcosynthesis, the injection into a vein of solutions of sodium pentothal, sodium amytal or some other hypnotic drug in order to cloud consciousness and remove inhibition is not only useful in war psychiatry (as will be mentioned in the chapter on military psychiatry) but is quite useful, too, in civilian practice.

Usually the material uncovered concerns relatively recent shocking and anxiety-producing emotional experiences, but sometimes in startling fashion, material that reaches far back into childhood is brought to light.

A man, forty-seven years old, was admitted to my service at the City Hospital. He was amnesic, having completely lost in memory his name and identity. He told a rambling story of having worked in Hollywood, doing something "important" in the "movie" industry. (From his sister we learned that he had never been in Hollywood or had any connection with the "movies" and, indeed, had spent all his life in Philadelphia.)

During the first pentothal interview, he broke through his amnesia, correctly named and identified himself and gave many of the facts of the last few years of his life. In a second interview, in answer to questioning he rapidly retraced the years of his life. He drew the picture of a child yearning for the love of his mother, who had been deserted by his father. She gave him little affection, but lavished it on her favorite, a brother, two years older than the patient. Our patient had only one eye and under the influence of the drug, he told us (which we verified) that his brother had put the other eye out with a stick while they were scuffling. This was when he was three years old, and in a voice choked with emotion, he said that *the only happy time of his childhood had been when his brother brought him home after the accident, his mother took him in her arms, held him closely and kissed and petted him.*

The Rorschach test is the ink blot test, so-called, since the figures or designs were made originally by placing ink on paper, folding and blotting it. Ten cards with varying designs and shadings, some of them with red and blue coloring, are presented to the patient, one after another, after an explanation has been given. The patient is scored according to a standardized score which rates his ideas of the identification of the figures, the amount of detail, color and form, the number of responses, the time consumed, the wealth or paucity of the imagination, emotional reactions, bizarre answers, etc.

In skilled hands, the Rorschach test gives the therapist very helpful information—the basic personality outline of the patient emerges; his capacity for self-control; his intellectual type, capacity and quality; the emotional reaction and control; the nature of the emotional conflict. Sometimes the diagnosis is made. I repeat that expert knowledge and training are needed, perhaps not so much to give the test, but to interpret it correctly. Anyone can see the shadows on an x-ray plate, but only a thoroughly experienced radiographer knows what they mean.

When the physician advises the patient or the family that

drastic therapy is needed, usually he means insulin or electro-shock and, sometimes, a brain operation. Also, there are other treatments that are drastic. Some years ago my former col-league, Harold Palmer, and I utilized narcosis therapy, that is, the induction of sleep, lasting from a few days to three weeks, from the administration of rather heavy daily doses of such hypnotic drugs as sodium amytal. Sometimes the re-sults were quite good. Some of the patients upon awakening experienced a kind of psychic rebirth. Many of their symp-toms had disappeared and seemingly they had obtained con-siderable emotional release and relief in their dreams, and more particularly in the outpourings of their emotional con-flicts, when the narcosis was decreased and they were in the no-man's land twixt consciousness and unconsciousness. Some-times such material was effectively used later, as the basis of psychotherapeutic discussions with the patient.

Needless to say, all the drastic therapies, with the possible exception of electroshock (under carefully controlled out-patient conditions, electroshock may be given for ambulatory patients), are, or at least should be, hospital procedures. Care-ful preliminary examinations to determine the condition of the body organs are best made in the hospital. In the hospital, too, and only in the hospital is it possible to operate carefully medically supervised treatment units with skillful nursing. Vari-ous emergencies and complications may occur and the absence of proper conditions and resources may mean the difference between life and death.

There are many modifications of the drastic therapies and their techniques are constantly being improved. The various modifications need not be discussed. However, it might be worthwhile mentioning that an important modification of elec-troshock is electroshock narcosis. It is now in the developmen-tal stage.

The treatment field for insulin shock therapy, originated by Manfred Sakel, is schizophrenia—by no means for every schizophrenic, but those patients selected by a competent psychiatrist. The initial dose of insulin is small, but it is rapidly increased until the phase of shock is reached. Generally, the patient in shock sweats profusely, the pulse becomes rapid, the blood pressure drops, the skin is pale, wet and cold; the breathing is deep and heavy. The patient is in deep coma. The shock is terminated, usually after an hour, by giving sugar solution by mouth, sometimes by injecting it into the veins. The shock treatment is continued for thirty to fifty days or even longer, according to the improvement shown by the patient. Insulin shock, and indeed all the drastic therapies, should be followed by periods of psychotherapy which brings to light and views the conflicts and problems of the patient.

Electroshock, which acts by producing convulsive seizures, was devised by Bini and Cerletti. Fortunately, it has replaced largely the convulsions produced by the drug metrazol. Metrazol was frightening treatment since it is doubtful that consciousness was completely abolished. At least some patients reported terrifying aura (the warning to the patient that the convulsion is about to occur)—darting streaks of fire before the eyes and loud explosive noises. It was difficult to induce patients to take a second treatment. In electroshock, delivered by an accurate machine, consciousness is immediately annihilated. Many modifications and safeguards have been added to electroshock and perhaps the most important is the injection of curare. This drug very much lessens the danger of fractures of the spine and other bones during the convulsion. In the hands of a skillful operator electroshock is a relatively safe procedure. The mortality rate is definitely less than 1 per cent and there are reported series of several thousand treatments with only a single fracture.

Electroshock has been given a very wide treatment coverage, personally I think somewhat too extensive. It has been
used in practically all the psychoses and psychoneuroses. In
schizophrenia it is sometimes of considerable value, particularly if the external emotional reactions are retained and are
active. As specific treatment, I am rather dubious as to the usefulness of electroshock in the psychoneuroses. Sometimes it is
helpful in a few long-standing obsessive-compulsive patients
in whom other therapy has not been effective. Occasionally, in
some neurotic patients, in whom a marked depressive segment
blocks spontaneity, a few (but a very few) electroshock treatments may make the patient more responsive to psychotherapy. In my opinion, many electric treatments block rather
than open the pathways of psychotherapy. For one thing, there
may be considerable blurring of memory and even erasure
of certain areas of recollection. Incidentally, it is good practice
to warn the patient that electroshock treatment may produce
interference with memory. This tends at least to lessen the
alarm and sometimes panic which the patient may feel when
he is confronted with gaps in memory, although, of course, he
may forget that he was warned. Physicians, too, reassure patients that the amnesia is only temporary—at most a few days,
rarely more than a few weeks. Then the memory figures and
events reappear in the stream of consciousness.

Sometimes the forgetfulness is curiously selective. I had a
patient, a lady in late middle life, who was very depressed and
literally groveling in self-blame. Without any foundation in
fact, she believed that her "former" friends in the city in
which she lived accused her of trying to entice their servants
away from them, into her own employ. She said they referred
to her as "tricky," "cunning," "sly," even "immoral." They
were right, she said many times. She was a "horrible, miserable creature, and God surely would punish her." After the

second electrical treatment, the patient said to me, "I know there is something I should be worried about, but I can't remember what it is."

The priority treatment areas for electroshock are the severe depressions of late middle life, particularly during the so-called involutional time. Here, very often, the treatment accomplishes a recovery.* The next most favorable response is obtained in the depressive phase of manic-depressive psychosis. The excited phase is a poor third.

There is no definite rule as to the number of treatments to be given. Only a few may be needed but there may be as many as twenty in a series. The series may be repeated after a free interval, but usually the chances of improvement from the repeat series are not very promising. Often, insulin and electroshock are combined.

In 1936, as the culmination of experimental injections which blocked the passageway of impulses from one area of the brain to another, Moniz, a Portuguese surgeon, recommended prefrontal leukotomy for chronic, intractable depressions characterized by severe agitation and motor restlessness. Since that time there have been many modifications and refinements of the operation, which I would not think of attempting to describe. In any event, some of the fibres between the frontal lobe and the optic thalamus are severed. The optic thalamus is a very important link in the chain of human emotions and their expression. No matter what perfection of surgical technique may be attained, it is well to remember that brain tissue is severed, and when brain tissue is cut, its function is destroyed. It does not and cannot grow together again, like skin or other

---

* Recently, very favorable reports have been made concerning the effectiveness of intravenous injection of ether solutions in the treatment of depressions.

parts of the body. Not all the king's men and horses of science can put the brain together again.

It is my considered opinion that these operations are being used too extensively. Some time ago, I was asked to give an opinion of an article submitted for publication to a prominent and widely read magazine. In the article, the prefrontal operation was enthusiastically advocated, not only for the psychoses, but for functional illness, alcoholism, sexual psychopathy, and many other conditions. The fact that the operation had not been made available for all psychoneurotic veterans was deplored as a grave injustice! Needless to say, I decided against publication. The article was not factually true, and it would have given rise to hope in the families of many chronic mental patients—false hope, which would have ended in disillusion and cruel disappointment.

It is not yet possible to form any accurate estimate of the overall final result of the many operations that have been performed. Unquestionably, some patients are very much benefited. Unquestionably, too, there is a price to be paid in the coin of mental deterioration—particularly emotional loss. Often the loss is so small that the game is worth the candle. Sometimes, too, the deterioration is very serious so that the description "human zombie" is not too inept.

Since the operation was originally devised, I have been on the lookout for promising patient material. In thirteen years I have found only eighteen patients who fulfilled my own criteria. Perhaps my criteria are rather rigid, but I do think they are sound.

Here are the criteria:

1. Chronic mental illness—chronic not only from the standpoint of the diagnosis, but also by reason of long duration.

2. Failure of all other methods of drastic therapy, usually

including insulin and electroshock and, above all else, thorough psychotherapy.

3. No bodily or brain contraindications to the operation.

4. A highly important criterion—impulsive, aggressive and often homicidal behavior motivated by compelling hallucinosis, usually hearing "voices."

In one of my patients, a woman thirty-five years old, the voices were so insulting and deriding and accused her of such "horrible and beastly" sex practices that she was constantly in a state of desperate panic. Three nurses were needed to prevent her from gouging out her ear drums with anything she could lay her hands on and she frequently attacked the nurses with homicidal intent.

The operation, done more than six years ago, was remarkably successful. She is so much better that two years ago her family took the necessary legal steps to reinstate her in charge of her financial affairs. Yet she still hears "voices," although I doubt whether any of her friends know it. Occasionally, I encounter her in a public restaurant and watching intently, now and then I can see her lips moving silently—answering "voices." But the people with whom she is lunching suspect naught of this. She is carrying on gay and sprightly conversation with them. The "voices" have become insignificant. The operation has torn them loose from the emotional matrix in which they were once so deeply imbedded.

All but two of my patients (one of these had an agitated depression and died soon after the operation; the other was an obsessive-compulsive patient of twenty-four years' duration who was helped only slightly) were long-standing sufferers of schizophrenia. Of course, there are other patients who are helped by the operation, including some instances of chronic, intractable pain.

Of my sixteen schizophrenic patients, twelve showed varying degrees of improvement, from considerable to not very much. In all of these twelve patients, their care is much easier and they get more satisfaction out of their hospital lives. In three patients, the gain has been phenomenal and they certainly lead normal or near-normal lives. In one patient, operated on three years ago, a kind of medical miracle has been achieved. During almost eighteen years' residency in a mental hospital, she was almost continuously impulsively and dangerously violent at the behest of "voices." Now she lives happily and successfully outside a hospital, participating in the usual personal and social activities of everyday life. With the exception of an occasional feeling of irritability which she contains within herself and does not translate into behavior, other than a rare "Oh, damn," no trace of her former mental symptoms remains. Let no criteria be taken from this single case. A bolt of lightning is more apt to strike twice in the same place and in the same way than is the leukotome of the brain surgeon.

Psychoanalysis is a highly specialized technique for exploring the unconscious mind. I will not attempt to describe it. Perhaps it has been too much publicized and not always accurately.

Psychoanalysis is at once a psychology, a philosophy and a method of treatment. As a treatment technique, it is applicable chiefly to neurotic and minor mental disabilities, though it is now being used extensively in the treatment of psychotic patients. Psychoanalysis could scarcely have a higher or nobler objective. It endeavors to free the patient from the fetters of neurotic inhibitions, repressions and disabilities which were forged in childhood and which bind him fast to parental dominance or its surrogate. It tries to show him how to attain emotional maturity. It attempts to lead the neurotic cripple to a promised land, where he will become emotionally straight and strong and where, it is hoped, he will be able to live on equal terms with his fellow men.

In order to reach this objective, psychoanalysis explores that mental "no-man's land"—the unconscious. The geography and contents of this country are beyond the horizons of the consciousness of the patient and some of the trails which the psychoanalyst follows in the journeys through this territory have very faint markings. The explorer takes his bearings mainly from the intellectually unsupervised or "free" associations of the patient and from his dreams. The important trails are the back trails, the straggling lanes and dark byways leading to the childhood and infancy of the patient. Indeed, sometimes they are penetrated much farther than this and seemingly traced back into the very womb of the mother and even beyond, into that dim, shadowy jungle where long before the dawn of recorded history our prehistoric ancestors were struggling tooth and nail to retain a precarious hold upon the ledges of evolution.

There is not the space available to give psychoanalysis the meed of praise it deserves for its contributions to psychiatry. At least a few should be mentioned. While psychoanalysis did not discover the unconscious, it did clarify the concept and make it applicable to the treatment of patient.

Psychoanalysis led the assault against the strongly entrenched citadel of self-sufficient objective psychiatry, smugly satisfied with lengthy descriptions of what patients said and did, with little or no attempt to interpret hidden meanings behind word and act. It demanded that there be an inquiry into the subjective aspects of patients and their symptoms. In effect, psychoanalysis said, and said wisely, that much more important than the mere description of symptoms was the attempt to uncover in the obscured mental life of the patient the starting point and the reason for the symptoms.

In pre-psychoanalytic days the neurotic patient was not much encouraged to talk—at least about himself. By and large, he was required to be silent and listen to the psychiatrist. Psychoanalysis loosed his tongue. It not only encouraged the patient to talk, and to talk freely, but it gave him *carte blanche* to say anything he wished. The net result was good. Today, unrestricted freedom of expression is a recognized component of every form of psychotherapy.

Before the advent of psychoanalysis, the discussion of sex, its developmental phases, its incompletions, its deviations, and in general, its importance as a dynamic factor in the production of nervous and mental disorders, if not exactly taboo, nevertheless was much more honored in the breach than in the observance. Psychoanalysis insisted emphatically that its studies indicated that sex was of the utmost importance and to ignore its influence was both stupid and dangerous. Thereupon it focused upon sex in all its ramifications a penetrating and revealing battery of individual and phylogenetic searchlights. Critics of psychoanalysis are wont to declare that psychoanalysts became too absorbed in what the searchlights revealed. They say that many psychoanalysts were blinded by the glare and became myopic for non-sexual vistas. Nevertheless, it remains quite true that the dark places of sex needed to be illuminated and psychoanalysis did just that. For these and many other benefits, psychiatry is in debt to the teachings of psychoanalysis.

All human institutions and disciplines are fallible and, in my mind, psychoanalysis is not an exception. It, too, has its difficulties and its faults. Some of these will be indicated in the subsequent discussion of psychotherapy, but at this time I would like to mention several major difficulties, as I see them.

Not all psychoanalysts by any means, but far too many, are

too ready to assume theory, and sometimes quite conjectural theory, as fact. There is a more or less universal pattern of medical thinking concerning the scientific requirements needed before mere theory may be held and taught and practiced as proven fact. True enough, psychological disciplines should be given more leeway than laboratory procedures, which are capable of being exactly measured. Nevertheless, the criteria to which any theory should be subjected before it can be regarded as factual are not and should not be too casually regarded. I think that too many analysts do not realize that at least a few scientific steps must be taken before one may pass from the level of theorizing—"It may be so, sometimes it is so, but much more study is needed"—to the higher plateau adjoining the land of medical fact, where it is permissible to declare—"I am ready to assert that my conclusions are correct, because . . ." This tempered attitude of true science is aptly expressed by the words which Sinclair Lewis' Martin Arrowsmith wrote in his notebook at the conclusion of long, arduous and exhaustively checked research in his laboratory: "I have observed a principle, which I shall temporarily call the "X" principle, in pus from a staphylococcus infection, which checks the growth of several strains of staphylococcus and which dissolves the staphylococci from the pus in question."

In *Arrowsmith*, Lewis' hero-scientist had made a monumental discovery and the exact and cautious words with which he described it conveyed the correct attitude of real science and of the true scientist. Its counterpart may be found on every page of the annals of medical discovery.

Granting that a psychological discipline should not be expected to fulfill the same rigid requirements, yet if it is truly scientific in its objectives, it should at least approach somewhere near such criteria. Too much psychoanalysis and too many psychoanalysts do not even remotely make this approach. Too often, the merest theory is announced with all the positiveness and authority of an *ex cathedra* pronouncement.

This brings me to the question of dogma. Many psychoanalysts are flexible in their attitudes toward Freudian dogma. Too many are rigidly inflexible. Not even the slightest deviation is tolerated. Actually, often I have found the adherence stricter than in some ancient churches, in which in addition to dogma, there is a considerable segment of pious practices, recommended to the faithful, but not mandatory in either belief or practice. In complete Freudian orthodoxy, deviations are punished by something that is perilously close to excommunication. Sometimes in analytical groups differences of opinion, as to the length of time a trainee should be analyzed, the subject matter to be taught, etc., cannot be, or, at least, are not settled by modification and compromise, but lead to splitting of the group, so that one faction regards the other as schismatic and vice-versa. Surely there should be more mature methods of settling opinion differences.

Many years ago one heard frequently the criticism that there is no way of making a scientific assay of psychoanalysis. One still hears the same criticism. At least in part it was true then and it is still true. It is only partly correct that anyone who has not been psychoanalyzed himself cannot have any understanding or appreciation of analysis, since he has not experienced it personally. Certainly in all other areas of human knowledge one may gain important and true perspectives, by studying them carefully and objectively. Contrariwise, it took me a long time to realize that quite a number of analysts are precluded from a scientific objective viewpoint about psychoanalysis, precisely because they *have* been analyzed. The analysis has erected a high wall of emotional defense against any criticism or agnosticism about psychoanalysis, a wall so thick that it cannot be breached.

Obviously, unless psychoanalysis is an exception to all human disciplines, which it is not, then, of course, it will undergo many modifications and changes, both in theory and practice. It would be sad, indeed, if the lineal psychiatric descendants of the intrepid pioneers and explorers of the early psychoanalytic days settled down to the mere possession of the territory they have inherited—instead of constantly re-surveying it, razing those structures upon it that are no longer serviceable, building new and useful additions, and, all in all, improving their heritage.

A number of analysts have excellent backgrounds in various scientific areas, neurology, neurophysiology, neurochemistry, pharmacology. They have come to the study and practice of psychoanalysis as the most satisfactory field for their labors. Freud, himself, was a very capable neurologist. These men will be always complete psychiatrists (remembering that man is a total functioning organism) even though they may not mention the words "body" or "brain." On the other hand, there are far too many psychoanalysts who have mislaid the body and the brain—mislaid them so hopelessly that they can never find them again. They are only dimly aware and only faintly interested in the significance of the advances that have been made at the physiological, electrical, chemical and pharmacological levels of mind-body and particularly mind-brain structure and functioning. This attitude has produced a truly unfortunate isolationism between general medicine and psychoanalysis—a serious loss to both.

My brief critique of analysis is meant to be constructive and helpful. I am very hopeful of the final outcome. There is enough receptiveness in medicine and psychiatry and enough moderation and questing agnosticism in the majority of analysts so that emotional barriers will be leveled. Then will come mutual understanding and co-operation and practice will be on a very high level. The benefits that will accrue to all those who are sick are beyond calculation.

Not all, and not even the majority of functionally sick patients need psychoanalytical therapy. At least they do not need a formal, orthodox psychoanalysis. It is fortunate that they do not. A skillful, conscientious, hardworking analyst can carry a case load of about eight patients. He sees them daily and spends an hour with each patient. If the situation is at all complicated, about three years are required to complete the analysis. About one-half the patients are freed completely of their symptoms, so that they can carry on their lives satisfactorily at a reasonably emotionally mature personal and social level. Since there are hundreds of thousands of sick people whose illnesses are preponderantly on a functional basis, it is obvious that the direct treatment contribution of unmodified orthodox psychoanalysis can be only fractional.

Even if the time factor did not forbid it, there are many other good reasons why it would be unwise to analyze every patient. In many patients, the conflict material is not very deeply imbedded in the non-conscious mind and the free association, dream analysis and other techniques of analysis are not needed to unearth it, or at least to uncover enough of it so that the patient gains sufficient understanding and emotional growth to make a good go of his life.

Often, when the external pressures are prominent and fairly severe, in a fairly well-co-ordinated personality, psychotherapy of less depth than analysis suffices. A patient of mine discovered his wife's infidelity in a very shocking and humiliating way. Soon after this, his only child, a son, came down with tuberculosis. About this time, too, he sustained severe financial reverses. It is true that these environmental blows activated painful childhood experiences and repressions centering around the desertion of his mother by his father when he was six years old. Nevertheless, a rather short period of "support therapy" removed a motley assortment of psychosomatic symptoms, enabled him to face the painful realities with understanding and courage and eventually to rebuild his life in constructive, enduring fashion.

Finally, as within the area of human illness which is preponderantly organic, there are many patients who cannot recover completely, no matter how skillful and drastic the treatment, so, too, in psychiatry are there many sick people who cannot be made entirely well, no matter how brilliant be the psychotherapy they receive. And yet they need treatment. Good, sound "support therapy" often not only gives them the help they urgently need but makes the difference between being able to lead their lives with at least moderate satisfaction and happiness rather than struggling feebly and ineffectually in a morass of shame, guilt, self-degradation and misery. Perhaps a certain number of overt homosexuals furnish a fair example. True enough, no amount of psychotherapy will change the sex pattern in the particular group I have in mind, turning them away from the unfortunate sexual love of their own sex and magically endowing them with physical and emotional heterosexual desire and capacity. Nevertheless, the counsel of a wise psychotherapist whom they respect and, who, while not condoning their behavior still does not despise them, who understands their problems and difficulties, personal and social, frequently keeps them from complete futility and despair.

I have used the term "support therapy" in quotation marks, as I have not yet explained its meaning. It distinctly does not mean that the doctor stands by the patient, occasionally giving him an encouraging pat or scolding him, or preaching at him and supplying him with some Pollyanna bromides and aphorisms about how he should lead his life. On the contrary, it employs constantly and skillfully many methods and techniques which presently will be developed. Advisedly, it is designated as "support" to distinguish it from the deeper therapy of analysis which in a sense is "target therapy." It (analysis) aims directly at the target of repressed material in the unconscious, beyond the frontiers of the patient's conscious remembrance and seeks to expose the psychopathology in all its implications. Nevertheless, skillfully practiced support therapy is far from being merely on the surface. Almost always it touches the periphery of the repressed, troubling, symptom-producing material, and more often than not, it penetrates it deeply. A physician who can talk with a patient about his problems for an hour without getting some idea of what is hidden in the psyche needs much more psychiatric training.

Since there is only one psychiatrist where at least six are needed, since, too, in perhaps 60 per cent of human illness the functional markings are heavier than the organic and, finally, since modern medicine cannot be practiced without careful attention to the significant psychiatric perspectives of sickness, it becomes obvious that the bulk of so-called psychiatric patients must and indeed should be treated not by psychiatrists, but by general practitioners, internists, obstetricians, dermatologists, surgeons and, in short, all doctors. Of course, the doctor must have some knowledge and understanding of human psychology, of the personality, particularly of its unconscious terrain, of the significance of repressions and of emotional conflicts in shaping symptoms and the various mechanisms of defense used by patients in building the psychoneuroses and in making other compromises with reality. Such understanding and knowledge is comparable to the things the doctor must know about anatomy, physiology, chemistry, tissue pathology of disease, etc., before he can undertake to treat successfully heart disease, tuberculosis, rheumatism or even measles.

A few years ago I proposed a definition of psychotherapy. I think it is still valid. It is flexible enough so that it does not close any legitimate avenue of treatment. "Psychotherapy is any honest measure of treatment emerging from the relationship between patient and doctor which improves the understanding and attitude of the patient toward himself, toward his illness and toward his environment." The definition may be put into helpful practice not only in psychiatry but in the management of all sickness.

In all treatment, notably in psychotherapy, there is a constant interaction between patient and physician. At this place, it is proper to begin to sketch in the first lines of the profile of the characteristics and attitude of the psychotherapist to whom you go for help. He will be sincerely interested, since it is altogether likely that he likes people. Most doctors do. Furthermore, since he has studied and practiced medicine, the most exacting and self-revealing of the humane disciplines, it is reasonable to assume that he has attained a considerable degree of emotional maturity. Therefore, he should have an objective attitude which does not preclude lively interest and warm sympathy. It does rule out hasty, ill-considered grossly partisan attitudes for or against his patients. An insight into his own life, with its mistakes, his own biases and prejudices and those of many patients, should teach him at least that first impressions are apt to be erroneous. Not every husband is a cruel, sadistic tyrant, nor is every wife a nagging scold. He should be firm, but kindly and explanatory, much like a good father or an older brother. The psychotherapist should be humble—not with hypocritical Uriah Heepish humbleness, but with true humility, the humility of one who is permitted to explore that least-known but most important territory—the human mind. To this initial, crude sketch of the personality of the psychotherapist, I will from time to time add other characteristics; I hope that finally a more or less finished portrait will emerge.

Usually, in ordinary psychotherapy, a physical examination is the first step. Already I have discussed some of the concrete reasons which make a physical examination mandatory. For instance, the possible discovery of serious pathology of organs. The examination of the psychotherapist is more than that. It is treatment. Occasionally it may solve the problem. At least, I am led to infer this from a case note given to me by a friend of mine, a well-known allergist. He claims that he saved the marriage and happiness of two young people who were becoming increasingly hostile toward each other by prescribing non-allergic cosmetics for the wife after he discovered in his examinations that her husband was markedly allergic to the cosmetics she had been using. Recently, I read that a judge had granted a divorce to a wife who, though she professed deep love for her husband, was "physically allergic" to him! Be that as it may, I said the examination was treatment because the psychotherapist is always alert to turn his findings to useful treatment purposes.

Sometimes a thorough physical examination may dispose of mild neurotic reactions, perhaps on the basis of an insignificant heart murmur or some other trivial condition. But the therapist must be sure of his findings, and then firm and decisive in his attitude. If he lets the patient lead him into the mazes of speculative theory—"cardiograms are not always conclusive"—"mild symptoms may become very serious"—"people do die unexpectedly of heart disease" and the like, then he has lost the opportunity to deal decisively with a neurotic exaggeration.

Families of patients are sometimes surprised that the doctor pays so much attention to some seemingly slight difficulty—a little acne in a young girl, obesity, a slight eye cast, outstanding ears, a little hesitancy in pronouncing words or what not. The therapist knows full well that these findings are not the cause of the extensive neurosis, but he may know from his penetration of the emotional conflicts that seemingly small, unimportant disorders and deformities may be the central focusing point for accumulated, deep and crippling inferiority reactions, having their origin in repressed childhood experiences. Then it may be good judgment to correct the difficulty, in order to clear the ground for more effective psychotherapy.

Many psychoanalysts do not make physical examinations of patients. They feel the examination establishes too intimate a relationship and carries the danger of producing too much emotional dependency on the part of the patient. This is of small moment, providing each patient does have an adequate physical examination by some physician. A number of analysts adhering strongly to dogma will not prescribe even a simple remedy for a patient being analyzed who may have only a cold. I may be wrong, but I think this is gilding the lily a bit too heavily. Perhaps the very unwillingness to prescribe may be negatively interpreted by the patient and endowed with personal meaning. One patient who in the early stages of her treatment was sent to me by her analyst for a prescription said, "I think Dr. J. is very deeply concerned about my health. He will not prescribe for me for fear of making a mistake, just as he would not prescribe for his wife if she were sick. He didn't tell me that, but I know." No doubt the patient's erroneous interpretation was rectified in the course of the analysis.

Many people think that even in the course of ordinary psychotherapy, the doctor is not interested in the physical phenomena of sickness. "He isn't that kind of a doctor." Untrue. Actually, there is no reason why the psychiatrist or any psychiatrically minded physician would not utilize any of the resources of modern practice, including drugs and even surgical interventions. There is one mandatory condition. The medicine or other physical treatment measures must never be given with the mumbo-jumbo and mystery of the ancient medicine man. The patient must understand *thoroughly* that the medicine or other treatment *cannot cure* an illness due to an unconscious unsolved emotional conflict. With this condition carefully observed, there are situations in which various treatment techniques may be very useful, perhaps in alleviating some very disturbing symptom, which when cleared away paves the way for more rapid psychotherapeutic progress. But never should the therapist break faith with the tenets of psychological medicine. Once I almost did, unwittingly. One of my patients, a young woman, suffered tremendously from terrific abdominal tension feelings, one of the expressions of her severe anxiety. I prescribed a harmless drug which, physiologically tested, often was effective in relieving spasm of unstriped muscle fibre. It was at the end of a busy day, I was tired and did not caution the patient sufficiently that the medicine was not a panacea, or treatment-short-cut. At best it might provide temporary relief from a distressing symptom. To my surprise, she called me the next day joyfully to tell me that she would not have to see me again since the medicine had "cured" her. It took a number of therapeutic sessions to undo the effect of my carelessness.

The simplest aspect of psychotherapy is reassurance. Usually, in hit or miss fashion, we use it daily to bolster up our friends who are worried. In therapy, it should be employed carefully and exactly, or else it does more harm than good. Merely carelessly to mouth a phrase to a patient like "You look fine today" means nothing at all. On the other hand, such a simple greeting to a patient as "You look fit and strong today" may do much good, if it is given sincerely and with foreplanned thought, in view of the therapist's knowledge of the problems of the patient. For instance, with one of my patients, I frequently complimented him on how well and strong he looked. In him there had been tremendous inner turmoil concerning the physical effect of masturbation, fatigue, loss of strength, bodily decay. It dated back to his childhood and was strongly conditioned emotionally by the attitude of his father about his boyhood masturbation—a well-intentioned attitude, but ignorant, rigid, severe and frightening. In the course of treatment, he had accomplished complete intellectual understanding and insight. There still remained some traces of the once deeply impressed emotional fear. So when I told him from time to time how well he looked, he knew I was not in any way subscribing to his previous erroneous thinking, but merely reassuring him, helping him to attain the final emotional maturing of his ego—which he did attain.

To be effective, reassurance must be kept within the framework of truth. Within this framework, the skillful therapist uses reassurance with telling effect. Often in one interview, the therapist may be able to give the patient enormous relief of mind. If he can truthfully, as often as he can, emphatically reassure the patient he is not "insane," that the illness is not a psychosis, that his condition is not due to inheritance, and that the outlook for recovery is excellent, then he may remove a psychic cancer of fear which the patient has been secretly hugging to his breast, greatly increasing his anxiety. The therapist, too, by reassurance can sometimes remove or at least dilute distressing guilt feelings in patients who have errant, "abnormal" sex thoughts, or perhaps because they have wished that someone they "should love" were dead. Human beings have the greatest difficulty in accepting such ambivalent thoughts. In our dim, remote history, apparently not only wishing for the death of others but the personal fulfillment of the wish was quite common.

Occupational therapy is a strong and reliable arm of psychotherapy. The therapist who knows his business prescribes it thoughtfully and with an alert eye to the inner difficulties and conflicts of his patients. Of course, he does not subscribe to the still far too prevalent idea: "You are just neurotic. All nonsense. What you need is good, hard work."

The therapist helps find an occupation which is likely to meet each patient's needs. He knows at least these few things:

1. Occupation blocks the retreat into unreality. It is a symbol of real, everyday living and therefore the patient feels less apart from his fellow men.

2. The occupation is designed to the measure of the chief motif of the patient's reactions. Some patients are so flooded by inadequacy and inferiority or may have such a large segment of masochism in their personalities that they would be overwhelmed by being given complex work, even though intellectually quite capable of doing it. At first, they may do much better with very simple work, like making a rag rug. The gradual progress to more intricate occupation often is a mark of the emotional growth of the personality and the improvement in the psychoneurosis. Generally speaking, handwork crafts and skills are more helpful than purely intellectual exercises. The finished product is concrete evidence of reality.

3. With many patients, the therapist sees to it that the occupation is an antidote to the patient's unconscious conflicts and contains the element of helping others. Often this is highly significant. It acts as an inner atonement for the self-blame

of patients for what they feel has been selfishness in their previous lives, or, sometimes, for torturing neurotic guilt feelings, the origins of which are hidden from the patient's awareness.

One of my patients, a middle-aged woman who was very neurotic, with many psychosomatic complaints, attributed her recovery to my suggestion that she study Braille and help to make books for the blind. What she did not realize at the time was that I had in mind the fact that her symptoms and her guilt came from repressed feelings centering around her "neglect" of her old mother, who died insane and blind.

Occasionally, in dramatic fashion, occupation may be directly curative. I have in my study a beautifully executed sculpture—a tiny female figure in the cruel, crushing grasp of a comparatively huge fist. Some time ago we were asked to treat a talented sculptress, who for many years had suffered from extremely severe migraine, so painful and disabling that she became very depressed, and her mind filled with suicidal thoughts. It was suggested that she take some modeling clay to her room and try to occupy herself. One night she felt an attack of migraine coming on. She got out of bed and modeled from the clay the fist-figure piece, as expressive of the pain of migraine. From that moment on, for many years, until the time of her death, she never had another attack of migraine or any nervous or mental symptoms.

When the psychotherapist suggests this or that occupation for a patient, he is not merely advising something which will help pass the time. He is, from his understanding of the conflicts and problems of the patient, using occupation skillfully to strengthen the ego of the patient, helping to overcome the difficulties.

Entertainment, diversions and particularly hobbies, occupy a fairly large area in sound therapy. The therapist employs them with the same thinking and criteria as in occupational therapy. Sometimes a hobby may be a direct outlet for mental conflicts. Because of repressions of their early lives, some patients have a great deal of fear and guilt revolving around sexual curiosity. Sometimes they may be much helped and their curiosity "legitimately" satisfied by suggesting that they study natural history as a hobby.

Maurice Levine gives a case history which I summarize, since in practice I have encountered similar situations and since, too, it illustrates the advantages of avocation in therapy. A woman who was somewhat inadequate and immature made a very satisfactory marriage. For many years she was happy and her life was complete with her husband and children. Then the children grew up and began to seek new pastures. Her ego was decompensated. Life for her, with its round of pleasant duties and responsibilities, was over. She then developed fatigue, fear of being alone, many bodily symptoms; in fact, she became a "nervous" invalid. These reactions represented camouflaged or inhibited hostility and anger against her children for "leaving" her and constituted an unconscious effort to hold them and her husband closely bound to her. Psychotherapy, which included the development of an active interest in women's clubs, particularly in that part of their programs designed to help children, saved the situation for this woman.

Here we stumble upon another qualification of the good therapist. He is a human being, and, like other human beings, he has his likes and dislikes. Personally, he may be allergic to women's clubs, "teas," bridge, interior decorating, golf, or what not, but should his patients need any of these activities, he is mature enough to surmount his own prejudices.

A therapist may or may not work out a schedule of daily routine of activities for some of his patients. Admittedly such a schedule is a crutch, but it may be a much-needed crutch

The judgment involved perhaps is somewhat comparable to the decisions of the orthopedist in the matter of braces and supports for his patients. Some patients will do better without artificial aids; others will need them for a short time only; other patients for a long time. Some patients may need the decisive finality of a daily schedule at the beginning of treatment. Others at very critical times when the going is rough. Sometimes the schedule helps in the matter of morbid indecision, when the patient is so torn by his psychoneurotic doubts that he cannot turn one way or another. Activity is paralyzed. The schedule, perhaps "Take a walk from two to three in the afternoon," may lift the intolerable weight of self-decision from the patient's sagging mental shoulders. In a general way, the attitude of the therapist in regard to scheduling the patient's day is much like that of a wise father. At first he participates in considerable measure, but gradually, and then rapidly, he puts the child in the position of making his own decisions. And, of course, the chief objective of the schedule is to teach the patient to do without it.

The discussion about the schedule presents an opportunity to expose another facet of the characteristics of the good therapist, not only in this detail, but in his general attitude toward his patients. When the doctor walks into his office, he does not leave his own life experiences and his reactions to them on the other side of the door. Such individual experiences and their inner repercussions tend to group themselves into one of two personality conformations. In the first, the therapist has great sympathy, perhaps too much sympathy for the frailties of his fellow men. In the second, he erects too high an altar to the ideal of innate strength and self-reliance. Without insight into his own life history, in the one instance he would help and support his patients too much—keeping them at the level of immature emotional dependency. If life has made him worship strength and resourcefulness, and if he lacked discrimination, he would not give his patients enough understanding and support. He would expect too much of them, too quickly. Being a therapist, he has come to some appreciation of himself and of other human beings and what life has done to him and to them, so that to some extent he can discount his own reactions. No matter what has happened to him in his life, he is more or less objective, with warm sympathy, but not spilling over into cloying and futile sentimentality.

In modern psychotherapy there is no place for threats, intimidation, fear or the production of pain, electrically or otherwise conditioned. The therapist is not a witch doctor. However, there are situations which the physician can meet only with an exhibition of authoritative firmness, or perhaps he may feel it wise to ignore the symptoms. Some patients, very likely as the result of spoiling or perhaps too much frustration in their childhoods, have developed regressive behavior patterns, attempting to meet their problems by resorting to infantile weapons. At the least difficulty in the course of treatment, these patients may go into angry tirades against the therapist, tear out their hair, storm and rage, strike the doctor, exhibit childlike jealousy tantrums, make suicidal threats and stage obviously artificial suicidal attempts or have "on the spot" amazing "convulsions," in which they twist and writhe much more than any real epileptic ever did. A girl of sixteen had such a convulsion on the floor of my office, when I pointed out some of her inadequacies and immaturities in meeting her problems. I said to her very firmly, "Stop that. You have enough real symptoms, without making up any. Besides, you will get your dress wrinkled and dusty." She got up promptly, brushed her dress and said, "O.K. Let's forget it." Another patient, a boy of eighteen, said, "I have a sharp razor blade in my pocket and I'm going to cut my wrists." I picked up a magazine and began to read it. The boy threw the razor blade into the wastepaper basket.

The experienced therapist knows that in these situations he must be sure of his ground—not teeter back and forth, one minute angry, the next frightened and sympathetic. If the patient senses that the therapist is uncertain and alarmed (perhaps the convulsion may mean some complication of serious organic disease) then he has a psychological ax to hold over the doctor's head. And he will hold it there, nicely poised, at least until he grows up emotionally. Or, the patient may partake of the doctor's doubt and become panicky. All in all, the attitude of the therapist in dealing with some of these regressive behaviorisms should be much like that of a wise father whose child is behaving very badly. He is kindly but firm and not too much upset—or excited about it—never cruel nor contemptuous.

Of all the techniques of psychotherapy, suggestion is far less useful than was formerly generally believed. Its first effect is often dramatically serviceable. It is easy to produce and tempting to use. All human beings are suggestible. For one thing, by responding to suggestion, one may acquire a reputation for being not only logical, but also amiable. Many of us like those who agree with us and we credit them with great intelligence. But the disadvantages of suggestion outweigh its advantages. It is too reminiscent of the grotesque mask and horns of the old medicine man. The static electrical spark or other devices are far too much like the ancient stage props and rituals. Used in mysterious fashion, suggestion appeals merely to the emotions of the patient, without reference to the symptom-motivating conflict. It merely displaces one illogical idea and puts one equally illogical in its place. After the shock of the electricity, the patient can move the paralyzed arm. He believes the electricity cured the palsy. This is just as erroneous as the belief that the arm was actually paralyzed. In suggestion, there is the ever-constant danger that the patient will discover the deception and lose his confidence in the therapist, confidence that can be built only on mutual honesty and trust. Finally, suggestion appeals to emotional immaturity and fosters too strong emotional dependencies. Many naïve patients, especially in the early stages of treatment, look for and even ask for a panacea, a "trick," some magic drug or treatment which suddenly will relieve them of their symptoms and make them well and happy like other people.

Suggestion does have a range of usefulness, but within the framework of frankness. Sometimes it may be employed to remove a symptom, like aphonia or loss of speech, which is blocking the progress of treatment. Sometimes, too, suggestion may remove a psychological block. In a very intelligent young woman I was treating for a complicated anxiety neurosis, there was just enough depression to interfere with the psychotherapy. She complained that while she understood her conflicts and problems intellectually, yet she could not get enough "feeling" about it to put what she had learned into practice. She became mildly self-blameful about her "stupidity." I suggested that she take one modified electroshock treatment, explaining that it would not produce any magic effect in itself, but that it might decrease her depression and spur her initiative. I explained, too, that no one knew just exactly how and why electroshock acted, but often it did remove depression. It worked splendidly.

Hypnotism depends chiefly on its strong suggestion appeal to the various levels of the conscious and unconscious mind. In skilled hands, with the patient understanding there is nothing supernatural about it, and divested of its weird "passes," incantations and hanky-poo, hypnotism has considerable value. Some therapists use it freely in treatment. Personally, I think it is more serviceable in certain situations in helping to uncover deeply hidden conflict material. The information so gained may be advantageously used in the further psychotherapy.

In every patient, the therapist estimates the relative amounts of internal and external strains and pressures and their seriousness and gravity. It is not an easy task. Inner repressed material was derived from once external emotional experiences, at least partly conscious, and traumatizing to the ego. Usually such highly charged material is welded into the personality during childhood, traceable to serious omissions in the child-parent relationship, perhaps insufficient affection and love or emotional possessiveness; in general, a disregard of the basic needs and rights of a child. This leaves pathological psychic vulnerable areas and there is always the danger that they may grow, spread and become malignant in adult life. External stresses already have been described. They are the sum total of the stresses of life that each one of us encounters, the thrusts and blows from the environment, some of them catastrophic. External and internal pressures do not remain separate and distinct. One merges into the other. Frequently, the external operates as a trigger mechanism, exploding repressed psychic material. Often the external-internal interplay is quite devious.

I had a patient whose contribution to the war effort was very great, even though it must remain unknown, since it is still "top secret." He was a convinced pacifist, but after a hard struggle with his superego, he put aside his beliefs to do what he decided was his patriotic duty. He directed certain highly important engineering projects, inventing and perfecting the deadly precision of war weapons. His responsibilities were staggering. Once in the laboratory, several of his co-workers lost their lives in a premature explosion and he, himself, was injured. When I saw him, he was laboring under great anxiety and had many psychosomatic symptoms. Prominent was a weight in his chest which made him breathe in rapid, jerky fashion, like a man struggling for air. He was depressed and self-blameful, insisting that he had permitted his fellow scientists to take undue risks. In fact, he was not very far from being psychotic.

In our first interview, and in subsequent ones, as we discussed his problem, he frequently interjected the apparently unrelated statement, "You know, Doctor, I have never been able to raise a patch of mint." (It is an old New England superstition, which I did not know at the time, that mint will not grow for a henpecked husband.) What my patient meant me to understand was that his wife constantly nagged him about his health, belittled his work and, though she was a well-informed woman, gave him no emotional confidence and support. All this reanimated a trauma to his childhood ego— a dominant mother, who denied him the demonstrative symbols of love and probably compensated for it unconsciously by constantly nagging the youngster about his health, getting his feet damp or playing too hard.

The psychotherapist is clear enough in his mind about what to do concerning the hidden unconscious mental conflicts of his patients. He must strip off as much of their camouflaging veneer as is possible and bring them to the surface, so that he and the patient together can view them on the table of consciousness. Before deciding what to do about external pressures, the therapist needs the guidance of certain criteria. For one thing, he will make a reasonably accurate measurement of each patient's ego reaction to his inner and outer difficulties. Our individual perspectives are very different. Some patients feel shamed if they bend before the external blows of fate.

They accept internal difficulties with comparatively little loss of psychological face. Since consciously they are not aware of the nature of these problems, they feel, "It is not my fault." With other patients, the pattern is reversed. They feel that no one can be blamed for succumbing to damage from the environment, but that they should have been able not to have incurred so many personality liabilities. To them it is a sign of weakness. In some degree, both are right.

In this area, as in all the areas of psychotherapy, the therapist has insight into his own personality limitations, and is able to rise above them in dealing with his patients. He may be a strong and rugged individualist who has met life successfully, neither taking nor giving quarter. Nevertheless, he does not expect this of his patients.

It is not a simple matter to know what to do, if anything, for each patient about external pressures. It brings up the very tricky matter of environmental manipulation. In civilian life, this is far more complicated than in war. In war, in the active theaters of combat, it was obvious that the personalities of some soldiers could not stand the overload of long-continued physical stress and emotional horrors. It was possible to give their egos surcease by removing them temporarily from the battle line. In civilian life, the decision, and the ways and means, are not so clear. After all, if a man has had financial reverses and is bankrupt, the therapist cannot restore his credit and make him affluent again. Nor can he restore to a woman the object of her deep love, of which she has been deprived by death or rejection. Here the analyst who adheres closely to his dogma has the advantage. He does not attempt to move the personal pieces in a patient's environment. His stake is the uncovering of the mental conflict and the understanding of it and its implications by the patient. This should be followed by better adjustment in life.

In ordinary psychotherapy, the therapist cautiously and tactfully manipulates the personal environment. He does it after he has had a view of the hidden recesses of the patient's psychic life and personality. In a patient who already has severe guilt reactions, it is scarcely wise to soften the environment so that everyone at home is extremely considerate, walking on their mental tip-toes so as not to disturb him. This serves only to deepen the guilt feeling.

On the other hand, in a man who had a deep, underlying, unconscious hostility toward his wife (masked by guilt feelings) because she was, again unconsciously, the surrogate for his mother who in his childhood had denied him love and dominated him—it was good judgment to have him remain for a time in a sanitarium. Here there was not the constant intensification of the mother-wife complex by daily contact with his wife. There are innumerable ways in which the experienced therapist can change patients' environmental media, so that the immediate surroundings become favorable rather than inimical.

Particularly at the beginning of treatment, many patients assail their physicians with a barrage of questions and requests for advice and decisions about practically every issue in their lives. Here, again, the orthodox psychoanalyst has the advantage. He declines to give direct advice or make decisions. Personally, I think the pendulum has swung too far. In the olden days of psychiatry (the passing of which is not to be regretted) too frequently the patient was merely a will-less pawn in the hands of his psychiatrist, who told him what moves to make in his life and just how to make them. Today I think the rigid, extreme, non-counseling attitude of some analysts goes too far, although, of course, it does adhere to strict dogma. The danger of advising and guiding, particularly if indiscriminate, is that too much emotional dependency is created in the patient. His ego becomes weaker, rather than stronger. However, I do believe that if the therapist has his exploring fingers on the outlines of the patient's conflict and knows the markings of the personality, then he may safely and beneficially give a limited amount of counsel and guidance. Naturally, the therapist does not make decisions for the patient about very serious steps in life—marriage, divorce, changing jobs, etc. The therapist is not a god, not even a demigod. At most, he might suggest that decisions be deferred until treatment has reached a more conclusive stage.

The decision about giving counsel and just how much and what kind of guidance to give must be strained through a double filter: the personality of the patient and that of the therapist. Some patients have potentially rugged egos which may be temporarily lamed by illness. They solve the central problem more readily if they are permitted to work out the everyday difficulties of their daily lives entirely on their own. Other patients falter and fumble about aimlessly and helplessly, unless they have at least a minimum of support and guidance.

From his evaluation of the repercussions of his own life experiences in shaping his personality, the therapist will know whether he is apt to err in the direction of being too abruptly and positively decisive or whether he tends to delay overlong or weigh matters a bit too meticulously. In dealing with his patients, he will make the necessary corrections and compromises in his attitude.

In every human being there is hostility and aggressiveness. A certain amount is practically normal. One reason is that we still retain traces, somewhere in us, of our blood-spattered phylogenetic history, man against man. Another more individual reason is that in childhood, our mothers and later our fathers and others in the family insisted on social conformity, which we did not wish and which we resented. In Chinese culture there is the negative extreme. Children are permitted to nurse, or at least suck at the breast, sometimes for several years, and there is little or no insistence on toilet training. I think that in our own culture there is too positive an attitude. There even may be neighborhood standards. The mother whose youngster is a month behind the time schedule in using the "pottie" may be humiliated and looked down upon socially by other mothers.

The hostility which comes under the scrutiny of the therapist is usually deep, serious and dated in childhood—firmly set into the personality by wanton disregard of the basic emotional needs of children. Since hatred of a mother or father cannot be openly supported in consciousness, it is often heavily blanketed by guilt feelings or/and fear symptoms. Some form of psychoanalytical technique may be needed to tear the hostility complex from its deeply anchored moorings, so that it may be brought to the surface and examined as it actually is, in all its implications. However, fairly often, the experienced therapist is able to trace its outlines rather exactly in the course of ordinary psychotherapeutic interviews. I have already given some summarized case histories, discussed some of the ways and means by which this is accomplished and indicated some of the clues which may lead to the apprehension of the offending psychic material. Sometimes the implications of patients' attitudes and symptoms are fairly obvious. From time to time, but by no means always, a phobic fear of being infected by dirt and germs, translated into unceasing and frantic efforts to keep the self and house spotlessly clean, may represent deep-seated guilt with overcompensation, masking hostility and a concealed death wish directed at wife or husband, mother or father or someone in the family.

I had a patient, a rather unattractive girl, fifteen years old. She had a hand phobia. She disliked all hands. Sometimes the

sight of hands filled her with horror, particularly the hands of
women and notably when the hands were well-kept and beautiful. She, herself, never had her nails manicured, and never
used nail polish. She said vividly tinted finger nails made her
feel like vomiting. She complained about women waving their
hands about, or displaying them prominently. This made her
feel "nervous" and disgusted her. "It is almost indecent."

She was in the art class at school, and I suggested to her
that at home she make some drawings of hands. She made a
great many and they were all rather horrible. Fat, asymmetri-
cal fingers and some thin and clawed, like talons, distorted,
swollen and sometimes shriveled joints, short uneven nails,
usually one or two fingers crudely amputated with an eraser.
After I had seen a hundred or more drawings, I said to her,
"Jane, whose hands are these?" Very hesitatingly, she replied,
"At first, I didn't know; now I know they are Mother's." Her
mother had beautiful hands with long, tapering fingers, about
which she was quite vain. Jane's hands were not pretty—short
fingers, and rather scrubby.

On the surface, Jane was pleasant enough to her mother,
but underneath there was a deep well of hostility. Jane's mother
had divorced her father when the child was four years old and
had married a year later. The stepfather treated Jane kindly
enough but she disliked him intensely.

Jane continued drawing hands, but as the treatment continued, they became more normal-looking and just before she
made a good adjustment, they were quite nice-looking hands.
In Jane's case, there was the opportunity to channel her hostility and aggressiveness into helpful outlets. With thorough
understanding of the "inside" situation, similar outlets may
be found from time to time.

The therapist, too, may utilize general outlets for hostility.
Certainly pent-up emotion is not good and may even be dan-

gerous. I think it was William James who advised a brisk walk or other physical exercise after a lover of music had listened to a moving symphony. That somewhat immature but great and lovable comedian, W. C. Fields, used to dictate a dozen blistering and scathing letters to various important personages, have them typed and sign them. Then he would put them aside for a few hours, read them, tear them up and throw the pieces into the wastebasket. I knew an important executive who was filled to overflowing with hostility toward Franklin Roosevelt. He claimed that he added considerable yardage to his golf drive by having the President's picture stenciled on his golf balls. Of course, he had a sense of humor. Incidentally, a sense of humor in the personality of the therapist is a valuable asset. It is an antidote to the pessimism, distrust and suspicion in many patients. But it must be kindly humor and not cynical wit. It must laugh with the patient—never at him.

In the area of hostility as in all other things, it is necessary for the therapist to take frequent, long searching looks into his own personality. Unless it be about something that is fundamentally evil, then there is no place for hate in the personality vocabulary of the therapist. The physician who hates Jews, or Negroes, or Catholics, or Methodists, New Dealers, Republicans, Democrats, or, indeed, whose personality is tainted not by honest disagreement or differences of opinion, but by illogical hatred of those who are not like him or do not think as he does, is not fit to deal with the emotional problems of human beings.

The therapist will hear many strange stories from his patients, some of them shocking and even horrible. The naked soul is not always a beautiful sight. All this makes it mandatory that the physician be truly non-condemning, non-critical, non-judgmental, accepting though not necessarily condoning. And every experienced therapist knows that mere words, however fairly spoken, will not suffice. If the situation a patient presents is such that his personality cannot accept it and view it objectively, then he will reveal, sooner or later, his intolerance, in his manner and even in his gestures and the intonation of his voice.

Of course, as I have said several times, doctors are human. Physicians, particularly those whose work in life brings them constantly into intimate relationship with human beings, cannot hope to escape occasional lapses—a little criticism or a flare of anger, a bit of sarcasm, now and then. If these reactions recur or become at all frequent, then the therapist will want to make a personality self-inventory. Perhaps he is overworked and terribly fatigued. Or he is nonplused at not having been able to penetrate deeply enough into the patient's unconscious conflict. Or perhaps he feels progress is not rapid enough. Or, more often, a vulnerable spot in his own psyche has been touched.

The therapist remembers, too, that no matter how obstinate or unpleasant a surface symptom may be, he has no personal reaction to it. A facial tic may be in itself an ugly thing, distorting the face with horrible grimaces. The therapist knows that buried beneath the tic, there may be a life drama so sad that he may well marvel that the tic or other symptom is not much worse than it is. Phobias or fears, viewed discretely, may seem irritating, particularly since the patient often realizes intellectually how futile and silly they are. When the tragic background of the phobia is revealed and the gallant efforts the patient has made to overcome his fear come into view, then the therapist may well be deeply compassionate. Compassion is an important facet of the therapist's character.

These happenings in the relationship between patient and doctor and many others lead to ego strengthening *identifica-*

tions and *transferences*. Often patients come to a better way of life, not only "nervously" better, but also ethically better.

Just as every human being has certain basic physical needs like sunshine, fresh air, exercise, food with its health-giving vitamins, so do we all have basic psychological needs. They are many, but certainly included are a reasonable amount of security and recognition. Without these, the ego is weak from emotional starvation, just as would be the body if there were a grossly insufficient number of food calories. Then we all need love and affection, both to receive and bestow it, and we need some satisfaction of our sexual desires. In our lives, too, there should be enough opportunity for activity, recreation and leisure. And we need a balance between emotional dependence and independence. In every human relationship, perhaps chiefly in marriage, there are times when there should be available the emotional warmth and strength derived from another person. Conversely, we need, too, opportunities to give emotional support to others, particularly to those we love and to express a certain amount of independence, assertion and even a bit of aggressiveness. Probably each one of us during our childhood needs to develop a certain amount of anxiety, not too much, but enough so that precipitation into the numerous anxieties of adult life involved in personal and social relationships will not be too abrupt and too frightening to the ego. It is altogether likely that in the process of producing the necessary conformity to reasonable social demands that must occur in childhood, quite enough opportunity is provided for the development of anxiety.

I would add another need, sadly wanting in this age of material largess but spiritual vacuum. I mean some spiritual values and convictions, obtaining satisfaction, comfort and strength by worshiping at altars other than those of Mammon.

These and other basic needs must begin to be satisfied in childhood, the pattern outline marked in, or else in adult life there will be large gaps in the ego personality, gaps of ego frustrations, which perhaps can never be filled in. In any event, the physician, in every patient, views these frustration gaps, measures them mentally and begins to plan to do whatever he can to help the patient find at least partial soul-satisfying compensations.

The problem of the therapist is somewhat akin to that of other doctors who utilize various replacement treatments on a physical level. It may be necessary to give vitamins if the food intake does not supply enough. Or from birth there may be too little of the highly important thyroid secretion. This basic need is manifested by many physical and mental symptoms and thyroid extract must be given. Or, often ovarian substance, if diseased ovaries are removed by surgical operation. Even an anatomical replacement may have to be made. Due to a developmental failure while the child is in the womb, there may be closure or some other malformation of the vagina. Later in life this may be corrected by surgical operation. These are only a few of the many replacements that may be made when something basic for satisfactory functioning is wanting.

The problem of the psychotherapist is equally important. Perhaps one or the other partner in a marriage is not receiving sufficient love and its demonstration by displays of affection. This is particularly serious and may be the focusing point of functional illness, if it revives a pattern of insufficient love and affection in the former child-parent relationship. The therapist sometimes may bring about a better situation, more likely to satisfy basic emotional needs, by a few sessions with that marriage partner, who in the matter of the manifestation of love takes too much and gives too little.

Sometimes when a husband is very immature emotionally,

he, having exhausted the possibility of making his wife be his mother, may in innumerable petty ways attempt to frustrate her basic maternal need to love and hold, fondle and protect her child. I knew one husband who even went to the extent of hiding the baby from his wife. In situations like this, it is unlikely that the therapist will be able to talk a husband or perhaps an immature wife into a more sensible, grown-up attitude. Often treatment by another psychiatrist will be needed. I say "another psychiatrist" advisedly. The wise therapist will decline to treat two members of the same family, particularly husband and wife. If he is foolhardy enough to try it, he will soon encounter enormous pressures to take one side or the other, usually prefaced by the statement, "Of course, I want to be fair about this, but . . ." Sooner or later, the therapist will find himself knocked out of the treatment ring, by a foul blow, from one or the other of his patients.

However, the skillful and experienced therapist will have many opportunities to supply some of the basic psychological needs of his patients.

Neurotic needs are in a very different category. To attempt to satisfy them is an extremely difficult and dubious procedure and usually is not highly successful. Neurotic demands do not represent frustrations of basic and innately normal needs. Usually they are selfish. They are demands and desires, even cravings for all sorts of things, from sentimental sympathy to cruel treatment. They are the outcroppings of the neurosis, which is a selfish reaction, albeit an unconscious one. They are dealt with better and more incisively by helping the patient achieve an understanding of his neurosis, its motivation, implications and significance.

Perhaps one may find an analogy in certain metabolic diseases: for instance, diabetes. In one sense, the diabetes represents a failure of satisfaction of certain basic metabolic needs.

But a craving for sweets or other symptoms may be the abnormal manifestations of the basic metabolic frustration. To satisfy them, for instance, by giving the patient all the sweets he wants would certainly do much more harm than good.

However, now and then the therapist may attempt to satisfy a neurotic need. At best it is a compromise but it may be a rather effective one. I treated a man, forty-five years old, a lawyer, who became extremely neurotic following the death of his father. His mother died when he was born. His father did not marry again, but devoted himself to his son. The patient never married. Father and son lived together, very happily, enjoyed each other's society and had many interests in common, professional and personal. It was too close a relationship and when his father died, my patient's ego sustained a well-nigh mortal blow. He developed many psychoneurotic symptoms, becoming extremely neurasthenic. Without going into the nature of the mental conflicts, I merely wish to mention one facet of my treatment which I think did a great deal in bringing about a fairly good adjustment. I suggested to my patient that he renew acquaintanceship with some of his father's old club cronies and get to know them better. He did this and among them he rediscovered a former friend of his father's, a retired Judge and a widower. Outwardly the Judge was a crusty old chap, but underneath he was lovable and warm-hearted and lonely. He and my patient formed a fine friendship, not too intense, but deep enough to give both men considerable intellectual and emotional satisfaction. Of course, the Judge was the father surrogate in my patient's psychic life. Of course, too, the need for a father surrogate was neurotic, but nevertheless, it was a real and demanding need.

The objective of any psychotherapy that is worth its salt is to heal and strengthen the ego of the patient. Without this, the patient cannot get well. The development, nature, function and operation of the ego, the rudder of the ship of the personality already has been discussed. And one of the stages of ego strengthening is the identification of the patient with the therapist. I think that many therapists do not quite realize the immense significance of the role they play for a patient during treatment. Often he is their sole source of strength, their only hope and refuge—the good and wise man, the great ideal upon which they seek to pattern their lives. The therapist represents the father and the mother—i.e., the kind of father and mother the patient unconsciously wanted in childhood, but did not have. The analyst actually becomes the father or mother figure, or both. The general therapist does not wish such an intimate relationship. He is merely in some degree *like* the good, kind, but wise father.

Treatment plateaus in psychotherapy are Confession, Ventilation, and the Psychiatric Interview.

Confession is the somewhat dramatic name given to the story the patient tells the doctor. If we were not indebted to psychoanalysis for anything else, we would still be deeply in its debt for emphasizing the value of just letting the patient talk. "Confession is good for the soul" may be a hackneyed phrase but it is a very true one. Confession at once decreases and devalues anxiety and tension. It does this in many ways.

In itself, the outpouring in words of pent-up thoughts and feelings increases general spontaneity. Long-hoarded things are gotten off the psychic chest. Frightening concealed ideas and emotions are robbed of much of their terror by objectifying them in a frame of words. At the same time, confession both lessens and punishes guilt. Lessens and dilutes the responsibility and guilt, since now they have been shared with someone else and that someone, a person of learning and wise judgment—the therapist. Furthermore, the patient often may find that the dimensions of his guilt are much smaller than he thought. Indeed, he may find that certain things, perhaps errant sex thoughts, are not "wrong" at all. Often, too, the patient may find that he has harmed others, those he loves, far less than he thought. Sometimes, of course, the reverse is true. And, confession also punishes guilt—healing punishment. It is shaming to the ego to reveal its nakedness and deformities to another human being. True enough, the therapist is not contemptuous, but neither does he justify unless he can do so honestly, nor does he condone.

While the patient does the talking, still occasionally the therapist may find it wise to tone down the confession a bit. Some patients are so masochistic that they verbally flagellate themselves unmercifully—and unconsciously enjoy it. Others are so exhibitionistic that they derive much satisfaction from displaying their inner chambers of horrors at its worst. A Catholic priest, a friend of mine, told me that he suffered much tribulation listening to confessions of oldish spinsters who confessed in endless detail and with lurid and elaborate adornments to "thought" sexual sins which they certainly had not entertained deliberately. He did say, "Go in peace, my child, you have not sinned." He felt like saying, "For heaven's sake, hurry and get out, and give the real, robust sinners who are waiting a chance to purge their souls."

Ventilation takes the material of the confession and from the psychiatric interviews into the open area of consciousness and patient and therapist together view it from all angles, look at its hidden meanings and its operation in the production and development of symptoms.

Of the many definitions of the psychiatric interview, I like best the one proposed by my good friend, Tom Rennie: "A psychiatric interview is not the same as a social conversation. It is a process specially devised to permit the patient to express anxieties and uncertainties, fully and without reservations, to the physician, who will not interfere or hamper the spontaneity by injecting his own personality or his own convictions into the situation. In essence, it is sensitive, objective, understanding, non-interfering listening."

As the patient talks, the therapist, though he may seem to be ever so casual, nevertheless is listening intently with the wide-open mental ears of his skill, experience and understanding. The first interview is usually the most critical and fruitful. It is likely that the patient has come prepared to unburden his soul. He has not yet identified the therapist with any of the figures of his past life. So he is apt to speak freely. Often, too, at least the top layers of the mental conflict are fairly close to the surface of consciousness, as it were, in the sub-soil of the unconscious, and can be uncovered without too much labor. Occasionally, after a patient has dwelt at length on the "gall-bladder trouble" or the "dropping of the stomach," I have said, "Now, wouldn't you like to tell me your real trouble?" Often there has been a prompt response, perhaps an outpouring of fear and anxiety, that the husband no longer loves her (or the wife him) and is being unfaithful.

Theoretically, in everyday psychotherapy the interview is on a conscious level. The patient tries to remember and tells what he recalls. Actually, however, much unconscious material is uncovered. Often the highroads of the remembered can be retraced to the back trails of the repressed, without too much trouble.

Many things come from the series of psychiatric interviews. If progress is being made, then there is an increasing strengthening of the *entente cordiale*, a better rapport, between patient and physician. The patient feels more confidence and security in the relationship. And there emerges something called transference.

Transference is hard to define. It presents so many gradations. In formal psychoanalysis, in a sense it is the love of the patient for the analyst, since he has become the figure of a strong love-object in the patient's early life, often a parent. The patient may interpret this literally and want to make, and actually make, demonstrations of love and affection. Or daydream vivid love scenes. Or, in negative transference, the patient may "hate" the analyst, scold and castigate him verbally or even try to punish him physically. Within the framework of psychoanalysis, the analyst recognizes the situation and works through it with the patient by continued free association, bringing into focus unconscious motivations for the behavior.

In ordinary psychotherapy, such complete transference is not desirable. There is a lesser degree. The therapist is for the patient the highly respected, authoritative, dependable figure, beloved in a general way, deeply admired, the source of strength and hope. The therapist understands. Above all, the therapist accepts him as he is and wants to help him. The therapist tries to keep the relationship on about this level.

I think something may be learned by a comparison of psychotherapy, including analysis, with a sacrament of an ancient church—the Sacrament of Penance of the Roman Catholic faith.* At first glance, and in some sense, basically they are antithetic to each other. For one thing, their rituals and settings are quite different. The penitent kneels on a knee-punishing hard, wooden bench. The analytic patient reclines on a couch. In psychotherapy, and particularly in psychoanalysis, there is no definite form or at best a very loose form of procedure. The ship of the psyche sails this way or that, sometimes drifting more or less aimlessly, its direction being given chiefly

* Long since I have given much thought to these considerations. For its clarification, I am indebted to the masterly essay of Father Victor White in *Commonweal.*

by the unsupervised thought associations of the patient. On the other hand, sacramental confession has a definite and very old form. There is the verbal confession made to the priest by the penitent, the feeling and expression of sorrow to God for having offended, the feeling and expression of a firm purpose of amendment (the earnest desire to lead a better life), the forgiveness or absolution of the priest (according to the dogma of his church), the imposition of the penance and, later, its performance. In these days, the penance is largely symbolic.

As Father White puts it, the material is fundamentally different. The sacrament considers largely conscious things— *malum culpae*—the evil that men do, willful misdeeds. The material considered in psychotherapy is largely unconscious —the evil men suffer—*malum poenae*. Chiefly these are the things that happen to us, involuntary misfortunes, thoughts, feelings, emotions, conflicts, behavior which cannot be helped.

In the administration of the Sacrament of Penance, the priest, according to dogma, has certain powers. He can forgive sins or withhold forgiveness; he may insist on restitution, as for instance, when something has been stolen or harmful scandal spread. He may and usually does give advice and counsel, perhaps particularly about avoiding what are called "occasions of sin," situations in which the penitent has placed himself unnecessarily in which there is great temptation to sin, and so on.

Neither the general therapist nor the analyst has nor does he attempt to exercise any power to forgive. True, the therapist is interested in the external conditions of his patients' lives, and rather cautiously may try to adjust them or perhaps help his patients meet them more squarely. True, too, he does give advice and counsel, but always having in mind the need of expanding the patient's self-knowledge and increasing his self-decision.

The orthodox analyst does not deal heavily with a patient's environmental situations, nor does he give much counsel. His interest in external factors is chiefly in how much they contributed to the formation and shaping of unconscious conflicts. He feels that if the patient comes to a thorough knowledge of his inner self, he will be able to work out his own problems in life, without advising or counseling. Of course, this does not always happen.

On the other hand, the confessional and psychotherapy are not as diametrically different from each other as would seem at first glance—particularly not in their long-range objectives. The conscious and unconscious are not rigidly separated from each other. There is no tightly fitting iron curtain between them. Everyday conscious behavior, particularly if it becomes habitual, seeps in and influences the personality. Conduct derived from unconscious trends and difficulties may readily become habit.

Modern psychology, I think, is coming to understand more and more that a cure of a neurosis involves at least some ethical and moral response and alteration. While the unconscious psychopathology producing a neurosis and more or less deliberate sin are very different, yet they both lead to amazingly similar behavior in everyday life. And in considerable degree in both instances, such behavior is selfish. In both neurosis and sin, there is the failure to meet the mature challenges and realities of life. As Father White aptly puts it, there are "shadowy compromises" never fully faced in the framework of life's conflicting demands. In both neurosis and sin there is a large behavior area of narcissism, self-indulgence, ego pampering. Even though theoretically, at least, in the case of wrongdoing the individual is responsible for his behavior—which in a neurosis he is not—yet both the sinner and the neurotic have failed to cultivate satisfactory behavior traits; rather they have accumulated undesirable and unhealthy ones. These traits, if too long and too frequently exercised, become stronger and it becomes increasingly difficult to relinquish them. Any psychiatrist will tell you just that about his chronic psychoneurotic patients and most chronic sinners will confirm it about themselves.

The target of any legitimate psychotherapy is to increase the awareness of the patient in regard to the inner motivations of his behavior; in short, to get to know himself better. The penitent, too, from the repeated examinations of his conscience should come to know and understand himself better. In any event, all this should lead to some change in both behavior and outlook upon life, enlargement of the conscious horizon, less absorption with self, more regard and consideration for others, an increasing growth of the superego. The place of religion in psychotherapy is not to be disregarded.

In 1932, Jung wrote, "During the past thirty years people from all civilized countries of the earth have consulted me. I have treated many hundreds of patients, the larger number being Protestants, a small number Jews, and not more than five or six believing Catholics. Among all my patients in the second half of life . . . there has not been one whose problem in the last resort was not that of finding a religious outlook on life. It is safe to say that every one of them fell ill because he had lost that which the living religions of every age had given their followers and none of them had been really healed who did not regain his religious outlook."

Of course, many psychiatrists would not concur in the inferences from Jung's opinion.

To return to the patient and the therapist. An allergist, treating a patient who is very sensitive to and made very sick by contact with some pollen or other substance, may decide to desensitize him by injecting small but gradually increasing doses of the offending material until an immunity is produced. So, too, may the therapist seek to desensitize a patient in the psychological area. To do this successfully he must have a good grasp of the nature of the underlying mental conflicts and considerable understanding of the particular patient's personality. Human beings over-react to all sorts of things. Even in these days, young people, boys as well as girls, may over-react enormously to the so-called "facts of life," usually meaning the facts of sex life. So, sometimes, may wives and even husbands develop neurotic guilt symptoms on the basis of "thought" or trifling behavior manifestations toward the opposite sex. "It's awful, but once in a while I feel excited when I meet an intelligent, athletic-looking young man. Think of that at my age, married for almost twenty years to a fine, good husband, whom I love and who loves me dearly. And I have three grown children."

In such situations, and knowing the deeper implications, the therapist may skillfully employ desensitization. Perhaps he may point out that marriage in itself does not magically remove the possibility of fluctuations in emotional reactions, that a factor in promoting ordinary social relationships is the "likes" and even strong likes we feel for other people. Perhaps some of this rests on the fact that those who interest us and to whom we respond emotionally resemble the people we love. Married people are still men and women who react impulsively to a very ancient biological endowment—sex attraction. Consideration must be given to the person who is being desensitized, increasing or decreasing the psychological injections as needed.

Sometimes direct sensitization is useful. I have sometimes materially lessened or even removed fears by teaching patients to modify gradually strong physical fear reactions. For instance, to learn to sit in a chair and try to read during a lightning storm, rather than making a headlong dive for bed and pulling the covers over the head. These methods are not likely to be effective if the phobia is very deep-seated and its inner motivations largely unknown.

Sometimes the development of lifelong fear reactions may be aborted if a danger is faced immediately or very soon after a mishap, perhaps a fall from a horse. During the war, we learned that among those surviving aviators whose ships had crashed, perhaps with the horrible death of some of their friends, there were a certain number whose fears were stopped in their tracks, and who were best helped and probably saved from years of neurotic invalidism by having them accept a briefing for another combat mission soon after the fatality. In these situations and comparable ones in civilian life, the therapist must have and must exude confidence. Uncertainty is contagious and fatal. Again, he is the strong, reliant father figure imparting confidence and emotional security.

Let us now assume that the emotional conflict is on the table of consciousness. It has been examined by patient and therapist, and progressively stripped of enough of its coverings so that the reasons for the defensive symptoms have become clear and the vista of more mature paths in life is unfolded. Then is the time for re-education. There is a realistic appraisal of the mistakes that have been made. In one sense, the patient learns intellectually that the way of the neurosis is the way of the child—demanding immediate gratifications. The way of satisfactory, mature personal and social living can never be solely or even mainly the satisfaction of immediate desires in impulsive conduct. Of necessity, it involves working toward a goal, postponements, modifications, reasonable compromises.

Usually, intellectual understanding alone, even if it be very highly developed, is not sufficient. Some degree of emotional outpouring and relief is generally required. This need not be, and usually is not the terrific emotional reactions we saw in some soldiers during the war, when under the inhibition-removing effect of pentothal, repressions were torn away, and the soldiers not only remembered but actually relived their former terrible battle experiences in all their details of stark fear and horror. In the relationship between patient and therapist, and in the transference that has been developed, there is likely to be the stimulus for milder but still adequate releasing and healing emotional reactions.

Within the limits of the space available, I have sketched in at least some of the more important things that happen between the patient and the therapist. Much more happens, much more can be done, and often much more is done. For instance, by way of merely one example, there is bibliotherapy. Many therapists are not only widely read professionally, but also have an extensive cultural literary background. They may gain considerable treatment ground by suggesting selected readings which bear on the problems of their patients and then discussing the material with them. There is a mine of helpful material in the great literary masterpieces of all ages —the Bible, Shakespeare, the classics of poetry, fiction and essay. Perhaps they are imperishable and have universal appeal because they express one quality of genius—the capacity to utter sublime and eternal truths without fully realizing their enormous significance and wide ramifications. This is the reason they ring true in the minds and hearts of men, in all times and ages.

Group Therapy. Group therapy is an important, rapidly growing and improving concept of treatment. A number of patients, ten to fifteen, but sometimes more or less, are gathered together with a group leader. The group leader may speak, but preferably briefly, perhaps explaining some mechanism, symptom or facet of functional illness. His objective is to promote general discussion, which almost always is forthcoming. For

one thing, there is obvious a leavening, desensitizing influence.
Patients learn, sometimes to their great surprise, that other
people suffer from symptoms like theirs. Often they have
hugged their symptoms to mental breasts, ashamed to talk
about them—"I thought no one else could be that way"—
"Well, for heaven's sake," said one patient to another in a
group therapy session, "you mean you are just like I am, climb
six flights of stairs because you're scared to ride in an eleva-
tor." And so the process of desensitization goes on. The realization that other patients have similar symptoms and the
understanding of the meaning of the symptoms breed that
healthy contempt that comes from familiarity. And let it not
be thought that the fact that a number of people are gathered
together precludes emotional reactions. In the free exchange
of opinion and discussion, often sympathetic, but, too, often
heated, there is the release and thinning out of much fear, depression, guilt and hostility. All in all, good group psychiatry
is a liberal education in the meaning and mechanics of the psychoneuroses. Often it is supplemented by individual therapy
and the period of treatment is sometimes appreciably shortened.

So the therapist with his training and experience and the
resources at his command is able to do something about it for
each patient.

15 | THE SILVER CORD

Perhaps in this day of streamlined science, of atomic and H bombs and other lethal war machines, of world disillusionment and weariness and of spiritual vacuum, there is no longer the opportunity to relearn the lessons of history and retrieve the mistakes that have been made. It may be too late.

Some students and prophets of history draw an alarming parallel between the present state of our civilization and culture and that of great, artistic Greece in 300 B.C. and of mighty, military Rome in 300 A.D. In Greece and Rome, divorce were prevalent; the moral obligations of marriage were flagrantly flaunted by husband and wives; laxity was the rule; there was a declining birth rate and much juvenile delinquency. In other words, ancient Greece and Rome disregarded something which no culture dares disregard, if it wishes to endure—the family. The family is the basis, the very foundation stone of society.

No doubt Greece and Rome felt secure upon their artistic and military pinnacles. It is peculiar to every civilization that the majority always feels that way. Everything seems so firm and strong and stable. It has lasted for such a long time. There seems no reason but to believe it will endure forever. A few prophets, warning of the decadence and extinction of past civilizations, are very faint voices crying in the wilderness. Few are willing to believe it can happen here, indeed that it has already begun to happen.

Our divorce record is shameful. While recently there has been some small improvement, yet the last complete accounting showed in the overall one divorce for every three marriages. In some large urban centers, the ratio was 1:2. In one city in 1946 there were 96 divorces to every 100 marriages!

Blessedly, too, the birth rate is more favorable, but it will have to rise considerably from the low level of 44 per cent of families no children, 22 per cent only one child. In 1920, 1921, 1922, 1923, marriages of college graduates produced less than one child per marriage.

In regard to the moral laxity of husbands and wives, Kinsey makes a strong statistical indictment of the American husband. It has been predicted that his forthcoming work on women will not show a much better picture. I trust this prediction is wrong and that the record of the composite American wife will redeem her erring spouse, statistically.

As to juvenile delinquency, J. Edgar Hoover has stated that while the most serious responsibility of the F.B.I. is to guard the secrets of the atomic bomb, juvenile delinquency is next on the priority list and in some respects is even more significant. In view of this somewhat pessimistic profile, it does not seem an overstatement to say, "It can happen here,"

The soundness of our Western civilization, and indeed, its very survival, does depend on the existence and continuance of the family. This has been nicely expressed in the noble language of Mr. Justice Birdseye (New York Supreme Court,

1857): "The family is the origin of all society and of all government . . . The whole frame of government and law exists only to protect and support the family."

Bills of divorcement conceal rather than reveal the real reasons for divorce. Cruel and barbarous treatment and indignities to person is the common formula. The personal indignity may consist of a slap or two, sometimes prearranged. Mental cruelty, which may mean variously reading the newspaper at the breakfast table, crumpling and disarranging the paper in order to take out the society page, the fashions or the sports sheet, derisive remarks about her Easter bonnet, making a fuss about the household expenses, unpleasant remarks about "his" or "her" relatives, not being willing to go out at night, or wanting to go out too much. Or the marital craft may be wrecked upon the rocks of too little income or too much income (recently a divorce was granted to a couple who claimed they got along well as long as they were in debt, but now that they were in the clear, they bored each other, since they had nothing to talk about), difficulty in finding a suitable house or apartment in which to live, one or the other not wanting children, differences in religion, annoying mothers-in-law, "fooling around" with other men and women. Sometimes some of these plaints have a measure of truth in them, but almost always they cover up the real, underlying reason for the divorce. Naturally enough, since this basic reason is not known, often it is not even suspected by the contending parties.

Psychiatrists are apt to have about the same degree of interest in these "reasons" for divorce as doctors in another field of medicine would have in a headache. The doctor wants a careful description of the headache, how long it has lasted, how frequently it appears, just where and how it hurts. But when he knows these things, he begins to think along the lines of possible explanations or causes for the headache. After all, the headache is merely a surface sign of something deeper. It might be due to too enthusiastic celebration at the fraternity banquet or too many dart games in the taproom with many liquid winnings poured into an empty stomach. But it might be indicative of serious gastrointestinal or other internal diseases. It might even mean a brain tumor. So, too, are the reasons given for divorce and for many marital troubles which do not culminate in divorce, reasons often stated with the utmost sincerity and conviction, merely surface symptoms of something underneath much more serious than "I just can't stand his mother" or "he is always nagging me." And, more often than not, that deeper and more valid reason is emotional immaturity in wife, in husband or in both. To gain some idea of what is meant by emotional immaturity, we may go to the top of the scale of emotional stature and describe emotional maturity. The dictionary defines maturity as the condition of being mature. Even a psychiatrist can do better than that.

This descriptive definition is on a somewhat idealistic plane. I doubt if any of us can succeed in living our personal and social lives continuously within the area of rarified atmosphere contained by the definition. For one thing, we would be very lonely. For another, we would bore others and defeat the achievement of satisfactory social relations. People would tend to feel hostile toward us because we were so perfect. Finally, it would be psychologically grotesque. The definition is a bull's-eye to aim at; we can only hope that the arrows of our aspiration toward mature emotional behavior will strike not too far away from the target.

"Maturity is a quality of personality made up of a number of elements. It is stick-to-itiveness, the ability to stick to a job, to work on it, and to struggle through it until it is finished, or until one has given all one has in the endeavor. It is the quality or capacity of giving more than is asked or required in a given situation. It is this characteristic that enables others to count on one; thus it is reliability. Persistence is an aspect of maturity; persistence to carry out a goal in the face of difficulties. Endurance enters into the concept of maturity; the endurance of difficulties, unpleasantness, discomfort, frustration, hardship. The ability to size things up, make one's own decisions, is a characteristic of maturity. This implies a considerable amount of independence. A mature person is not dependent unless ill. Maturity includes a determination, a will to succeed and achieve, a will to life. Of course, maturity represents the capacity to co-operate; to work with others, to work in an organization and under authority. The mature person is flexible, can defer to time, persons, circumstances. He can show tolerance, he can be patient and, above all, he has the qualities of adaptability and compromise. Basically, maturity represents a wholesome amalgamation of two things: 1. Dissatisfaction with the status quo, which calls forth aggressive, constructive effort, and 2. Social concern and devotion. Emotional maturity is the morale of the individual." *

I would add something else, the aspiration toward the spiritual—a spiritual fortress as contrasted with sole reliance on the material. If you wish, a co-operating, constructive reaction dependency on God. In psychiatry, unbroken and total dependencies upon other human beings are deplored as the sources of much functional illness. And yet, man cannot walk alone. He can accept and practice a dependency upon God without psychological loss of face. The right kind of dependency, loving God, imitating His love and mercy in our dealings and relations with our fellow man, is a source of strength and not weakness.

There you have it, at least an idea of emotional maturity. How do we get it? Whence does it come? These questions nat-

* From *Psychiatry of Two Wars*, Strecker and Appel (Lippincott).

urally bring into focus the mother, who traces in her child the first outline of either emotional maturity or immaturity.

The woman who has a baby faces an age-old dilemma. Upon the reasonable degree of success with which she solves the dilemma, there is inevitably revealed whether she is an emotionally mature mother or not. Motherhood is a dual function and both roles must be skillfully played. The first role and probably the more significant is that of the Great Lover and Protectress. She will want her child, she will love it, hold it closely to her breast and caress it, she will nurture it and defend and protect it from dangers. Often I am asked, is it not dangerous to love a child too much? I think the answer is no. For from the love and affection which the child receives from the mother in the early years of life, there is derived emotional security, the most important thing in the life of a child. Without this bedrock of early emotional security which comes from love, a sound personality cannot be built.

At cursory glance, the second role in the dual function of motherhood would seem to be at odds with the first. For the mother cannot be only the Lover. She must be also the Frustrator. She not only must love her child and hold it closely; she also must relinquish it, as it were, push it away. She must gradually loose the maternal apron strings which once tightly and rightly bound her child to her. She must understand that just as there must be weaning from the feeding at the breast, so, too, must there be a psychological weaning. She must learn to sever the psychological umbilical cord and she must be able to do it not only with sadness, but also with gladness in her heart. In emancipating her child, she is giving it a priceless heritage.* For only from the reasonable satisfaction of the dual

---

* The duality of motherhood is not expressed in two separate time divisions. Loving does not cease and then releasing begin. A mature mother never stops loving her children, no matter how old they are in years. But

mother (and later parental) function can the child grow up
emotionally and be given a sound, self-directing, self-acting
personality, a mature personality, which will be able to function satisfactorily in the usual give-and-take contacts and relations of adult life. Only those adults who in childhood have
learned not only to take but also to give will be able to meet
the test without too much frustrated stumbling, and, all too
often—abject failure.

There is a frightening finality for the future in the early
child-mother, later child-father and child-family relationships.
Here are the first social lessons. If they teach and ingrain emotional maturity, it is most fortunate. Sometimes, but scarcely
often enough to be counted on, maturity favoring conditions
in adult life, occasionally just the right kind of marriage (if
the immaturity is not too deep), may lessen the damage and
add some cubits to the emotional stature. But the process of
growing up emotionally, relatively easy for the child, is indeed
a very painful process for the adult. All in all, in a child's early
relationships, particularly with the mother, there is contained
in miniature an accurate forecast of that child's adult behavior
in his emotional experiences with all the human beings with
whom he may come into intimate contact. The record is contained therein, almost as surely as the ear of corn is in the ker-
nel or the flower in the seed.

I believe, too, that adult behavior is more or less predictable
from the kind and amount of emotional immaturity existing
during childhood. As a member of the President's Commission
on Selective Service in World War II, I was deeply concerned
about the almost 2,000,000 young Americans who were rejected as unfit to serve because of neuropsychiatric disorders
and illness. Of course, all these young men were sick. Many

---

neither does she fail to begin ever so slightly to release, emancipate and
prepare them for adult life, no matter how young they are.

were unavoidably sick, perhaps with psychoses or psychoneuroses, just as concrete and definite as tuberculosis or heart disease. But in far too many the sickness was not inevitable. It was the outgrowth and culmination of not having been permitted to grow up emotionally during childhood. Given the opportunity of knowing these young men when they were youngsters and, particularly, knowing their mothers, competent psychiatrists could have predicted the result with considerable accuracy. They would have known that the maternal apron strings were too short to reach to the training camps and certainly not flexible enough to be stretched overseas.

Why is emotional maturity so necessary for happy and successful adult living? Why does childhood-conditioned immaturity defeat its attainment? And why is it so productive of psychoneurotic and other functional breakdowns ten, twenty, thirty or even more years after childhood is over? Here, I think, is the course of events:

1. Notable deficits in fulfilling the dual function of motherhood and parenthood, by insufficient amounts of something that is as necessary for the child as food—love and affection. Sometimes this is not only negative but also positive: harshness, rigid and non-explanatory discipline and even cruelty. Then and/or failure to release and emancipate the child emotionally, with consequent lack of reasonably adequate preparation and experience for understanding and participating in grown-up human relationships.

2. From such deficits there results the inculcation into the personality of the child unconscious hostility toward the mother or parents, hostility of such amount and gravity that it cannot be psychologically digested or compromised. (Normally, there is of necessity a certain amount of hostility, since the mother must frustrate her child in some degree in the process of helping it learn the lessons of social conformity. Such

hostility is successfully compromised and is an important and constructive aspect of growing up.)

3. Even ordinary adult hostilities cannot be readily faced in consciousness. To admit them completely through the portals that guard the "not remembered" and to live with them openly would be too much of an insult to the ego. How much more impossible is it then to face hostility felt toward the supreme love objects, the mother and the father! It is inevitable that the inner, unacceptable hostility should engender unexplainable guilt feelings.

4. Here, then, is a psychological situation from which escape is imperative. Depending somewhat upon the individual markings of the personality and somewhat upon the conditions of adult life which the unprepared and highly vulnerable personality encounters, the particular method and route of escape are determined. It may be alcoholism. Or drugs. Or certain types of mental illness. More commonly, it is a psychoneurosis, frequently with a pretentious façade of psychosomatic symptoms—headache, backache, nausea, vomiting, heart symptoms, in fact, symptoms referable to any and every part of the body. The escape may be expressed chiefly in terms of dissatisfaction, incompletion, unhappiness and emotional failure in life. Perhaps this is the worst of all. It is, indeed, hard for a child to live in a world of grown-up men and women.

I shall now present a few thumbnail sketches of immature mothers I have known. They are authentic profiles and each one represents a large group. However, it must be remembered that the question of the identity of the emotionally immature mother cannot be answered by an unqualified "yes" or a categorical "no." There are innumerable gradations and shadings. Even the most nearly completely mature mother shows some tracings of immaturity. This is as it should be. Perfection would make her a sore tribulation to her children and everyone else who came into contact with her. Conversely, probably there are few 100 per cent emotionally immature mothers, although I have occasionally met one who almost fitted into this category. Still, there were a few fragments of maturity in their attitudes toward their children. An unadulterated emotionally immature mother would be totally destructive to her children.

There is the decisive mother. Usually not dictatorially decisive—"Bill, if you dare get that crew haircut I told you not to get, then I won't allow you to go out at night for three weeks"; or, "Jane, if I hear another word from you about getting that red dress for the party, instead of the gray one that suits you, then you can't go to the party at all." No, the usual technique is the softly decisive one. Mother does not complain if her will is not followed, but Jack and Mary both know they have hurt her deeply. Sometimes they even see the tears starting to her eyes. And they feel so miserable that they wish they had never opposed her.

Of course, children do need *explanatory* guidance, and haircuts and clothes are not overwhelmingly important, but they are symbolic of other things that are. The softly decisive mother, not by counseling, but by the deft and skillfully contrived ways of emotional immaturity, manages to decide not only haircuts and clothes, but opinions and attitudes, choice of playmates and companions, of studies and sports, of hobbies and later on of occupations in life. Children of such mothers, irrespective of how high their I.Q.'s may be, are poorly equipped to play the game of adult life, the rules of which call for at least some capacity to be self-decisive.

Then there is the in many ways admirable, "no trouble" mother. Usually, she looks worn out but if you tell her so, she is likely at first to deny it. "Why, I feel fine," and then perhaps grudgingly she will admit, "Well, maybe I do look a wee bit tired. If I am, it is my own fault. I just love to do things for the children."

The children of the "no trouble" mother live in the house of continuous service. Figuratively, there is a path from cellar to attic and just around the corner, trodden smooth by mother's footsteps, to get this or that for Jack or Susie. There are many detours to pick up clothing and other odds and ends, with which Jack and Susie have bestrewn the floor. At almost any hour of the day or night, it isn't too much trouble to prepare a meal or at least a snack. "Mother knows just how you like it." Nothing is ever too much trouble. Mother does everything for the youngsters, gladly and with a sweet, happy smile. No wonder they come to accept it as their due. Self-sacrificing though she be, yet the "no trouble" mother does not contribute much to the emotional growth of her children. And there is the added danger that not being able to find houses of "continuous service," like the one they knew in childhood, one or more of the children, after brief and unsatisfactory experiences outside may return to the "no trouble" house and mother, and remain forever enwombed.

Another likable mother is the Pollyanna mother. She is a sweet, gentle soul and with her children she lives in the House of Harmony. Should one of the youngsters raise his voice in argument with a brother or sister, this mother is apt to say, "Hush, Jim, we love each other too much to quarrel." Unfortunately, differences of opinion vigorously defended, arguments somewhat aggressively advanced, even occasional mild fisticuffs, are part of the process of growing up. Childhood has always been the arena in which these small battles are fought and it should be the practice ground upon which fair rules of contention are learned and observed. I doubt that we can expect more than that. A certain amount of self-assertion is needed in the world of adults. Again, here, there is the danger that the children of the Pollyanna mother, ill prepared for the world as it is, will find life as it is lived too rough and contentious and will be forever frustrated in seeking to find again the house of harmony of their childhood.

The "don't you dare punish my child" mother is rather less admirable. She places under the cloak of her complete protection perhaps an only child, but more likely one of the children whom she feels needs her particular solicitude. She cannot bear to see this child punished, no matter how merited or mild the punishment may be.

Sometimes she is quite articulate about it. She may put on an act, the histrionics of which would have excited the envy of the immortal Bernhardt. "You shall not touch my child." All this in the presence of the child, the scene brightly illuminated by the growth-inhibiting light of too much attention.

Even more harmful is the more usual quiet technique. The favored child accepts the punishment or censure bravely enough. The mother looks on silently without interference. It is an oft-repeated comedy. Mother and child are letter perfect in their roles. The youngster knows that as soon as the punishment is over, he can count on Mother to take him into her arms, lavish affection upon him, tell him how unfairly he has been treated, praise him for being "Mother's brave little boy," and promising him material rewards. To make matters worse, an increasingly closer pact is formed between mother and child. It is a magic circle of sweet whispered confidences and agreements, "just you and Mother" which excludes the father and the rest of the family.

All this is not an atmosphere that stimulates emotional growth. That child will later on have to face a very difficult and sometimes impossible job of attempting to adjust to an adult world, in which infractions of the code of the rights of others are never overlooked, and often are severely punished.

Somewhat lower down on the scale is the "frail" mother. Strangely enough, since she never mentions it, yet everyone, even the neighbors, seems to know that she gave her health and strength in bringing her children into the world. Her children know it, usually with sorrow and pity and feelings of guilt. The doctor says that Mother does not have any organic disease, "She just isn't strong."

The children gladly do all they can to be helpful. But much more than that is stipulated in the unwritten bond. Since the mother almost sacrificed her life in bearing them, the children should be willing to repay in kind. A life for a life. On the surface, it seems to be a fair bargain. Actually, it is unfair and cruelly exacting. Often at least one of the children, usually a daughter whose heart is filled with sympathy for the frail mother, dedicates her life to her. Gradually, as the years go by, all the threads of her personal and social life are severed. When finally the mother dies, it is too late to begin life anew. Marriage is no longer possible. Emotionally, there is nothing left. Nothing but a nervous breakdown.

Many times in my professional life I have talked with such women. It is truly pathetic. Some of them, when they realize how unfair the bargain has been, turn out the vials of their bitter resentment and hatred of the "frail" mother, who, nevertheless, has been strong enough to crush out their lives beneath the wheels of the chariot of her invalidism.

It is a relief to turn to the "pretty, addlepate" mother. She is single-minded in her unswerving devotion to the ritual of cosmetics and hairdo, but not in the usual way of women who are to be commended for their beautifying artistry which has made the world a much pleasanter place. The "pretty, addlepate" goes far beyond this. She practices an extreme artistry which is an unfailing source of joy and profit to beauty-salon proprietors.

Almost never does anyone, not even her children, see her unless she is turned out perfectly. She cannot be accused of spending too much time with her children. Frequently, particularly in the evening, she sallies forth on pleasure bent, but not always strictly maternal. As she bends over the youngsters to bid them good night, it is a beautiful sight. After she leaves, one can almost hear them saying to each other, "Mother is so beautiful and she smells so sweet." But it is not the odor of true maternity. It comes in bottles and is very expensive.

The danger, of course, is that there will be ingrained into the receptive personalities of the youngsters the dubious ideal of feminine pulchritude, transcending all else. The girls become eager novitiates in the rites of the body beautiful, and too often they have little else to offer in the emotional relationships of adult life. The boys become ardent devotees at the shrine of female beauty. When these youngsters seek marriage, they look for little that cannot be seen on the surface. As everyone knows, neither marriage nor any other important life relationship can endure unless it is built upon more solid and permanent foundations than the female figure, skin and hair. And, for that matter, neither the male body.

Many of the mothers of whom I have given brief glimpses are interesting, likable and pleasant women. They may be well educated and informed about many subjects and converse intelligently. Incidentally, education is no criterion of emotionally immature mothers. I know some women who are doing a splendidly mature job of raising their children, though they had only grade-school teaching. And I know a few Phi Beta Kappas who are very unsatisfactory and immature mothers.

There is one kind of immature mother, who in my opinion

is neither likable nor pleasant. In fact, I think she is detestable. Unconsciously, but nevertheless unerringly and unsparingly, she visits upon her children her revenge for the thwartings and frustrations of her own sexual life. Ruthlessly she divests sex of all its beautiful significance and presents it to her children as a horrible and loathsome thing. To her halfgrown daughter, just beginning to bud into womanhood, she speaks something like this: "Of course, darling, I hope that some day you will marry. Mother wants you to be very happy. But you must be careful of men. Don't trust them too far. The best of them are selfish. It seems they want you for only one thing—their pleasure. And they don't care what they do to you as long as they have their pleasure. They don't care how they break down your health. When you are sick and old before your time, then they will turn to younger and more attractive women and find their pleasure with them."

The theme song of this immature mother may vary in some of the details, but the result, as far as her daughter is concerned, is the same. There is deeply etched into her plastic personality the belief that all men, even the man she will some day marry, are lustful carnivores prowling the face of the earth seeking females to devour!

How can this child, come woman and wife, ever meet the mature responsibilities of the sexual aspects of marriage? Her mother has built around her a barrier of sexual fear and suspicion. It is unlikely that she will ever completely surmount it. It is highly improbable that she will be able to participate fully in the joys of sex. Abortively, perhaps, but certainly not in its completeness. For sex is much more than a physical relationship between husband and wife. It is, perhaps, the having of children and loving and rearing them together. It is home building. It is mutual trust and confidence. It is the sharing of happiness and sorrows. And it is much more. How can the wife, sex frightened and made cynical and suspicious by her mother during girlhood, do these things?

For her sons, such a mother usually draws a blueprint of the kind of girl she hopes they will marry. Apparently such girls are difficult to find in these degenerate days. It is definitely implied and often openly asserted that "girls nowadays are not like your mother was when she was a girl." No, definitely not. They are more apt to be creatures of lures and artifices, of slyness and cunning. "Before you know it, you are trapped. You must be very careful to find just exactly the right one."

The blueprint of "your future wife" is drawn so precisely and with so many specifications that it will be very difficult to find a girl who even remotely fulfills its rigid requirements. Should there be a girl who seems to measure up, how can a fellow be sure? How can he tell that she is not one of the female werewolves Mother so often warned him about?

Again, how can such a childhood-defrauded young man meet the adult emotional conditions of married life, sexual and otherwise? How can he inspire in his wife and build and share with her complete love, trust and confidence if unconsciously, and sometimes even consciously, he is compelled to react to the pattern of his childhood, looking for and expecting to find in his wife feminine "wiles, tricks and deceptions"? After all, Mother knew.

Sometimes, Pop is Mom. The word "Mom" slipped out. I had not intended to use it. Somewhat unfairly, it has been made synonymous with the immature mother who will not relinquish her emotional grasp upon her children. It should be an honored word in proportion to its use as a term of affection by the mature sons and daughters of the mothers who have helped them grow up. However, for this once, I will let it stand as indicative of emotional immaturity. And, conversely, I repeat that sometimes and far too often, "Pop is Mom."

I know of no more unenviable lot in life than that of the reasonably mature young woman who finds herself married to a very immature young husband. And she, perhaps rather more often than her immature sister, is likely to find herself so trapped. The call of her maternity is louder and the appeal to it more compelling. Nothing is more appealing to her than an awkward, helpless young man who needs looking after. So, she marries him.

At first it is an intriguing situation. She loves to pat his hair into place, tie his scarf, brush his clothes, fetch his slippers and aspirin and rub the hurt in his back. (Not that limited amounts of babying are not a normal part of marriage.)

Sooner or later, the situation loses its novelty and charm and begins to pall. This is particularly true when real babies begin to arrive. Here are creatures who are not only helpless and defenseless, but also tiny and lovable. Here is the real call to maternity, not the decoy call of the immature husband. She is happily busy in loving, feeding and guarding her youngsters and in helping them grow up. She becomes increasingly "fed up" with the pseudo-baby husband, perhaps six feet tall and weighing 180 pounds, who constantly wants to be petted, who does not share her love and interest in the children, and who seems rather to resent their presence. He is utterly useless in the house and sometimes cannot even be depended upon to play games with the youngsters, since he sulks if he loses.

Then the immature husband I have in mind conducts a campaign which may last for years. The objective of this campaign is to persuade his wife to be his mother. He uses every weapon of immaturity, no matter how unfair—childish blandishments, sulking, petty tyrannies, appeals for sympathy and coddling through pretended illness, sickly affairs with women. If his wife is reasonably mature, he loses the campaign. She declines to become his mother.

Then, if he happens to have a half-grown daughter, he does something very serious. The fact that it is unconscious, that he does not realize what he is doing, does not lessen the damage that is inflicted upon the daughter. In a few words, he courts his own daughter.

The conclusion is foregone. He woos and wins her easily. She is at the age when womanhood is stirring in her. As always, at this age, her father unconsciously is her man ideal. She becomes his eager and willing slave. Now she is the one who brings him his aspirin and slippers and rubs his "tired" head. (Again, a little of this is a normal and wholesome part of the father-daughter relationship, but a little is enough.) Into the small but receptive ear of his daughter, the immature father pours his troubles. The child-mother is an inexhaustible fount of sympathy and petting. Between child-father and child-mother there is an ever stronger bond. It is a pact which excludes the mother. There is an unspoken agreement between them that "Mother does not understand." The fact that the mother-seeking motivation of the immature father is unconscious does not save it from being psychological incest. What will happen to the daughter in her adult life is predictable. Should she marry an immature man—two children building a flimsy structure upon shifting sands—their house of cards will come tumbling down upon them. Should she marry a mature mate, there is a bare chance of the marriage being worked out, but not more than a bare chance. More likely is it that the husband will tire of the "little mother" who is little else.

I have sketched in the outlines of the disastrous situations which are very likely to result from notable failure to meet the double function of motherhood and parenthood. What can be done about it?

It is not sensible to blame individual immature mothers. They cannot help themselves much. They are the products of a system which in our country is beginning to resemble a matriarchy. One reason that the system flourishes and waxes strong is that it is fed by an unstinting praise and adulation— praise and adulation merely for being a mother, irrespective of the kind of mother or the type of children she has produced. There can scarcely be enough admiration for the real mother who adds more mature human beings to a world which needs them so much. But it seems neither reasonable nor sensible to stand in reverent awe before a mere collection of birth certificates.

Congress has investigated matters far less significant for the weal of the nation.

If a man makes a mousetrap which does not catch mice, there is no reason he should be praised simply for cluttering the market with another useless contraption. If I write a book, I hope to be praised for the things in it that prove useful. I am sure to be blamed for those things in the book which are not good and serviceable. This is as it should be. It is the product that counts. Children destined to become socially immature adults decrease the morale of society, impede social progress and are the source of much unhappiness to themselves and to those with whom they come into intimate contact.

A large part of the blame is to be laid at the door of what is becoming an altogether too frequent type—the typical American father. He subscribes too enthusiastically to the prevalent and dangerous doctrine that the raising of the children should be left in the hands of the mother. Preoccupied with business and professional interests and with stag pleasures, golf, bridge or poker ("necessary if I am to make and hold important business connections!"), the only contribution of some husbands and fathers seems to be frequent libations drunk "to the good little woman at home taking care of the children." It will not do. It is not enough.

It can be stated without reservation that every father has an important contribution to make to the emotional development of his children, boys and girls alike. It is a contribution so significant, so much determined by the fact that he is the father, that the mother, no matter how mature she happens to be, cannot make it alone.

The mother is left at home holding an empty emotional bag. She must, indeed, be very strong in her emotional maturity if she does not succumb, at least in some degree, to the temptation to fill it with dangerous emotional over-attachments to her children.

Only in a very small degree do we reward the mature mother for the important contribution she has made by giving her our public and political confidence. For the sake of the children of the nation, she should be widely utilized when she is beyond the childbearing period. No one understands better than she the needs of children. No one would guard their interests more zealously. She would favorably influence legislation that would protect those interests and rights. She would promote the kind of education that would increase the likelihood of many more children coming into their most precious heritage—emotional maturity. And yet, in spite of these facts, far too many citizens will cast their ballots for that male candidate who is adept at kissing the babies of the voters.

Finally, a great deal could be accomplished and probably the system would be dealt a death blow if the children, themselves, at the high-school level or even sooner, were suitably instructed as to the necessity and value of emotional maturity

in securing success and happiness in life. It would seem that
at least as important as learning how to bound the State of
Missouri or demonstrating a problem in algebra or geometry
would be instruction in the art and artistry of being a mature
wife or husband, mother or father. Children so taught would
increasingly appreciate the deep and lasting significance of
emotional maturity. Probably such children would scrutinize
the job their parents were doing for them. Immature parents
would resent any questioning attitude on the part of their children. Mature parents would like and profit by it.

For years, I have preached the gospel of emotional security
and maturity for children, not for a few children, but for all.
It is the fifth and the greatest human freedom. Those of us who
know about it should tell others who do not know.

Many centuries ago, there reigned a great Shah of Persia,
with unlimited dictatorial powers, even life or death, over his
subjects. He did have one duty. Once a year he had to speak
from the balcony of his palace. And because this was his only
obligation, he disliked the task very much.

The appointed day came and the Shah spoke to his people,
"Do you, my people, know what I am going to talk to you
about this year?" And, with one voice, they answered, "No,
mighty Shah, we do not know." And the Shah said, "Why
should I waste my time speaking to such ignorant people?"
and he retired from the balcony. But still he had to honor the
tradition.

The next day he appeared again, and spoke, "Do my people know what I am going to say?" And the people, hoping to
tempt him to speak to them, called out, "Yes, we do know,
great one." And the Shah answered disdainfully, "If you already know, there is no sense in my telling you."

But the people took counsel among themselves, appointed
a spokesman and instructed him how to reply. And the next

day, when the ruler again spoke from the palace balcony, "Tell me, my people, do you now know what it is I am about to say to you?" the spokesman answered, "Powerful One, some of us know, but some of us do not know."

"Very well," answered the Shah, "let those of you who know tell those who do not know."

So, let those of us who know how vital is the attainment during childhood of emotional maturity for adjustment during every day of adult life tell those who do not know.

Its achievement means much more than the difference for the individual between mental health or sickness, happiness or miserable frustration.

This chapter has been an indictment. In view of the seriousness of the situation, I think it is justified. In the following chapter, I shall attempt to give some suggestions which, if put into practice, may help children grow up emotionally.

16 | A DESIGN FOR CHILDHOOD

It is not an easy task to weave a design for childhood. There are almost too many threads from which to select. One cannot be sure how durable some of them will prove to be. Others may stand out too prominently in the completed pattern. This is one way of saying that the road of too great complexity in the psychology of childhood is beset by many dangers. One may easily take a wrong turn. If there are too many meandering byways, lanes and detours, we are likely to become so fascinated in their exploration that we may never find the child who waits at the end of the road.

At least we can be certain of a few simple facts. One is that there are children. Another, that they live in a medium which we call their environment. From these two facts we can infer a third: that something happens to the child as the result of its contact with the environment in which it lives. Something happens to the environment too.

The contact involves many physical factors that are very concrete in their effect upon the child—food, with its important vitamins, sunlight, fresh air, and many other things. We know well and sadly from the effect of malnutrition upon the war-orphaned children of Europe that if the supply of these needs is shut off or if it is insufficient in amount, the effect will be disastrous. Even death may result. At least there will be serious retardation and crippling of the child's growth and development. Likewise the child must draw upon its surroundings for the satisfaction of its psychological needs. It is fair to draw a parallel. If there is deprivation or an inadequate supply of psychological foodstuffs, then inevitably the psyche of the child will be seriously damaged, occasionally destroyed.

The psychic endowment that comes to each child as a result of the constant interchange, back-and-forth flow, between it and the environment is called the personality. In various places in this book, personality has been briefly described and its significance emphasized.

If the body situation, the general health and strength in each child represents the physiological equipment with which he must meet the physical stresses and strains of later life, then the personality is his psychological insulation and defense. The physical and the emotional are not two. They are one. They form the unit of total human functioning—a child.

No single school of psychiatric thought has completely explained the growth and shaping of the personality. We must still accept the operation of an unknown or X quantity. In every living organism, there is an innate potential for growing. See how beautifully it works in the physical structure. In the mother's womb, the buds of the organs of the baby, at first only to be identified by an expert, nourished by the one blood stream of the mother, grow into highly differentiated organs: heart, liver, lungs, spleen, etc. It would seem as if there existed in the organ buds the potential for the selection of the factors that will insure normal growth. After birth, the child is still incomplete. Its organs, muscles and bones are tiny and weak. It does not have all its appendages: hair and teeth. Again, the growth principle operates. From the nutrition delivered to the various parts of this small but complex structure, there is selected just what is needed to bring about a highly specialized maturity of organs and parts. So does the body grow up.

As there is an innate potential for physical maturity, so is there, too, a potential that unfolds into emotional or psychic adulthood. It should be repeated and again emphasized that the chief purpose of the emotional development of the child is to provide the opportunity to make for himself a workable personality, so that the conditions of adult life may be met satisfactorily, so that he may meet his fellow men on even terms, give and take, finding in life a reasonable measure of satisfaction and happiness.

What are some of the psychological potentials? And since the shaping of the environment is largely in the hands of adults, how may the environment be managed so that it will contain a sufficient supply of those things that may reasonably be expected to bring the psychological potentials into full flowering?

Fortunately, we do know the framework within which and only within which a satisfactory design of childhood can be woven. It is the framework of holding and loving the child, releasing and emancipating it. Only within such a properly proportioned framework can there be filled in the main motif of the design—emotional maturity.

One of the first psychological potentials is so simple that it is often overlooked. It is physical *motion*. The infant soon explores its surroundings—of course, not consciously, but as it were, instinctively. With hands and feet and, indeed, with the entire skin surface, it comes into contact with objects in its immediate vicinity and it notes and registers (again, not consciously) similarities and differences in shape, size, consistency, texture, temperature, big, little, hard, soft, rough, smooth, hot, cold, etc. From the very beginning, and very rapidly, there are stored up an enormous number of touching and feeling experiences and the reactions to them. And babies reach out eagerly to explore an ever-larger territory. They progress rapidly from crawling to toddling and then to upright, co-ordinated walking.

Motion is so important that it is probable that a bound child, that is, a child physically prevented from investigating its surroundings and therefore with the number of incoming sensations cut down to a minimum, would be seriously retarded mentally. No doubt you know some mother who boasts that her child is a good child because it is quiet. It sits nicely and quietly and does not get underfoot. But a quiet child is *not* a good child, *not* a sound child. The quiet child is being denied the golden opportunity to get mental and emotional growth. Children must have a free and unrestricted chance to come into contact with their environments, even though a few pieces of bric-a-brac might have to be sacrificed. If there were consciousness, freedom of movement is one of the first things a child would demand. Probably the child would say, "Give me the chance to move." Certainly it conveys this wish almost as clearly as it does the desire for food.

I cannot say that immature mothers restrict the opportunities of their babies for physical motion more than do mature mothers. I do not know. My impression is that they do. Several times I have observed that great event when a baby for the first time moves away from its mother. I have studied the expressions and attitudes of the mothers. It seemed to me that the immature mothers watched their children with more intentness, supervised them with more anxiety, circumscribed and limited them more closely.

I cannot escape the feeling that the phase of her child's physical activity sounds a warning note somewhere within the inner recesses of the immature mother: "Better be careful, your child is growing up, beginning to move away from you." It symbolizes and in miniature is the forerunner of the threatened total emancipation of the child later on.

All mothers call back their babies from their first crawling expeditions. I think there is a subtle difference in the "come-back-to-me" call of mature and immature mothers. In effect, the mature mother says, "Come back to me, baby, so that I may teach and help you to go farther away from me." But the immature mother says, "Come back to me, so that I may bind you more closely and teach you never to leave me."

Probably the most dynamic psychological potential is imitation. No explanation of the extreme importance of imitation in building mind and personality is needed. It is obvious.

The child learns to speak its native language, rightly called the "mother tongue" by imitating the sounds it hears from its mother and then from other adults in the family. At first, the sounds must be largely meaningless noises. But soon they are coupled with happenings that follow them. Experimentally, the baby tries a word and soon many words. It is learning to speak.

The play life of children startlingly reflects imitation. I suppose throughout all ages, little girls have taken an old skirt, a piece of cloth, a rag, anything they could find and draped it around themselves in imitation of the skirts of their mothers. If parents could be hidden observers of the game of "playing house" they might be rudely startled. For children faithfully mimic the faults of their parents. Perhaps the mother would hear her play "mother" little daughter soundly berate her play "father" small son for never getting home in time for meals and then "telling me all those silly lies." The father might ponder seriously if he heard himself in the miniature of his son deliver a series of choice epithets, liberally larded with profanity about "the so and so" who deliberately hides his favorite pipe or the sports sheet of the newspaper. Once unobserved, I saw a little girl who had been teased into tears by a playmate rush into the outstretched arms of her sister, the play "mother" who consoled her with caresses and these words, "Never mind, darling, that Smith girl is a nasty, dirty brat."

In the first semblance of being grown up there is the mirroring by imitation of what has been observed in the family and particularly in the mother.

Schoolteachers should be able to see themselves portrayed in the play life of children. With crude but accurate strokes the small Thespian cartoonists paint by word and pantomime the weaknesses, dissatisfactions, immaturities of their teachers and depict the revenge they sometimes take upon the children they teach for the frustrations of their own lives. When the subjects are not their own fathers and mothers, children can lampoon with cruel and direct realism. Once I came upon a group of little girls singing with such cherubic expressions upon their little faces that almost I could hear the rustle of angels' wings. But the words of the song were these:

> "Roses are red,
> Violets are blue,
> Teacher stinks
> And so do you."

Children imitating their parents are not merely mimicking. They are being impelled by two strong driving forces, identification and idealization. By identification they merge themselves into their parents, become a part of them. By idealization they place those whom they themselves are a part of, their parents, upon a very lofty pedestal.

Children are pitifully weak and insecure. The more they can identify with, become a part of their parents, the more freely can they borrow from them much-needed emotional strength. And the higher the pedestal upon which they can place their parents, the greater the emotional security they can feel. It is scarcely emphatic enough to say that children imitate their parents. They *must* imitate them. Most of us, when we were children, were willing to meet criticism and teasing from other youngsters, and even suffer an occasional bloodied nose in defense of the opinions of our parents. It was not so much that we were defending their opinions. We scarcely had enough intelligence to carry out a logical defense. After all, we had not listened to proof from the lips of our parents. Our position was not that vulnerable. Our parents said this or did that. It was quite enough for us. Children defend emotionally the parental citadel, with a determination, sometimes sadly worthy of a better cause. Never again in their lives will they have a stronger fortress.

Each parent and in a very special way, each mother, whether she be a true mother or spurious, represents such a citadel of strength and refuge for her children. This stronghold must not be removed too quickly. Neither can it be allowed to stand unchanged indefinitely. Children must be emancipated, given their independence and taught how to use it wisely. The emancipation must be accomplished gradually and tactfully, but it must be reasonably complete. Here is uncovered a basic difference between mature and immature mothers.

Whether she is learned in the ways of child psychology and able to fortify her true mother instincts by conscious knowledge or whether she is untutored but unconsciously guided, the real mother of men performs the releasing function of her motherhood as faithfully as she does the protecting function. Gradually she opens up more and more exits from the emotional citadel of her motherhood. She breaks down restraining walls. She weakens foundations. And, eventually, she leads her children into the outer world, girded and provisioned for adult life.

Albeit largely unconsciously, still does the immature mother sin deeply against the releasing function of motherhood. She "hangs on" to her children. She makes decisions for them, far beyond the time when they should be making up their own minds. Openly she encourages the children to lean upon her or else she leans upon them so heavily that they become emotionally absorbed in giving her support and strength. She continues to postpone the day of emancipation. Finally, it is too late. The immature mother has succeeded in perpetuating herself in her children. The handwriting is on the wall— nurses, older children, teachers, college professors, employers, adults at every economic and societal level to whom these embryo men and women are attracted; impractical and even dangerous ideas and movements with "crackpot" or demagogic and unscrupulous leaders—all these and many others form an endless procession of surrogates for the immature mother. It is imitation gone to seed—imitation that bears evil emotional and social fruit.

The real mother opens widely the doors of her emotional house. The imitation mother bars the exits and insulates and seals them against the outside world. In later life often, no matter how much the former children come to hate their emotional and social incarceration, even openly reviling the memory of the immature mother who jailed them, unless they have much skilled help, they remain imprisoned in the tomb of selfish, immature "love." Their prison is made of softer but stronger stuff than stone and steel.

The moral concerning imitation applies not only to parents but to every adult in contact with children. And which of us is not? If we wish to start their personalities in the right direction and prepare them to be able to meet the important issues in life, then we must provide helpful material to imitate. Accessible to imitation and in liberal amounts there should be integrity, straightforward dealing, truthfulness, courage, compassion, reflection, judgment, decision, tolerance. There should be a pattern of service to the community and to the nation. Too, at least some stirrings of internationalism. And some spiritual strivings. The early environment should be relatively free of the opposites of these so much needed attributes. Not dishonesty, deviousness, venal lying, moral cowardice, hasty, ill-considered judgment and action, indecision, prejudice and intolerance, gross materialism, absence of patriotism, lack of participation in community and national service and a vacuum instead of ideals of world-wide brotherhood. These things are the markings of those termites who are trying to undermine the foundations of democracy. The enduring, constructive pattern wrought by parents and others, suitable for imitation by children, might be expressed in a formula of daily living in which there is a reasonable balance between taking and giving, between the acceptance of privileges, but, in return, the performance of duties.

We must not expect children to imitate behavior described only by rather hypocritical mouthings. However nicely expressed, platitudinal admonitions alone will not serve. The firm and convincing tone of good-behavior example is needed.

Johnnie's father always gave the correct ethical replies to his questions. When Johnnie asked if it was wrong to lie or cheat or steal, his father always answered positively and in a shocked tone of voice that it was "very wrong." Furthermore, he delivered excellent sermonettes explaining just why it was wrong. But Johnnie had listened avidly when his father and mother discussed ways and means of evading payment of a large part of the income tax. Although Johnnie was small, his ears were large and his mind larger. Johnnie was the treasurer of the neighborhood boys' club. He hypothecated the club funds, made false entries and pyramided the money by various juvenile schemes. Finally, he lost all the money. Johnnie was ostracized by the other boys. Incidentally, the ostracism of children may be as cruel as that meted out by a tribe of savages to a member who has broken a tribal taboo. It was a sad and painful way for Johnnie to discover the clay feet of his parents.

Some people consistently carry into their adult lives the imitation of the remembrance of the virtues of their parents. It is a noble practice. It would also be profitable to carry out enough introspection to enable us to pick out at least a few of the things in ourselves, dating from our childhood imitativeness that have hampered us seriously in adult living. We might be stimulated to do all we can to prevent our children from being similarly burdened.

Suggestibility is an important and wide-open channel, through which there flows from the environment into a child's personality a stream of material which makes for later weal or woe. Suggestibility is more subtle than imitation. Imitation is direct. A child sees something done by an adult, and within the range of its capacity, it faithfully reproduces what it has seen and heard. Suggestibility is indirect. The child picks up from the environment a certain inclination or hint. Then, in its behavior it acts upon the suggestion. All human beings are suggestible and children are notably so. It is not an overstatement to say that all normal children literally drink in suggestions from the environment, from hundreds of sources. In some shape or fashion, much of this suggestion becomes a part of their personalities. Naturally, when the fountain of suggestion is those two heroic figures in the emotional life of the child, the mother and the father, then the suggestion is all the more eagerly imbibed and remains the more deeply impressed. For instance, the mother who, when her little daughter stumbles and breaks a teacup says to the visitor, "Poor Betty, she is so nervous. You know she gets that from her father's family," is directly suggesting nervousness. If the child continues to be subjected to such harmful suggestions, one may predict the inevitable result—a nervous child. A boy who lived in the atmosphere of his father's hypochondriasis and who had listened to many dinner-table pronouncements about the "toxic" symptoms like headache, which came from certain foods, and the generally unsatisfactory state of his father's bowels, when questioned about his future occupation, replied, "Well, I'd like to be an engineer, but I guess I'll be a neurotic like my father."

Suggestibility recalls the conditioned reflex. Pavlov, the great Russian physiologist, by associating the ringing of a bell with feeding and then merely showing a dog meat, finally was able so to condition the dog that the ringing of the bell alone sufficed to produce the flow of the digestive juices. A psychological conditioned reflex is a behavior response to a secondary stimulus that has become associated with the initial or primary one. Sometimes the difficult behavior of youngsters—perhaps "nervous indigestion," "nervous insomnia," bed-wetting, etc. —is the result of badly conditioned reflexes. For instance, bedtime, which should be normally associated with the idea of sleep and conditioned by reasonable peace and quiet, is often subjected to the secondary stimuli of extreme hilariousness and rough play and the reading of luridly colored stories.

Better sleep-favoring conditions can be secured by using affectionate explanation to the children and without resorting to rigid, authoritative discipline.

Healy felt that lying and stealing in boys were often conditioned reactions, suggested by the powerful primary stimulus of receiving disturbing sex information under secretive "gang" conditions.

A fear of dogs was stopped in a baby who had been frightened by the family dog springing up on the perambulator in an excess of friendliness. During a period of a few weeks, the dog was brought closer and closer while baby was being fed. The final link in the newly forged chain of conditioned reflexes was the feeding of the baby with its hand resting on the dog's head. Sometimes psychiatrists see fixed and irremovable fears in adults that had very simple beginnings and could have been aborted in childhood.

But, let us return to mature and immature mothers and .he suggestions their behavior makes and imprints upon their children. A nice illustration is found in their respective reactions when one of the children is hurt, perhaps falls and bumps his nose. Both mothers are apprehensive. But from then on, their conduct differs. The mature mother strives to conceal her fear, knowing its display would increase the child's fright. She becomes the Master Physician. She does not belittle the hurt before she has thoroughly examined it. Then, even though the injury is slight, she applies a remedy, if it is only a bit of ice. A definite remedy appeals to anyone who is hurt, so the mother endows the remedy with healing properties, "It will make it feel better." This mother does not get excited; she emanates confidence and security. She knows the child is searching her face and bearing for telltale signs that the hurt is "bad." The child is calmed. The mother sympathizes with her hurt youngster but not in maudlin fashion. Then, since she knows that not only the youngster's nose, but also his ego has been hurt, she makes this beautiful suggestion: "Sure, darling, I know how it hurts, but a man like you can stand it for a little while." Thus, the retreat to baby immaturity is blocked. It is the simple, loving artistry of motherhood.

I have outlined a more or less perfect job. Many mothers miss out on some of the details but still turn in a very satisfactory score. But as a physician to her children, the decidedly immature mother does not rate very high. For one thing, her emotional concern shuttles back and forth between her child and herself. Sometimes she compensates for her own alarm by vociferously blaming the child for carelessness or "dumbness." She dispenses harmful suggestions with a lavish hand: "You might have been killed" . . . "You are lucky you didn't break your leg" . . . "Maybe you have a concussion." Rarely does she examine the hurt carefully and calmly. Usually she is hasty and frantic about it, sometimes outshrieking the child and dispatching post-haste various messengers for the doctor. If she applies a remedy, she is likely to do it over-elaborately, either with loudly and excitedly expressed doubts as to its efficacy or with such extravagant claims for its merits that even a moron child would scarcely be deceived. If she sympathizes, she really lets down her emotional hair and smothers the child with loving endearments and blandishments. Almost never does the typical immature mother neglect the opportunity to push the child back a few steps from maturity. When her child is hurt, she unconsciously knows the stage is set for tying the silver cord more firmly.

Suggestibility is a weapon of great strength and flexibility. It should be used frequently in shaping the personality of the child. It is a double-edged weapon. It should be plied with bold strokes to make suggestions that will add worthwhile traits to character formation and it should skillfully feint away the suggestion of those things that would detract from making a sound personality. In the discussion of imitation, a list of things desirable to imitate was given. The same things should be conveyed by suggestion.

I doubt that there ever lived a normal man, no matter how superior or indifferent he appeared to be to the attention and plaudits of his fellow men, who secretly or even unconsciously did not prize his place in the sun, even though it was only a small place. Inevitably it must be so, since the love of power begins in childhood. Some psychoanalysts feel it originated when the child was in the mother's womb—fetal omnipotence. I am not too much interested, since even the most immature mother is not responsible for what the baby did before it was born.

Love of power may be defined as a more or less unconscious wish to dominate the immediate surroundings. It is readily discoverable as an objective reality in early childhood. It should be easily understood by all of us, since we carry it into our grown-up life. Do we not find satisfaction in dominating our personal surroundings, even though it be only in a very limited way? Do we not tend to hang on to whatever bits of power we have secured? Is there not in each one of us an unwillingness to relinquish our small dominions? I presume this is the real reason that prima donnas and actors make so many farewell appearances and also the reason why it has become imperative to fix rigidly a retiring age for professors, even for professors of psychiatry.

Without going into the deeper psychological reasons for the love of power, it is not hard to see why it should be so prominent in childhood. Within the limitations of not doing actual harm, everything is done to keep the baby comfortable, satisfied and happy. Without conscious process of reasoning, the child nevertheless senses its power over the environment. For instance, there is more than an even chance that the production of a certain kind of noise called crying will send adults in the vicinity scurrying about doing things to relieve an unpleasant situation. This cannot happen day after day without inducing an appreciation and a savoring of dominance and a desire to retain it.

All too soon comes the bitter disillusionment. The stage of happy dominance over others must come to an end. The child must learn that adults and even other children have rights, that these rights must be respected and often large concessions must be made. Inevitably in the child there is the conflict between the demands of society and his own wish to retain or, later, to regain the power of his babyhood. In reality it is one of the tragedies of childhood. Sometimes it is a silent tragedy; often it is manifest as most perplexing behavior.

Sometimes parents and even physicians are puzzled by the atrocious behavior of a child who is beginning to recover from a long illness. The explanation is simple enough, but its implications are very serious. The child has had a painful, lengthy and exhausting illness. The sickness comes to an end and convalescence begins. Naturally, the adults of the family want to make up for the pain and discomfort the child has suffered. It is permitted to have its own way far beyond any reasonable limits. Few children can withstand the temptation to reach out and attempt to grasp the golden apple of infantile power, heretofore kept out of reach. The situation needs skillful management. It is critical. The wrong attitude may mar the child's future.

In the home circle and in the schoolroom, we can observe children seeking the lost power of babyhood by trying to hold the center of the stage by misconduct.

Frankie was a fine, normal boy, seven years old. He was an only child, but he had many companions and got on well. One evening at the dinner table, he announced suddenly, "I'm not going to eat tonight." Surprised and concerned, his parents plied him with questions: "Was he sick?" "Didn't he like the dinner?" "Would he like something else?" And so on.

Politely, Frankie replied, No, he wasn't sick. The food was all right. He didn't want anything else. He just didn't want anything else. He just didn't care to eat. Why? No answer.

This behavior was repeated about a dozen times in a few months. The reactions of the mother and father became more marked. Each time there was quite a scene. Questions, entreaties, tears on the mother's part, anger and a little profanity from the father. But Frankie would not eat.

Finally, the parents consulted a psychiatrist. He listened to their story, asked a few questions, and said, "My advice is the next time it happens don't do anything. That is all. Thank you."

The parents were disappointed. They had hoped for a prescription for medicine. But since they had paid a rather large fee, they decided to follow the psychiatrist's advice.

The next time Frankie came to the table and announced that he did not intend to eat, his parents were silent, began their dinners, paying no attention to him. Frankie repeated several times, "I am not going to eat." No response from his parents. Then the boy went into a kind of hysteria of rage, pounding the table with his fists, and shouting at the top of his lungs, "Don't you hear what I say, Mother, I'm not going to eat, aren't you going to cry?" And to his father, "Don't you hear, aren't you going to swear?"

It was Frankie's swan song, but his final bid for babyhood power. There was no further difficulty.

How can we manage the childhood drives to regain dominance without too much damage to the developing ego? A common mistake is to overemphasize its manifestations by too much attention. The error is in one of two extremes. The first is too much severity. Brutally the child is brought face to face with the hard fact that the days of power are over. There is harsh punishment, even physical beating, for the smallest nonconformity. Recently I examined a frightened, nervously sick girl, fifteen years old. Her mother had frequently punished her by locking her in a closet overnight, without food or water. Once her father pushed her into a creek for some slight misbehavior. Many adults who as children were subjected to such cruel treatment become so twisted in their personalities that throughout all their lives they are afraid and defeated. Others may project upon society the ill-usage they received, becoming bitter, antisocial and dangerous agitators, occasionally even ruthless dictators.

The other extreme is spoiling. Unwise and very questionably "kind" adults may permit children to hang on to their babyhood kingdom of power overlong. An only child or perhaps one child, the favorite, is permitted to remain in the highly artificial position of continued dominance. Other children are made to concede beyond reasonable limits. "Let him have his way." One or the other parent is forced to give in. Hurts are assuaged by more concessions. Finally comes the day of reckoning. Realistic conditions of life are encountered. They must be faced. It is too late. It cannot be done. The badly spoiled child now adult almost inevitably is defeated. The habit pattern has been too deeply imprinted. There are childish attempts to gain the center of the stage. The adult environment counters with indifference or active opposition. The final result is either bitterly disillusioned retirement from the world of adult emotional relationships or perhaps the learning, over a long period of time and in a pathetically trying and sad way, a lesson that could have been taught much more naturally and with much less difficulty in childhood.

Every woman who has children gambles with them in the game of retention of their infantile power. The child sees only the table stakes, the desire of the moment, to regain the baby dominance. He cannot see the real stakes, his future maturity, adjustment and happiness. As the game is played, the immature mother has the advantage over the mature one. She, the mature mother, can offer only future values, the promise of a remote capacity to live life unhandicapped, on even terms with other grown-up men and women. To the child, the present power is more attractive. He cannot know it is only a bauble. The immature mother plays her blue chips lavishly. On the surface, the child is an easy winner. His immature mother yields to him almost all of the pleasant, carefree dominance of his baby days. As he gaily rakes in his winnings, a behavior "king for a day," he knows naught of the future and cares less. It will be a long time before he misses the few chips his mother retains after each hand has been played. These chips are the real stake in the game. They represent the emotional hold of the immature mother upon the child, and increasingly they decrease the chances of winning adult maturity. Finally, Mother has all the chips and the child is so deeply in debt to her emotionally and his adult adjustment is so heavily mortgaged that it is unlikely that he will be able to escape social bankruptcy.

When persistent efforts to hold power in childhood are an attempt to compensate for a deep sense of inferiority, then the situation is very complicated and difficult. What is a sense of inferiority? It is an emotional pattern that forces the individual, sometimes consciously, but chiefly unconsciously, constantly to compare himself to others, or in a broader sense, to the environment and always to his own belittlement. We know how handicapping this is to an adult. But usually adults can do something about it. With help it is often possible to ease the friction somewhat by slight modifications of the environment and changes in the personal life. But the child is well nigh helpless. His avenues of legitimate escape are few and limited. It is not so strange, then, to find children lying and stealing and being daring about sex in efforts to compensate for nagging inferiority feelings and to find a "place in the sun" of attention.

"Disappointment, failure, defeat, personality infirmity are the crop from the seeds of the inferiority complex. We hate to be neglected. Or to be unloved. And to be relegated to a lowly position. We wish to master our difficulties, feel strong and succeed.

"The intense, tormenting sensitiveness of inferiority is frequently determined by physical factors. A little fellow I knew had had infantile paralysis. One leg remained weak and he limped. After convalescence, he attempted to re-enter play activities. At first his playmates were considerate. But after a time, with the almost brutal realism of childhood, they became impatient of his inability to 'keep up'. He saw plainly he was not wanted. One boy even called him 'limpy'. Little Jack's house of cards crashed to the ground. Unwanted and miserable, he retired into himself. But the yearning for a 'place in the sun' would not be stilled. He began to steal money, considerable sums, from his mother's pocketbook. With the money he took his former playmates to the movies, treated them lavishly to soda and candy, bought them presents. For a short time, at least, he could buy the right to be with other boys on equal terms. Fortunately, the situation had not gone so far but that it could be retrieved.

"A fairly common cause of inferiority in boys is a real or fancied underdevelopment of the sexual organs. I know a man of thirty-five, whose attitude toward life in all its relations, his marriage, his business, his social life, is one of hopeless discouragement and failure. When a boy in school, another boy in the shower room in the presence of a group of youngsters made a mocking remark about his sex organs, which were a trifle undersized. After that, he avoided undressing before the other boys. Next, he invented all sorts of excuses for staying away from gym and athletic field. Then he assumed an interest in the violin so that he could explain, at least partly, his athletic and social derelictions. He became less and less inclined to associate with others. He grew peculiar and asocial. Marriage in later life to a charming and tactful woman failed to lift him from the depths of his inferiority. Any physical defect, even an insignificant one, may have far-reaching effects and it is important to institute wholesome and rational compensatory activities as soon as possible." *

Psychoanalysts have written very interestingly and somewhat convincingly about the penis amputation phantasy in girls and the inferiority reactions following in its wake.

"I knew a young woman who had splendid physical and mental qualities. She was quite tall, but pretty of face and beautifully proportioned. Beginning in childhood, on the basis of her size, she was simply overwhelmed by inferiority feelings. With an exceedingly well-developed, informed and cultured mind, nevertheless, she was socially very awkward. Her inferiority-derived self-consciousness blocked the utterance of her thoughts. Unusually endowed in two directions, music and sculpturing, she twice turned her back on her accomplishments, when a little more effort might very well have meant not only a personal but also a public success. She was well born and wealthy, but to her these natural and acquired ad-

* From *Discovering Ourselves*, by Strecker and Appel. Second Edition. Macmillan, New York.

vantages did not compensate for the fact that she was 'as tall as a man'." *

In this connection it is interesting to note that often small men are sensitive about their stature and go about with a chip on their shoulders, daring the world to "knock it off."

"Any deviation from the average, either in appearance or physical function may undermine the morale to the point of serious inferiority.

"Environmental emotionally upsetting reasons for inferiority are legion. A youngster is receiving poor marks in school and stands low in the class. He becomes discouraged. Instead of giving him understanding and help, his parents scold him. He tries harder but the specter of failure is always before him —a frightening specter. He fails even more. All confidence departs. 'I am no good—I can't do it.' Headache, crying spells, then a so-called 'nervous breakdown'. It is the only escape from the inferiority he must try to meet without help.

"An average child with brilliant parents starts life under considerable disadvantage. It is even worse when brothers or sisters are superior students or athletically and socially accomplished above the average. Such a situation, unless very intelligently handled, carries in it the potentiality of disaster. The mediocre child is very likely to develop the idea that he does not 'belong'. It does not seem worthwhile to try to strengthen the few capacities which he does possess. His parents are not proud of him as of the others. Why try? He can never hope to do as well in school as Jane. Or make the football team like Bill. Or talk to girls as does Jack. Too often, capabilities which though not striking are solid enough, as for instance, aptitude along mechanical lines, are forever lost and a sense of uncompensated inferiority is permitted to ruin a life.

* *Ibid.*

"Many children become inferior-minded because of home conditions. Parental quarreling, separation, divorce, alcoholism, in short, anything at all of which the child feels ashamed, either secretly ashamed or humiliated in the eyes of his companions, are potent factors. One of the most pathetic stories I ever heard came pouring out from the very soul of a boy of nine, who was going home from boarding school for the Christmas holiday. For weeks he had listened to his friends excitedly telling of the good times they were going to have in their own homes with their families. And he was going to spend ten days with his mother in her fashionable apartment and ten days with his father in a large and ornate hotel!

"Inferiority reactions are common in children of foreign families. Take an orthodox Jewish family transplanted from Russia. The children are educated in our schools. They assimilate our mores. The parents are too old to change. The daughter, a girl of seventeen, meets at a dance and becomes interested in a young man who is studying law. She is a bright girl who dresses attractively in the latest American fashion. The young man responds to her attractions. The affair progresses to the point where he should meet her family. Then the girl thinks of her humble home. Her father is an itinerant merchant of the pushcart class. Her mother adheres to the orthodox dress. The house is poorly furnished and in a dirty section of the city. The neighbors are far too neighborly. The girl cannot face the issue. She is ashamed of her parents, their manners, their surroundings. She is ashamed to bring her sweetheart home. She breaks off with him, loses interest, stays at home and sulks. Untold suffering results from such supposed inferiorities. Clear thinking would have shown her that she had much reason to be proud of her family. They had had the initiative and foresight to uproot themselves and start life anew where their children would have more opportunities. Manners of eating and sleeping and de-luxe bathrooms are not the real criteria of true nobility of living.

"Whatever may be its *raison d'être,* once inferiority has become a prominent part of the personality, the battle is joined. Whether recognized or not by the individual, it inevitably produces cravings, yearnings, desires, strivings for relief. There can be no status quo. Either the person will beat it down and rise above it, or else it will destroy him. Efforts to outdistance the inferiority are called compensations.

"A common compensation is the development of apparent superiority. Many people at first glance seem to radiate the very essence of self-assurance. Often they have a breezy, confident manner. On closer acquaintance the armor of surface confidence is penetrated and the core of inadequacy and inferiority revealed. Often they have been failures or at best have led quite mediocre lives. Little in the record justifies superiority. Their dogmatic opinions are not worth much. Yet with an air of absolute accuracy and finality they will inform you of the stocks which are about to go up, the size of next year's wheat crop, the team that will win the pennant, who will be elected President, the kind of hat to buy. Their range of information is too wide and too dogmatic to be sound. They are experts—pseudo-experts. Their manner contrasts strongly with the modesty and reserve that usually mark the real expert. Too often the superior attitude is only a surface compensation for inner inadequacy.

"Perhaps the most usual way of compensating for weakness and insecurity is to wave the magic wand of phantasy. All of us use it throughout life. The play life of children, especially their secret play, is largely phantasy. Phantasy is golden and boundless. A magic thought or two and the scrubby, dirty little girl of the slums is transformed into a golden-haired princess, the sordid tenement room into a glittering castle. Made-up fairy stories allow the child whose life is meager and cramped to live in a wonderful world, where one may be blessed by a fairy godmother, frightened by ogres and giants, loved by the handsome prince or gain the favor of the beautiful daughter of the powerful king. Whatever be the material from which the phantasy is woven, the child in its imagination lives happily and successfully ever after.

"There is another form of compensation, sometimes unwisely fostered by parents—the specialist attitude. Jimmy is doing fairly well in school. In studies and athletics he is just about average. But he wants to be a star. He wants to shine. Keenly he feels his inability to rise above the average and he is nagged by discontent. Suddenly he has the solution. He develops an unusual out-of-the-way interest—astronomy, philosophy, Egyptology or even the saxophone. Generally, the interest is in an abstract sphere, far removed from the real interests of the average boy of Jimmy's age. Jimmy begins to read voraciously. Or to practice on the saxophone day and night. Time is taken from regular studies and marks fall to a lower level. The special study requires so much time that Jimmy skips athletics whenever possible. Even social contacts are avoided. He absents himself from meetings of the boys' club and makes excuses for not attending parties. All this is done ostensibly, and perhaps consciously on the basis of an absorbing interest in this or that. The compelling motive, however, is escape from the unpleasant facts of undistinguished competition with his fellows in the classroom or on the athletic field. The specialist attitude has *not* developed on the basis of particular ability for an unusual subject. It is merely a chance selection compensatory for inferiority. (There are instances where there is genuine and great ability and even genius, but they are rare.) Jimmy finds that average or even only mediocre capacity in an unusual field brings distinction. Too often his parents are flattered and aid and abet him. Perhaps they have begotten a genius. Jimmy has won the recognition he coveted. It has been won too easily and at too great a loss. For one thing the school lessons have been neglected. At first, Jimmy poses. Then he may actually develop an asocial attitude. He prefers to be alone. He is not being prepared for life. It may be predicted that he will meet it very inadequately. The path to unhappiness and disaster has been opened.

"Compensation for inferiorities may be obtained by traveling 'The Path of Opposites'. Presented with a list of words and asked to call out the first word of response that enters the mind, we are apt to show our inclination to the opposite. 'Light' is likely to bring out 'dark,' 'long'—'short,' 'day'—'night'. It seems to be a psychological law. If our love is blocked, it may change to hate. The child whose will is blocked, may scream, pummel and scratch its mother. But soon the situation changes and affection is lavished as never before.

"The tendency to swing to extremes is found throughout life. The lover finds his attentions repulsed and becomes bitter. But the way is opened for reconciliation and he swings back with renewed and stronger protestations of affection. The politician is read out of the party by the leader. He becomes vehement in his denunciations. But when truce is declared and the pipe of peace smoked, his expressions of sentiment and tender regard for the leader often are excessive and ludicrous. The father whose childhood was hemmed in by too many restraints may give his own children unwise latitude and freedoms. New York and Hollywood are overcrowded by young men and women who as boys and girls led very restricted lives in small towns. Often the explanation of overdone behavior of this sort is insecurity and inferiority. The exaggerated response may carry a person along temporarily. Usually in the long run it is unsatisfactory. Generally there are available wiser courses of endeavor and action." *

So that we may recognize for our children the dangerous pitfalls, the negative side of inferiority and its compensations have been stressed. There are positive and constructive aspects of inferiority.

"The inferiority complex has been called the 'golden complex'. It would be a sorry world without this sense of the imperfect, without appreciation of our limitations. As Browning wrote, 'It is the spark that disturbs our clod.' It keeps us striving to reach beyond our poor selves. It prevents us from reclining in smug satisfaction with what we have and what we are. It is the very breath of inspiration and progress.

> Poor vaunt of life indeed,
> Were man but formed to feed
> On joy, to solely seek and find a feast.

"The very lack of success and perfection keeps us in the fight, struggling, and enables us to make more of ourselves. 'Gifts should prove their use,' said Rabbi Ben Ezra, but often they would remain unproved were it not for the spur and lash of inferiority. It enables us to rise from our dead selves. We are given strength to 'welcome each rebuff that turns earth's smoothness rough, each sting that bids nor sit nor stand but go.' This is the philosophy of the inferiority complex, which enables us to transmute its base metal into gold.

"The inferiority sense has much social value. It makes our friends livable, human. People with overgrown feelings of superiority lack imagination and sympathy. They are less attractive and have less capacity for friendship. Therefore, inferiority may be a boon and blessing rather than a handicap.

* *Ibid.*

True enough, if it goes too far, it is damaging and crippling to the personality. Usually it proves to be relative. Although we may be somewhat inadequate in some fields, yet if we seek for them, we are almost sure to find compensations in real excellences in other directions.

"Compensations may be wise or unwise. The boy whose leg is shortened a bit by infantile paralysis eventually may become an expert swimmer. Through perseverance the stammering Demosthenes became a great orator. A blind man cannot become a painter or sculptor but he may become a superior organist. A Helen Keller may compensate for blindness and deafness by remarkable development of tactile and intellectual co-ordinating capacity. Here are but a few of many examples of defeating inferiorities on their own terrain.

"In every walk of life, there are resources that do not involve the setting up of fictitious and impractical goals, adoption of visionary specialist attitudes, extreme swings along the path of opposites, unwisely selected activities, overcompensation, cessation of effort and retreat into phantasy. There are legitimate, wholesome and practical compensations that add to the meaning of life and enhance its satisfactions.

"The presence of a decided sense of inferiority in children involves a problem not only for the child but for the parents. Wisely handled, it may yield eventually the fruits of success, adjustment and happiness. Unwisely managed, it may result in failure, maladjustment in life, much unhappiness. The first step is the recognition of inferiority feelings. Parents cannot help their children fight the battle, unless there is some appreciation of the enemy. Sometimes it is necessary to seek psychiatric help to discover the source of the inferiority. But, sometimes, too, parents have enough wit, understanding and love to come to a fairly accurate estimate of the situation.

This may be sufficient to pave the way for an intelligent, well-ordered attack upon the difficulty." *

The childhood drive to regain the power of infancy may be a critical phase of personality development. Parents should not take the reins into their own hands, but they should be watchful and helpful and prepared to block detours which lead to dead ends.

I sometimes wonder if human beings would have survived if they had not carried over into adult life the intense curiosity that is so characteristic of the child. Had our remote ancestors not been curious enough to learn all they could about the habits of their enemies, the prehistoric monsters, instead of vanquishing them, they themselves might have been destroyed. We owe to curiosity the marvels and labor-easing devices of everyday life, from the miracle drug, penicillin, to electric lights, telephones and the radio. Science is simply informed curiosity. Curiosity is common alike to child and noted scientist. The chief difference is that the curiosity of the scientist is fortified and directed by highly specialized information. Otherwise child and scientist, driven by curiosity, like to take things apart and put them together, to find out how they work. No doubt we are indebted for the doubtful blessing of the atom bomb to those scientists who wondered whether the atom could be split.

Nothing quite approaches the driving force of the curiosity of childhood. One may have a measure of sympathy for the father returning home, weary from a hard day's work, bombarded at the door by a barrage of questions from his children. Why can ducks swim? Chickens can't. Why does our dog wag his tail when he is glad? When kitty does it, we know she is

* From *Discovering Ourselves,* by Strecker and Appel. Second Edition. Macmillan, New York.

mad. And so on. Only a small part of a child's education is supplied in the schoolroom. Much more of it comes from the answers to the eternal question mark in the mind of the child. I
am afraid there is no surcease for parents or others who are in
contact with youngsters. There would be real reason for concern if our children did not ask questions. Childish curiosity
should, indeed must, be satisfied. You could not succeed in
shutting off the flow of water in a brooklet by building a dam
across it. The force of the water would make other channels
and find its egress through them. This is what happens to sti-
fled curiosity in children. It finds unsatisfactory and even
harmful answers. The questions of young children should be
answered simply, directly, truthfully. As children grow older,
they can be directed to authoritative sources of information.
"Bill, look it up in the encyclopedia under atom, then tell me
what you find and we can talk it over." Knowledge acquired
by a little effort adds significantly to the growth of the personality.

There are still some adults who feel sex curiosity in children
is abnormal. When it is stronger than ordinary curiosity, they
feel it is a sign of depravity. They are horrified at the little boy
who wants to know about his own sex organs and the sex organs of his baby sister. Should they discover him examining
them, they are aghast at the monstrosity they have brought
into the world. It is all normal enough and the explanation is
simple. Sex is one of the strongest potentials, strong enough to
be dignified as an instinct. Of course, it unfolds itself even
early in childhood. The second part of the reason why sex
curiosity in children is much stronger than any other kind of
curiosity, is an artificial one, created by adults. We still clothe
the subject of sex in far too much mystery. Many otherwise
reasonably intelligent adults place it on the forbidden list for
children. Too often, there is a hush and an air of deep mys-

tery, should a child wander into an adult discussion of sex. One of the ladies immediately begins to make gestures of warning, usually accompanied by odd grimaces. Usually another lady contributes the time-honored formula, "Hush, little pitchers have big ears." Naïvely, it is assumed that now the youngster will have no more interest in the matter. Certainly it should not be difficult to understand that curiosity blocked, made difficult of satisfaction, is multiplied a hundredfold. Children are more curious about sex than anything else, because sex is a dominant instinct and it would be less than normal if it did not call forth strong curiosity. Also, it has been made extremely attractive by concealment.

What should be done about sex curiosity? I do not think that formal lectures to children are particularly useful. For parents and others there are available many helpful sources of information—comparative sex life of plants and animals, zoological gardens, a few good books.

All these things are heavily outweighed by the properly receptive atmosphere in the home. If it is such that children do not hesitate to ask natural questions about sex almost as readily as they ask for information about other things, then the right foundation has been laid. This is one of the really important legacies parents can give their children. Often before a psychiatrist can really treat an adult psychoneurotic patient effectively, he has to clear away an immense amount of cobwebbed debris, odds and ends of ignorance, misinformation and bad habit formation about sex, which since childhood has cluttered up the psyche of the patient.

Furthermore, a frank, receptive attitude toward children in their interest about sex naturally leads to talks, initiated by the youngsters. Begun in very simple manner, these talks grow in complexity and are a constant source of help. Something very definite is added to the personality which in adult life will pay immense dividends of mental security, health and happiness.

In the role of "Information, Please" on the forum of sex curiosity in children, the mature mother is an expert. Immature mothers operate under a fourfold handicap. Probably as children they did not have much opportunity to grow up sexually. Immaturity is likely to crystallize at sex. Frequently immature mothers have come into womanhood ignorant of the extent and beauty of sex, sometimes so fearful of it that they have taboos which would make a South Sea islander smile. Often they are very prudish. When I hear a woman with children describe sex as "nasty" or "dirty," I feel reasonably sure she is an immature mother. Usually when immature mothers refer to sex, they mean exclusively the sexual act. They are apt to hint darkly or even declare openly that "it" is the only thing men want from women. Naturally, if a woman is an immature mother because of a scurvy trick played upon her by her childhood environment about sex information, then she cannot give her children much that is helpful about sex. Unfortunately, she can and often does burden them with her ignorance, fears and prudery.

The real mother, because she is mature, probably has had a more normal and complete sex life than her immature sister. First and foremost, this mother is a thoroughgoing woman who does not belittle sex and strives to live it as fully and as nobly as the circumstances of her life permit. Obviously, the woman whose sex life has been reasonably complete is a much better sex mentor for children than one whose sexual experiences have been abortive and fragmentary. However, it takes two people complementing each other to attain the summits of sex. Even though a woman be every inch a woman and mother, she may have been sexually defrauded by an immature life partner. Neither mature nor immature mothers are immune from sexual thwartings and frustrations, although the immature are much more liable to frustrations, since emotionally they are not statured enough to measure up to the requirements of adult sexual life. In any event, real mothers do not visit upon their children their own sexual disappointments. Commonly, immature mothers do. Mature mothers accept their sexual problems and mistakes sportingly. They believe and practice that every child is entitled to a fair start from scratch in the somewhat hazardous game of sex.

Immature mothers have fewer scruples. From the ashes of their own sexual lives, there does not emerge the phoenix of correction of mistakes, wisdom and fair opportunity for their children. Rather there arises a mournful dirge of caution and calculation, warnings to be careful or the male sexual ogres will devour them or the harlots get them. There is much misinformation and, all in all, a sordid bespattering of something innately fine which should be placed on a basis of honest realism but at the same time a high and ideal level. The basic reason why so many immature mothers build flimsily the foundations of sex upon the quicksands of immaturity is an unconscious one. Complete and satisfactory preparation for adult sex life is the most serious threat to their domain. Should their children accomplish it, then inevitably the silver cords which bind them would be severed. Therefore, immature mothers, not realizing the extent of the grievous wrong they are doing their children, deprive them of the opportunity of growing up sexually. Unless this segment of growth is attained, the whole future emotional and social structure will be dwarfed.

There are a few more potentials of maturity which go into the shaping of the personality. One is savagery. In the life of almost all boys there comes a time when they want to go west to kill Indians. In these days the call of the wild is more likely to bring out the responses of being an international spy, a

superman or an aerial dispenser of atom bombs. It may be
that the savage manifestations of modern youngsters represent
a condensed recapitulation of the eras of primitive savagery
through which we passed on the long way we have traveled to
reach our present plane of civilization. Although it is not unimportant, yet I am less interested in what happened millions
of years ago than in the children of this day. Objectively many
manifestations of savagery may be observed in children, particularly boys. It is the rough and tough stage of maturing,
marked by overvehemence in language and conduct and much
fighting, wrestling and general pummeling, all punctuated by
weird, ear-splitting noises. It is hard for mothers to understand
and accept the fact that for a time their male offspring are going to behave outrageously. And some of the neighbors predict
that those young Jones hellions will surely come to a bad end.
It is unlikely.

For one thing, the savage phase represents a normal stepping away from the earlier complete emotional security of the
child-mother relationship. It is a kind of defiant self-assertion.
Probably, too, the aggressiveness releases inner hostilities engendered in the process of conforming socially.

Usually, the mature mother deals with the savagery in her
young sons satisfactorily enough. She takes it seriously, but
not too literally. She is even apt to participate mildly in it. I
knew a boy who until he enlisted in the Navy at the age of seventeen frequently used to "horse-bite" his mother. A "horse-
bite" is a sudden, vigorous gripping of the fingers on the
leg. He could always count on a thoroughly satisfactory feminine squeal. Mothers never forget to be properly femininely
shocked but duly impressed at the bold, daring feats of their
youngsters.

The immature mother is more likely to be frightened and
confused by boyhood savagery. In her confusion she may be

unduly severe about it. Or she may be so "hurt" that the boy feels ashamed and guilty.

Now, I come to a personal opinion in which there may be a very large area of honest and intelligent controversy. I believe that during the time of childish savagery there should be developed the spirit of competition. Understandingly and properly, perhaps as an aftermath of two brutal and destructive wars, there is an increasing tendency to decry competition in children. In some of our schools it has been practically abolished. It is right enough that competition should be minimized. Children should not be spurred on to merciless rivalry. However, I am inclined to think that later on in life every child will meet situations best prepared for by fostering the desire to win. Perhaps I am preaching a bad doctrine. Possibly, as in the problem of disarmament, someone must be willing to risk the first move. Still, thus far, at least, in life as we know it, it seems impossible to escape competition. The games and activities of childhood teach fair play and honesty and unwillingness to take unfair advantage but leave to the child some satisfaction of victory.

Modern life has recognized the claims and needs of savagery. It is a time when reserves of physical strength should be accumulated and self-reliance and love of nature should be encouraged. Among the normal outlets for so-called "animal spirits" are Boy Scouts, summer camps and athletic competitions.

I should like to dwell briefly on one more personality potential—romancing. Its coin of usage is untruth, but still, it is not big lie-telling. Only if unduly prolonged beyond its usual phase does it become lying. Among other things childish romancing is the first flowering of the imagination. In children it is apt to come out in the telling of tall stories that would have shamed the fame of Baron Munchausen. Here is a daily installment in the serial story of Gerald H., not quite six years old: "Coming home from school today, Mom, I saved a little girl. Two big fellows were twisting her arm. I tripped one and knocked out the biggest one with a punch in the nose." And when Anne, about the same age, says, "A man wanted to buy me candy and lots of presents and take me for a ride in his big car," it does not necessarily mean an abduction attempt. It may mean merely that a kind-hearted chap on a hot day said to Anne, "Here, kid, here's a nickel, get yourself an ice-cream cone." Or, perhaps not even that much fact.

The romancing of childhood should not be brutally crushed. If in effect you say to a child, "That is a lie and you are a liar," then you are distorting or even destroying something potentially beautiful, just beginning to grow. Children can be taught truthfulness gradually, tactfully, skillfully. For one thing, this is the time to introduce the minds of children to good imaginative literature. There material outlets and compensations will be found for the rapidly growing imagination.

Mature mothers maintain a watchful and helpful policy of neutrality toward the romancing of their children. They are not too admiringly and naïvely credulous. True enough, the romancing of children does contain some of the precious stuff of which poets make their masterpieces. But mothers do not jump to the conclusion that they have borne a great poet. Yet mothers do not shame the little teller of lies by sarcastic skepticism. The youngsters do not expect complete belief. They do like and need someone who will not too openly scorn and make fun of their stories. Mother is the ideal audience. She listens. She is interested. And then, gently, she is a friendly critic of too great extravagances in the story. She knows the need of an outlet for childish imagination. She does not choke off the expressive words. That may open the road to excessive daydreaming and phantasy. As she listens, mother is on the alert for opportunities to inculcate the principles of truthfulness. All in all, she is masterly in shaping the conclusion eventually that a story can be enthralling as a story without its being necessary to pretend that it really happened.

Mothers who have not grown up are rarely middle-of-the-roaders in the matter of the romancing of their children. They veer very strongly to one side or the other. I think something depends on how prominently they figure in the romancing. If they are the heroines of the romance, they seem willing to have it continued as a long serial story. If they are excluded they are more likely to remember the demands of truthfulness. They are not enthusiastic about their children having private lives. It is too ominous for the future.

There are other potentials, but I have given the important ones. Children do not, like Topsy, just grow up. The growth of their emotions, as well as that of their flesh and blood, is deeply rooted in the environmental soil of the home. From this soil the human emotional growth must draw its sustenance. The nature and direction of the personality growth is early determined, and frequently they cannot be too much diverted and changed. The psychological potentials must be carefully tended and nurtured.

To build a hypothetically normal child, india rubber would be useful. To encompass the long range and wide variance found in any group of normal children, much flexibility is needed. Included there should be the ability and desire to move, readiness and willingness to imitate, an alert response to suggestion, a reasonable amount of love of power, a strong leaven of curiosity, a dash of savagery, and a spark of romancing. These are the important potentials that must be satisfied in order to build sound personalities for children and integrate them satisfactorily.

Although they scarcely need it, perhaps I have supplied

mature mothers with some explanation of why they behave as mothers. I am more concerned with trying to show some women why they misbehave as immature mothers. I cannot believe that any sane woman who has borne children would wish to harm them. If the lives of their children are threatened by some immediate danger, like fire or drowning, many immature mothers would and often actually do give their lives to save them. Unfortunately, they do not see and understand the more remote threat to something even more precious than life —emotional maturity. If they could see and completely understand the extent of this peril, then no power on earth could prevent them from making whatever self-sacrifice is required to emancipate children.

What I have written applies not only to the mother, but equally strongly to the father in the paternal segment of his relationship to his children. Indeed it applies to every adult who is privileged to be able to influence the personality growth of children.

I have described at least some of the material from which parents may knit suitable and long-wearing psychological garments for their children. But the husband must be willing to do more than simply hold the ball of yarn for his wife. Some husbands are not even willing to do that much.

It might be useful for husbands and fathers to submit themselves to this questionnaire:

1. Because you are the breadwinner, do you consider that the responsibility for bringing up the children falls to your wife?

2. At the end of the day, do you feel you have a right to peace and quiet at home, and that your children should respect that right?

3. Do you participate in the life and interests of your children and give them some opportunity to participate in yours?

4. Do your youngsters feel free to ask you questions about sex?

5. If your wife disciplines a child, do you interfere or argue about it before the child?

6. Do you accept your share of responsibility in meting out and carrying through just and necessary disciplining of the children?

7. Are your children afraid of you?

8. Do you often react to the errors and misbehavior of your children with violent outbursts of temper?

9. If you felt you had unjustly punished or scolded a child, because you, yourself, were in a jittery state, would you afterwards acknowledge this to the child and talk it out frankly?

10. Do you get your children to obey by promising or giving them rewards?

11. Do you ever run down or belittle your wife to the children?

12. If the men of your family had all been professors, ministers, professional men or white-collar workers and your son, who had a real flair for mechanics and a very low scholastic aptitude wanted to go into the garage business, would you refuse to accept his decision gracefully? *

I am sure I need not supply the answers. Fathers know them. Let them put them into practice in their relationships with their children.

* From the author's book, *Their Mothers' Sons*. Lippincott and Company, Philadelphia, Pa.

No ONE should write of war without condemning it. No one who has participated in war can write about it without condemning it. And particularly no psychiatrist who has been in contact with war at close range can do aught else but turn from it with horror and loathing, sorrowing that men and women may still be tempted to the bloody debauch of war.

However, we cannot disregard war, horrible as it is. I am told that since Christ came on earth, almost 2000 years ago, to teach His simple but true doctrine of love for our fellow men and peace on earth, there have been fewer than 300 years of peace.

I wish I did not have to mention the economics of war, for I have little taste for mathematics. However, even a psychiatrist may safely predict that the ultimate cost of the psychiatric disabilities of the last global war will be found in those astronomical spaces penetrated only by the infinity of higher mathematics. Each psychiatric casualty of World War I cost $34,000. In that conflict, of all sickness, surgical and medical, the neuropsychiatric breakdowns were 1:7; exclusive of wounds, 1:3. All through World War II, the Army discharged soldiers with psychiatric diagnoses, chiefly psychoneuroses, at the rate of several thousands per month. In one current year, the psychoneurotic discharges reached a peak of 100,000. One may safely predict that both relatively and absolutely, the dollar expenditure will be very much greater than in World War I.

There is such an intimate relationship between military psychiatric disabilities and morale that one is tempted to think in terms of cause and effect. For weal or woe, in human affairs the deciding imponderable is morale. Morale is so intangible it cannot be defined, and yet is so real it wins or loses wars, preserves or destroys nations. Never did great military leaders underestimate the power of morale. They knew that without its buttressing strength, military genius was powerless. Napoleon said that one-fourth of the victory was in the men and material, three-fourths in the spirit of the men. The retreat which ended at St. Helena began when the spirit of the French army was broken by a Russian winter.

On a field of battle, or on the fighting deck of a battleship, a physical wound, even though it be mortal, definitely raises morale. The men who witness a fellow soldier, often a friend, mortally wounded or slain by the enemy, are activated by the twin lash of anger and desire for revenge, and become what in battle is prized above all else—effective killing machines. On the other hand, should a companion in battle suddenly fall to the ground without physical wound, perhaps writhing in an hysterical convulsion, or should he give an exhibition of uncontrolled fear, then there is a focal point from which emanate waves of questioning, perplexity, mystification and fear, and from which fighting morale recedes to a low ebb.

Less dramatic but equally deteriorating to military morale is the appearance of psychiatric disabilities, far from the sound of guns, in training areas in the continental United States. In those training areas, thousands of men were striving to achieve adjustment to separation from family and home, to the regimentation and discipline of military life, to the hazard and fear of future combat. These men were keenly conscious of those fellow soldiers who fell by the wayside, psychiatrically disabled, perhaps to be discharged from the service. Their thinking was apt to be untutored and direct. In effect, they said, "What manner of sickness is this? There are no broken bones. There is no fever. Nothing wrong can be found in the body." If such thoughts entered the mind at a time when the soldier was homesick, dissatisfied with military routine and apprehensive about the threatening future, then there was likely to emerge the tempting question, "Is this the way out of it all?" Good soldierly morale may be distorted and destroyed even while it is struggling to become an effective part of the personality.

I do not believe that World War II or any war of the future will produce a new kind of mental disease or psychoneurosis. Yet in that war as never before conditions so often modified and grossly distorted the basic psychoneurosis that it was difficult to identify. In civilian life it would have been recognized promptly enough. In war it was often necessary first to scrape off the encrustations deposited by physical deprivations, exhaustion, tropical disease and acute fear reactions.

World War II was not a battle of trenches, which from my own personal experience were not too uncomfortable and had considerable self-preservative merit. World War II was fought not only upon the earth's surface but in the skies at oxygen-deprivation heights, beneath the surface of the sea, in subarctic wastes, on burning desert sands.

It was not a battle of only moderately deadly instruments and machines of war, like the airplanes of World War I, gallantly dogfighting their way through the skies, but otherwise ineffective. Instead it was a war of giant aerial fortresses, dropping massive bombs with deadly precision, of huge battleships and submarines, of deadly artillery and crushing tanks, of rocket planes and torpedoes, of land and sea mines, of flame throwers capable of directing streams of searing liquid fire.

Perhaps in the amazing increase in the engineering precision and death-dealing power of war machines is to be found some of the reason for the switch in frequency which has occurred in two psychoneuroses. In World War I, the common neurosis was relatively simple, somewhat naïve conversion hysteria. In this neurosis, the unconscious emotional conflict between the instinct of self-preservation and the protective behavior it activated to avoid danger to life and acquired soldierly training and ideals and the behavior they demanded to risk life often was converted into incapacitating functional symptoms—paralysis, aphonia, deafness, blindness and many others. Naturally, the man who cannot walk, talk, hear or see cannot fight. Furthermore, his *amour propre*, his ego, was not outraged, since as far as he was concerned, he really could not walk, talk, hear or see.

In World War II, conversion hysteria was not so common. Chiefly, there were anxiety reactions. In these it appeared that much deeper emotional recesses were penetrated. In so-called combat fatigue, there were horrible catastrophic nightmares in which terrifying battle experiences were relived with startling intensity and gross displays of naked fear. Too, there were "startle" reactions in which sudden accidental sounds, like the dropping of a book, were subconsciously reminiscent of battle sounds, producing severe and uncontrollable trembling. Feelings of guilt in which survivors of war disasters were tortured by thoughts that either through omission or commission, directly or indirectly, they had participated in the death of fellow soldiers, perhaps friends, were quite common. It scarcely seems likely that in a few decades the ethical stratum of man's superego should have progressed so rapidly. More likely is it that the calamitous and horrifying situations produced by modern war machines probe into deeper and more sensitive emotional levels.

It seems likely, too, that such desperate war situations may strip the protective layers from the core of human emotions. Formerly, such exposures were relatively infrequent, occasionally in an expedition trapped in the polar wastes or in a mine disaster. Furthermore, behavior reactions to war situations, in which the emotional impact is brutal and long-continued, would seem to indicate that fear may be dissected into several layers. At least there are a number of somewhat distinctive behavior responses, varying from mild manifestations, like restlessness and overprecision in performing purposeful movements, to complete stupor.

In the try-out for the World War, the Spanish civil war, some of these fear levels were revealed. In the first stages of fear a man might button a garment, then survey it critically, then unbutton it, pat it here and there, pull it this way and that, button it again and so on. Or he might close a door softly, look it over, open and close it again, many, many times. At a deeper level of fear, men and women ran through the streets under a downpour of bombs, holding a chip of wood over their heads for protection. Torpor and deep insensitive stupor were common. It is possible that we have come perilously close to the saturation point of human emotions, and while there may not be a limit to the resources of engineering genius in perfecting machines of war, there is a limit to the capacity of human emotions to survive the psychic devastation and degradation which are produced.

There may be another reason why conversion hysteria is less

common not only in war but also in civilian life. In as little as twenty-five years, the public has imbibed considerable information concerning the workings of the mind. It may be that one result has been that the unconscious but very obvious deception of hysteria is no longer as available to many personalities as formerly. Almost everyone else realizes, even though the patient does not know it, that the hysteric has organically sound eyes, ears, organs of speech and legs, and yet cannot see, hear, speak or walk. And there are so many incongruities and contradictions which people have come to understand.

A lady about to cross a busy intersection of streets suddenly could not see. She would not step off the curb for fear of being killed by an automobile. Yet, a few minutes later, she suddenly reached over to remove a tiny white thread from her friend's dress.

It is to be emphasized that many, indeed the majority of psychiatric disabilities, did not appear as a result of combat experiences but were detected by the hundreds of thousands at induction or in training areas in the continental limits. By no means all, but far too many of these conditions consisted of somewhat vague neurotic symptoms, "I feel nervous," "tense," "jittery." Or, there were rather indefinite psychosomatic symptoms, "headache," "sort of lightheaded," "back hurts," "feel tired," etc. Or, there were exhibitions of bad behavior. One could not escape a strong suspicion that often the symptoms were not far from pretense. It is to be emphasized, too, that often these manifestations were not restricted to, but merely sharply focused in, the regimented and disciplinary setting of military life. If such symptoms had occurred in those young men whose civilian life records had been useful and constructive, then perhaps they might be regarded as a logical protest against the waste and horror of war. However, too often the civilian record was a trail of inadequacy, selfish behavior, instability and lack of social responsiveness. What does this mean? Some thoughtful observers believe it indicates a softening, a deterioration of our youth. This is a broad assertion. It should not be accepted without sufficient validation. It is a problem which needs thorough thought, discussion and clarification. It is not too much to say that, unsolved, it threatens the security of our democratic civilization.

I believe it is true that the particular type of psychiatric war reactions (or, for that matter, those of civilian life) is determined largely by the innate markings of the personality in which it occurs. Animals meet threats from reality with those weapons which are tried and trusted. When survival is threatened, "poundage" animals like the elephant or rhinoceros charge and attempt to annihilate the reality which threatens their lives; large cats, like the tiger add agility and cunning to muscular power and the biting and tearing strength of fang and claw. The opossum feigns death. Myriads of insects rely on beautifully delicate protective camouflage and escape destruction by achieving inconspicuousness, merging imperceptibly into the trunk of a tree or a blade of grass. So, too, do human beings threatened with psychic disruption employ those psychological weapons which experience has demonstrated as readily available and naturally usable by their particular personalities. Why not? It is normal and natural enough. Psychologically, each one of us meets the realities of our lives somewhat differently from any other person. So in miniature in our everyday lives, quite within the bounds of average mental health, we all of us employ various crutches upon which we come to depend somewhat and in the use of which we become very adept. Some of us rationalize a bit, that is, succeed more or less in letting ourselves believe the things we would like to believe. Others do a little projection, that is, tend to blame others or the conditions of life for things in which they themselves are at fault. All this is quite usual and commonplace. Should a break come, for instance, a psychoneurosis, it is not at all surprising that the house of its symptoms should be built chiefly from the ingredients which make up the personality of the individual who has the psychoneurosis. Probably this is at least a part of the explanation of why one patient develops hysteria, another neurasthenia or an anxiety state, while in still another, the illness is dominated by fears, obsessive thinking and compulsive behavior.

War not only reverses all the customary routine and activities of civilian life, but it is reality at its worst, starkly fearsome, cruel and threatening. It is easy to understand that the varying personalities of soldiers will react in different ways to war's hardships and hazards. During the war, notably in the very active and dangerous sectors, there was a considerable number of mental breakdowns with all sorts of symptoms— depression, stupor, hearing voices, suspicion and ideas of persecution and many other symptoms. Many of these mental breaks looked just like schizophrenia in civilian psychiatry, and at first were so diagnosed.

We were not surprised that there were such mental breakdowns. Conditions often were beyond human endurance. But we were very much surprised to note that many of these very sick psychotic patients recovered in a very short time, sometimes a week or even less. In civilian life, it was usual for many psychoses just like these to be months or more getting well. And some never recovered.

At first these patients were removed at once to a port of debarkation to be shipped promptly to the continental United States. Often the ship doctors could not believe the written record of pronounced mental symptoms only a week or so before could be correct. The soldier patients were quite normal. I think here is the explanation: Every personality, even the soundest, has a saturation point. Frequently under the devastating conditions of modern warfare, this point was reached. Then from the hidden unconscious recesses of the personality, there came to the surface certain traits, some of which are present in all of us, but are kept safely inhibited. With inhibition removed, they were elaborated into various mental symptoms. The basic soundness of the personality was attested to by the fact that in a short time there was a rebound to normality and the symptoms disappeared.

Although there were many variations in the presenting symptoms of psychiatric casualties, yet I believe that the pattern of the mental conflicts from which they emerge in war is universal. Briefly stated, again, it is an unconscious struggle between the respective behavior demands of the instinct of self-preservation, so dominant that it operates automatically in attempting to remove us from the path of any danger to life and even strives to protect us from trivial discomforts, versus a constellation of behavior patterns acquired in military service, through training and discipline. These behavior reactions are numerous and complex, including such practical segments as the fear of being shot for cowardice, and sometimes such ideological concepts as to fight and if necessary, to die, in order to preserve a form of government. The demands of these two opposing elements of the conflict are scarcely reconcilable and it is not surprising that frequently a satisfactory compromise could not be effected and the conflict came to an end as a psychiatric disability.

This elemental conflict was present unconsciously in every man, soldier and officer, who was in the zone of war danger. I do not mean that, for instance, we would greet each other by saying, "Well, how is the old conflict between self-preservation and soldierly ideals this morning? Do you think it will get through the day without a smash-up?" But, just the same, hidden deep in the psyche, the question was there. And when for any given personality the pressures became too great—pressures of filthy, sordid conditions of life, physical depletion and great fatigue, a gruesome sight (such as a buddy's head blown off by a shell)—then there was a smash-up.

I believe, too, that the conflict was operative not only in the sector of active combat, but also far from the front lines where there is no danger and even in continental areas. Indeed, I believe it operated even in those soldiers who developed psychiatric disabilities a few days after induction into the Army or even before induction. In these men there was only a weak and ineffectual struggle against urgent and probably pampered self-preservative demands. On the other hand, in those who succumbed to real "combat fatigue," the conflict almost literally was a death struggle. Many of these men were not broken until great hardships, exhaustion, tropical diseases and soul-searing and revolting emotional experiences were placed in the balances against them. Such men were as honorably wounded as those who were struck down by the fire of the enemy.

As I come to give the picture of the outlook, namely, the chances for recovery, I find myself writing as I did in the official Government account of the Psychiatry of World War I. Much the same criteria hold good:

1. The more satisfactory the previous personality and the sounder its integration, the better the outlook.

This is understandable. The stronger, more durable and more flexible the material, particularly human psychological material, the more difficult it is to damage it permanently, and if it does tear or bend, it is still innately sound and can be more readily repaired.

2. The shorter the time elapsing between the occurrence of the casualty and the initial psychiatric treatment, the better the outlook.

This, too, is quite understandable. It is true in civilian life. The less time and opportunity there has been for patterns of psychotic and psychoneurotic behavior to become fixed and habitual, the more hopeful the chance of tracing them to their sources and eradicating them.

It is particularly true in war. Early, perhaps only a few hours after the symptoms of the war neurosis have appeared, while they are still "warm," there has not been time enough for secondary-gain objectives to be definitely shaped in the personality. Once shaped, they present a stubborn obstacle to treatment. It must be remembered that the secondary gain is an enormously important stake. It means removal permanently from the constant threat to life and the miserable conditions of war.

3. Within reasonable limits, the closer to the battle line psychiatric patients are treated, the better the chances for recovery.

At first glance, this is scarcely what we would have expected. Proximity to an active theater of combat would not seem to be the place, nor would it have the facilities to make war-sickened minds well. Yet, the statement is true.

I think one reason why many men with war neuroses did better within the sound of the guns is because only in this terrain could they come to realize that removal from danger and a discharge back to civilian life, after all, was not an unmixed blessing. If the personality has basic soundness and the ego is reasonably strong, then unconsciously, and even consciously, it comes to evaluate the "loss of face" involved in being invalided home—"loss of face" before others and, more significant, "loss of face" inside self, in the inner revealing mirror of the soul.

"After all, many of the fellows, some of them friends of mine, are up there, just a few kilometers away. They are fighting. A lot of them will get through it all right and later on go home together feeling pretty good. And their families will feel pretty good about them. Of course, I'm sick. I couldn't help it. Not my fault. Nothing disgraceful about a psychoneurosis. It's the same as a bullet wound. But I guess it's kinda hard to explain. People won't say anything, but they might think I was yellow. Anyhow, I hate to go home without the outfit. We been together. I guess I would have to go home with a lot of psychoneurotics—some of them nuts."

This is about what a young soldier said to me when he was given a choice between going back to a hospital or returning to the line. He had had a moderately severe psychoneurosis. In two days from the time of our conversation, he was back with his outfit. His attitude was a fair index of the kind of thinking in the minds of a considerable number of soldiers who had broken with a war neurosis.

4. The more severe the external factors, deprivation, exhaustion, acute and severe emotional shocks, the better the outlook.

This, too, is surprising. One would expect that these added strains would so sap the resistance that recovery would not be likely. However, it must be taken into account that a heavy load and often an overload of bodily and mental stress was needed to bring about the break. This is a hallmark of a stable and resistant personality which often will rebound under simple treatment. Generally speaking, the soldiers who were in combat areas tended to have relatively sounder personalities. They had been screened several times, selective service, induction, and in training areas.

War psychiatry did not devise any totally new treatment formulae, but many of the known treatment techniques of civilian psychiatry were skillfully modified and adapted to war conditions. In our army hospitals in England, I saw some good results from a combination of narcosis and insulin. Sleep, lasting from one to three days, was produced by various hypnotic medicines. The insulin, in doses not large enough to effect coma, was given for about two weeks. Incidentally, the average gain in weight was about twelve pounds. Narcosynthesis was often successful. A drug—sodium pentothal, or other hypnotic—was given into a vein. The dose was carefully controlled so that the patient did not lapse into sleep, but enough so that repression was broken through and the lid of inhibition lifted. Frequently, by means of skillful suggestion, the soldier relived and re-enacted his battle experiences. For instance, again he experienced the fear and horror he felt when he saw his buddy blown into pieces by a war missile. Not only was great relief afforded by the emotional outpouring but there was spread out before the psychiatrist information about the details of the horrible war happenings which had been so revolting to the ego that they had to be repressed. The psychiatrist, armed with this knowledge, was able to deal intelligently with the patient and bring together into a normally functioning unit the traumatized and fragmented personality.

Group therapy was very useful. The group leader brought patients together in small groups, gave them an explanatory start and then encouraged them to talk over their symptoms. Unquestionably, the exchange of experiences and opinions between patients shortened the time required to bring the patient face to face with the real underlying reasons for his breakdown. Without such self-knowledge and facing of unconscious issues, recovery cannot occur. The group becomes familiar with the operations of the usual mechanisms unconsciously employed to produce the psychoneurotic escape. Probably every psychoneurotic patient at first believes that what has happened to him is unique—nothing quite like it ever happened to anyone else. The members of the group, talking it over, find that something similar has happened to each one of them, and that often it has a simple and understandable reason. The psychoneurosis is divested of its mysteries.

Near the front, where time was often a controlling factor, and in the situations that were not too complex, the main reliance was on simple measures—rest, perhaps secured by giving hypnotic medicines, plenty of good and hot food, removal of the worst symptoms by suggestion, reassurance and desensitization of the ego from the insult of not having been able to continue in action, the production of insight by explanation of the nature of the underlying conflict and the mechanisms involved in the production of the symptoms.

This last is highly important. Under war conditions, close to the line of battle, it is about the only insulation that can be given against relapses, not only in military, but also in civilian life. It may mean the difference between a minor psychoneurotic flurry, successfully overcome for all time to come, or a lifelong history of neurotic invalidism.

The explanation given to the soldier who has been relieved of his symptoms before he goes back to the battle line must be carefully measured to his educational and cultural level.

Some years ago, I was examining a graduate student for qualification as a psychiatrist. I said to him, "Assume that as a military psychiatrist, you have successfully relieved by suggestion a young man of his psychoneurotic symptoms—hysterical deafness and amnesia. He is now about ready to go back to duty. He does not understand why he broke down, and why suddenly he could not hear and could not remember a period of almost ten hours. How are you going to explain it to him? There is very little history. Apparently he participated in a sharp engagement with the enemy, but did not get back with his company after it was over, being left on the field with the dead and wounded. Later he was picked up by the stretcher bearers and brought to the dressing station, deaf and amnesic. I talked with him for a few minutes. He comes from the lower East Side of New York. He says he hated his father, who was very strict and 'mean' to him when he was a child. He was only able to go as far as the sixth grade in school, because he had to work. In civilian life he was a plumber's helper. He is ashamed of his breakdown and asked me if I thought he was a 'quitter'. He wants to know just what happened to him and why it happened. What are you going to tell him? Tell me just what you would say to him?"

The candidate answered about like this: "I would say to him that there had been an irreconcilable conflict between the behavior demanded by his self-preservative instinct, his most ancient and strongest biological endowment, and the conduct required of him as a soldier. I would explain that the conflict reached its critical point when he was left on the field amidst the wounded and the dead. He then came to an unconscious pathological solution of his conflict. His psyche could not endure the situation any longer; his whole personality, and particularly his superego, could no longer tolerate the sordid business of war, the filth, the blood and destruction, the constant threat to his survival. So, by various mechanisms, his unconscious mind rescued him from the intolerable situation, fitting the symptoms nicely to his needs, making him deaf so that he could no longer hear the cries and groans of the wounded and amnesic so that he no longer could remember his horrible experiences. I would tell him, too, that no doubt the Army and particularly some of his company officers were surrogates for his own father-figure whose authority he had hated so much during his childhood. And, when he thwarted their wills by becoming militarily incapacitated, he was thwarting and defying his Jove-like father." And so on, much more.

I said to him, "Fine, and what words would you use?"

He said, "Just as I told you."

It was splendid and very impressive. The young candidate had an excellent knowledge of psychopathology. The explanation would have been suitable if the patient had been a Ph.D. from Harvard. It scarcely met the needs of the boy from the East Side of New York who had had only a very elementary education.

Perhaps an explanation somewhat like this would have been more appropriate: "Well, Jones, it's something like this. Nobody likes war. It's rotten, dirty business and every sensible person knows it. And nobody wants to get killed, you or I or anybody else. Don't kid yourself, or let anybody else kid you. Everyone up here or in any other dangerous spot is afraid inside himself, whether he shows it or not, and whether he knows it or not. Even your company commander and the big boss (the commanding general). If things don't get too tough we get through it somehow and do a pretty good job. But if things get too tough, too many breaks against us, something is likely to happen inside of us, which takes us out of it for a little while. We don't know it is happening, we don't want it to happen, but sometimes it happens anyhow. And, remember, Jones, what is tough for one guy might not be so tough for another fellow, but maybe the first one can stand something the other couldn't. I hate the whine of those artillery shells before they hit. Maybe you don't mind that. I guess you were hard hit by being left on the field with the dead and wounded, likely to be shot by the enemy. The groans of the wounded don't sound so good. And the dead ones don't look so good. So something inside your mind said, 'Hell, this is too much, I'm going to get you out of it.' You lost your hearing so you would not have to listen to the cries of the wounded. And you lost your memory so you wouldn't have to remember all those terrible things But it wasn't your fault. You didn't make it work out that way.

It just did. But it's O.K. now. You can hear again and remember. And you have some idea of how this kind of sickness could get a fellow. I don't believe it will happen to you again. You're a good soldier. Your 'top' said that you were one of the best. Your 'buddies' like you and are depending on you to get back and give them a hand."

More of this, much more, but clothed in the same language.

Will the vast experience of neuropsychiatry in the global war be intelligently applied in the military framework? Having failed in our preparation twice within twenty-five years, and having paid a heavy penalty for our failures, it is inconceivable that we should again be remiss in filling the lamps of military psychiatry with the oil of organization and personnel. No matter how small the peacetime army may be, there should be maintained in the Offices of the Surgeons General of the Army, Navy and Air Forces, at least a nucleus of neuropsychiatric organization, a viable nucleus capable of rapid expansion and in close touch with qualified civilian psychiatric personnel, available for service should the need arise. Even such a modest provision would be in jeopardy unless the Surgeon General is made a member of the General Staff. It is incomprehensible that the Surgeon General who during World War II was responsible for the medical health and care of more than 8,000,000 men should have been in a military echelon under the nonmedical line, which, if it wished to do so, could override his judgment in medical matters.

Many generations to come will have to pay for the huge neuropsychiatric morbidity rate of the war. Surely prevention will be one of the priority considerations in the military psychiatry of the future.

I was intimately connected with it, but I do not believe I could give the neuropsychiatric phase of induction more than a bare passing mark. Even the relatively small amount of screening it accomplished was remarkable in view of the dearth of psychiatrists and the pressure of time, permitting on the average less than five minutes to discover disabilities which rarely have external markings, as do physical handicaps like a hernia or heart disease. I am fully aware of the fact that almost 2,000,000 young Americans were found unfit for military service because of neuropsychiatric handicaps. This was an enormous segment of our manpower. The point is that the solution of the problem was not to be found in numbers. I know that many of those rejected could have rendered effective service in many useful ways. We did not have the organization either to sort out their capacities or to find places for them in the Army where they could exercise them. Conversely, far too large a segment of those who were inducted were of no use whatsoever. Indeed, they impeded the war effort, since considerable manpower was needed to care for them in the neuropsychiatric wards of military hospitals. We would have been better prepared if there had been on record a survey of the national health, and if the war service act had been less selective and had mobilized every citizen from 18 to 70, each one assigned to his and her proper place in the total war effort. Modern war is a total business and must be met in total fashion.

Effective psychiatric prevention must deal with morale. An army may march to its objective on its belly, but it captures the objective by its morale. Morale is much more than the sum of a man's chemistry or organs or mental functions. Perhaps it is faith and courage, devotion to the nation and what it stands for in spite of its imperfections, willingness to live for what it is and can be, and, should the imperative need arise, die for it. Good morale does not arise spontaneously. It must be produced, honestly but deliberately. Its foundation is in simple things: appetizing, well-cooked food, satisfactory living conditions, neat, well-fitting uniforms and shoes, interesting diversions and sports. Medical care should be of such quality that the soldiers have unshakable confidence in their medical officers, not only for a current illness, but for the sickness or emergency of the future, in encampment or battle.

Proper relationship with officers, commissioned and non-commissioned, is morale-making. It should be such that the soldier will not hesitate to talk over military and home problems and will find wise and friendly counsel.

Mass exercises and drills have morale-making value. From them are derived the security and confidence that come from the strength and bond of numbers.

Conditioning men for campaign and battle must mean something more than mere familiarizing with troop movements and hardening to the sights and noises of war. Equally important is psychological self-understanding and conditioning. No soldier should be permitted to enter battle with the belief that in some magic way, suddenly he will be unafraid. Certainly he will experience fear—the natural protest of his strongest and most ancient function, self-preservation. Neither should he be taught that fear can be suppressed. No more can it be suppressed than can the beat of the heart be stilled. The soldier can and should be taught to mobilize his resources, so that he may learn to control his behavior when he is afraid. If this lesson is taught correctly and learned thoroughly, then fear becomes an effective fighting ally, motivating behavior, not only producing satisfactory military action, but also giving the soldier the best chance of escaping with his life.

Incidentally, one might ask, "How much of his body should a man expose to the fire of the enemy in order to be a good soldier?" Certainly if he gives his life bravely, but at once, as did many of the soldiers of our late fanatical Asiatic enemy, he is scarcely an effective soldier, since he is lost without having inflicted any damage on the enemy. If a soldier never risks exposure to the bullets of the enemy, he is a poor soldier —dangerously disruptive of morale. Somewhere between these two extremes lies the correct compromise formula which equals the most satisfactory soldier, and in this formula will be retained considerable behavior representation derived from self-preservative drives.

Much has been written of the ideologies and idealism of war and the necessity of giving soldiers satisfactory answers to the question, "Why are we fighting this war?" My contact with soldiers in and from various combat areas led me to think that, almost irrespective of educational and cultural levels, before any serious attention will be given to any considerations of ideology and idealism, we must satisfy the urgent need for faith in two things. Military morale of the future must be able to provide such faith.

1. That the civilians at home are backing him, not only by buying war bonds, but by token of their attitudes and daily behavior. The morale barometer of troops in the field dropped appreciably with the news of the coal strike and other strikes.

2. Every soldier needs confidence in the personality and quality of his leadership. It is true that an army good in its morale is apt to grumble, but underneath there is quiet confidence in the officers, belief in their capacity to look after them, participation with them in the knowledge of the objectives to be taken and the importance of each man in taking them, abiding faith that they will be led to ultimate victory.

It is to the credit side of psychiatry that we have learned much about the ingredients that go into the building of good soldierly morale. I have indicated but a few of the factors. Even if only these few could be constantly and thoroughly observed, unquestionably there would result considerable lowering of the incidence of war psychiatric disabilities.

Some of the psychiatric lessons of World War II have been

truly impressive. Apparently there is the real danger of devitalizing and bankrupting human emotions, so that they will respond strongly only to stimuli that are material, with a consequent weak and enervated response to the stimuli of much-needed philosophical and spiritual checks and balances. No matter to what technical heights a civilization and culture may soar, no matter how comfortable and even luxurious the products and gadgets of machines may make everyday living, it is still true that a civilization devoid of nonmaterial philosophies and spiritual assets and without benefit of their influences is doomed to fail and perish miserably.

A considerable segment of the young men discharged from the Army after a short trial of service and a larger number rejected at induction are best described as having been temperamentally unsuited for military service. True, they did have various indefinite neurotic and psychosomatic symptoms and some of them showed psychopathic traits (frequently absent without leave, intolerant of discipline, constantly grousing, always at sick call, etc.), but as every service psychiatrist knew, the basic reason why they could not be accepted or had to be discharged was because they could not adjust to military life. The record shows, too, that the majority had not adjusted satisfactorily to civilian life.

One makes no progress at all by precipitating arguments as to whether these men were really sick. Of course, they were sick, even if sometimes there was a considerable element of malingering in some of the situations. Much more important is it to know what the sickness expresses. What is its origin? What is its significance?

The psychiatric reading at the first level beneath the surface symptoms apparently discovered, often unconsciously, but sometimes consciously in these men, not only an inability, but also an unwillingness to serve. Here is a profound disturbance of the "I and You" relationship. The origin is in childhood. As children, these young men learned only to take, not to give.

Faulty human biology and constitution cannot be blamed too much. For one thing, in the group under consideration as revealed in the huge laboratory of manpower, seeking adequate soldier material by induction and testing men by military service, generally speaking, there was not so much evidence of intellectual inferiority but rather was there obvious evidence of emotional and social immaturity. Much more indictable were the defects in childhood training, particularly in the child-parent relationships—grievous failures in teaching. Apparently a reasonable amount of social obligation and responsiveness is not learned. The "I" is enormously large, the "you" pitifully small. Too often there is not even a minimum of habituation by practice of contribution to the social welfare of community and nation. Since such lessons can be impressed but very faintly by verbal precept, and deeply only be example, one cannot escape the conclusion that far too many adults who are responsible for the emotional development and spiritual growth of children are themselves emotionally and socially immature in their attitudes and behavior patterns.

War is a sorry, wasteful business, but at least we can reclaim it a bit by noting the errors we made and firmly resolve never to make them again. Mistakes in war carry the gravest penalties. As consultant in psychiatry to the three services, Army, Navy and Air Forces, I was in a position to follow psychiatric operations closely.

Called to Washington before the outbreak of hostilities, I was shocked to learn that in certain high medical military circles, it was not even known that there was a book, Volume X, an official and excellent account, *Neuropsychiatry of World War I*. Had this account been known and carefully studied, many mistakes could have been avoided. For instance, there was stubborn opposition to training and commissioning Divisional Psychiatrists. The Divisional Psychiatrist is the backbone of the psychiatric army service. He is many things—the division family psychological doctor, the man who can help you with your problems, the "trouble shooter," the morale builder, the director of cleaning up the division so that not too much fragile psychological material goes "overseas" and who, in the field, sorts out the psychiatric casualties, those who could be treated at the front and in a short time made well and sent back to duty, from those who were going to be a long time sick, and who should go back to the continental limits. Otherwise, they would seriously clog the line of communications, a military mortal sin. True enough, with the advent of the new Surgeon General, my good friend, Norman Kirk, a fine, able man, as much of the lost ground was reclaimed as was possible. But by then it was a matter of somewhat too little personnel and a bit too late. Operating under this handicap, the divisional psychiatrists nevertheless did a satisfactory job, sometimes outstandingly good.

The Army trusted too much to induction. Induction was full of loopholes and because of the necessity of operating according to a rigid time table, the psychiatric loopholes were very large gaps. In some measure this accounted for the enormous number of medical discharges for psychoneuroses—as stated, amounting to 100,000 in one year. I believe there was a connection between this and the fact that the army psychiatric service finally was not able to continue, on account of the large numbers, to treat functional illnesses in its general hospitals; so-called convalescent camps had to be provided. Much good work was done in these camps, but, all in all, they were not satisfactory set-ups. It was objectionable to amputate this large group of sick men from the body of the medically and surgically sick and, as it were, to isolate them. Too, the return to duty from the convalescent camps was relatively quite small.

In this area the Navy did better. It accepted induction, but with its tongue in its cheek. By some device which has not been completely explained, the Navy was able, in its boot camps, to subject young men to a trial of duty lasting as long as ninety days. If they were found inadequate, "temperamentally un-suited," their military connection could be severed. Legally they had never been in the naval service. It was a saving grace. It meant that some 90,000 more hospital beds were made available. It meant, too, that throughout the war the functional psychiatric breakdowns were treated in naval gen-eral hospitals, along with medical, surgical, orthopedic and other conditions. It was not easy to accomplish. There were strong efforts to segregate functional patients in encampments, but all such efforts broke against the solid determination of the Surgeon General and his psychiatric consultants.

I visited practically all naval hospitals in the United States and one in England. With but very few exceptions, I doubt if they could be surpassed. The commanding officers, execu-tives and staffs were men of exceptional professional skills, humane attitudes and broad cultural backgrounds.

In some places, by no means all, but far too many, the army medical corps was seduced by the line officers. In army par-lance, the psychiatric personnel was persuaded to "wash their dirty linen." Many men could not be made into soldiers. Then, often pressure was brought to have these men admitted to the psychiatric wards of army hospitals with additional pressure to have them discharged with a psychoneurotic label. In this way the line officers escaped censure for not having made these men into serviceable soldiers. After all, no one can be expected to do anything with a "psycho." It is true that line officers in the lower echelons were themselves subjected to pressure from above. They were expected to make satisfactory soldiers of the human material assigned to them, unless it was sick. No other excuses. Sometimes the attempt was not successful because the leadership was feeble. But often it failed because the material was too flimsy—shoddy stuff. Even able and conscientious military craftsmen cannot make silk purses from sows' ears. Nevertheless, the medical department should have resisted the pressure. They should have declined to provide a psychoneurotic exit. And they had the right and the authority to decline. In medical matters the authority of the medical officer is supreme and not even the General of the Armies can make him act contrary to his medical conscience.

The final outcome was bad. Psychoneurotic discharges mounted to the skies. Finally, the Commanding General ordered an investigation, and a Commission, of which I was a member, was appointed to assist the Inspector General. Intensive studies were made over a long period of time and many samplings were taken here and overseas. At least a partial solution was provided. Hereafter, a man could be discharged for military incapacity, inaptitude, temperamental unfitness for being a soldier. And, if the circumstances warranted it, the discharge could be an honorable one.

Most regrettable was the feud between the medical departments of the Army and the Air Forces. I do not know that it was anyone's fault. The beginnings of the feud were shrouded in mystery. Seemingly long before the war began, the medical department of the Air Forces, dissatisfied with the medical care the airmen were receiving, seized power, carved out its own medical empire and, during the war, ran its own show, with separate officers and, at the higher echelons, having only strictly formal relations with the Army's Surgeon General. Naturally, like all of the Air Forces, the medical department was young, virile, somewhat belligerent. Some remarkable feats were accomplished. For instance, an entire hospital and its equipment was flown to Alaska and set down in a few days. Nevertheless, the situation, to say the least, was very paradoxical. Then the Air Forces was not a separate branch of our services. Legally, the Surgeon General of the Army should have been in charge of all the medical personnel and services. Technically, he was. Actually, there was a tremendous amount of valuable time and effort wasted in having all kinds of orders issued, having them countermanded in a few days, in bickering, quarreling, in laying elaborate and devious plans to frustrate and circumvent each other. Even during peace it would have been wasteful. In war, it was extremely serious.

The psychiatric department of the Army had good leadership, and allowing for the enormous obstacle of the dearth of skilled personnel and a few mistakes, it turned in a good record. The Army hospitals, particularly in England, were modern and scientific, capably and efficiently conducted. At the front, the Army psychiatric personnel carried out effectively a well-rehearsed treatment plan. Many of the accomplishments were remarkable. Some of the mental hygiene units, doing preventive work, were models. For one thing, they established the functional unity and bond of psychiatrist, psychologist and psychiatric social worker for all time to come in civilian psychiatry.

One of the Navy's psychiatric mistakes antedated the war. I think it was a typical "brass hat" mistake. As is well known, the physical requirements of the Navy were and still are very strict. This was as it should have been. But it should have been amended so that it did not apply too rigidly to civilian medical officers in certain specialties like psychiatry, who were willing and often, indeed, preferred to enter the Navy. The Army took them quickly enough. Finally, regulations were softened, but not until considerable valuable psychiatric personnel was lost for Navy service. Of course, the original intent of the regulation was wise. In battle, on a fighting ship, there is a definite order of command. Should the captain, the operations officer, and others be killed in action, the command eventually might devolve upon the ship surgeon. Even should this happen, it is doubtful that he would be a psychiatrist from civilian life. If so, I fear the ship would be lost, even though his hearing and color vision were perfect.

Faced not only by a dearth of psychiatric personnel, but by real poverty, the Navy, with the active support of the Surgeon General, Ross McIntire (a fine, intelligent and most reasonable officer, very sympathetic to psychiatry), accomplished something fairly close to a miracle. Two and three blades of psychiatric grass were made to grow where before there was only one; and that often poor and scraggly. Three months of very intensive psychiatric courses were given to groups of selected medical officers. At first these officers were flippantly referred to as "three-month wonders," but I noted as time went on and they turned in psychiatric performances far above the average, the term was used with increasing admiration and respect. Since the war, at least half of the Navy medical officers who took the psychiatric indoctrination courses have become career psychiatrists.

Overseas, the Navy should have had a fleet psychiatrist. He was as much needed as the fleet surgeon. A fleet psychiatrist and the plan he would have formulated would have greatly improved the immediate care and treatment of psychiatric casualties. It is true that in many of the Navy actions, particularly on the small islands, there was not room for anything but fighting and immediate first aid, such as blood transfusions. Often these islands were hell's half acres of destruction and death. But there were other opportunities. Give a good psychiatrist a niche somewhere, almost anywhere, and he will accomplish something useful.

The Surgeon General of the Navy was an easy man to deal with. Before I accepted the appointment, I had a talk with him, in which I outlined my thoughts. He agreed. I want to record the fact that the Surgeon General kept his word in every detail. For instance, as an index of this, we had decided that any reserve psychiatric officer could write me directly about anything without going through channels, making suggestions, complaints, what not. If the matter was important, I would then take it up with the Surgeon General for proper action. This plan operated successfully and, through it, the quality of the psychiatric service was notably improved. Several times, as a result of the investigation of complaints received, high-ranking medical officers were relieved of their commands because of their hopelessly archaic attitude toward psychiatry and psychiatric patients.

Perhaps the outstanding accomplishment of the Air Forces medically was in some of their convalescent hospitals. Several I visited were vocational centers of the highest caliber. Patients were well trained in practically every useful vocation and I feel sure that now many of them are not only better fitted to earn their livelihoods but are happier because of what they learned in Air Forces Convalescent Hospitals.

I have in my memory a picture from an Air Forces Convalescent Hospital near Denver. A gallant aviator, his back broken in combat, who would never be able to walk again, had a cheerful conversation with me. He had completed several courses of study successfully. When I saw him, he was happily sketching with the aid of a blueprint suspended over his bed the plans for a house he was going to have built for himself and his wife, after his discharge from the hospital.

The Air Forces of the Army (and naval aviation) carried out well-planned and satisfactory courses of study and training, which made young medical officers into flight surgeons.

On the airfields these flight surgeons did very well what they had to do. The trouble was that outside of emergency and first aid and setting simple fractures, they did not have anything very important to do, medically and surgically. Serious, complicated and interesting sickness and surgical conditions were promptly removed to hospitals. Flight surgeons could establish and maintain some kind of casual contact with hospitals, and in some fashion follow the courses of the illness, provided the hospitals were not too far away. But these contacts were entirely too casual to mean very much. In vain we importuned the authorities to arrange periods of rotating services in the hospitals for the flight surgeons—even brief periods. Our requests were denied on the plea of great and immediate urgent need. I am still unconvinced that the need was great and urgent enough to justify separating for long periods of time intelligent, ambitious and energetic young men from contact with modern medicine, surgery, their specialties, and psychiatry, and the advances that were being rapidly made.

The medical corps of the Air Forces did not have sufficient voice and authority in the matter of replacements for fighting and ground aviation personnel. The higher medical echelons were not insistent and emphatic enough. All over the world, in the far reaches of aviation, there were many forgotten men, exhausted, war weary and broken in spirit, who had served unbelievably long tours of duty under punishing climactic conditions. Long since they should have been replaced.

The psychiatry of the Merchant Marine Service, operating under the bar sinister of not being in the military service, even though the men faced great hardships, danger and death, nevertheless turned in an excellent account. The "Havens" where men with psychiatric breakdowns were given a few weeks' treatment, never more, returned many seamen to duty, free of symptoms, with revived morale.

Some of the psychiatric mistakes were inevitable. In such a huge effort, with such little time available for preparation, it is noteworthy that so few mistakes were actually made. It is immensely to the credit of psychiatry that in time of the catastrophe of war it contributed as much as the record proves to the art and science and humanitarian need of healing and prevention.

POSTSCRIPT

THE WORLD finds increasing difficulty in extricating itself from its many serious predicaments. Often, overnight, predicaments become crises. We do not know which way to turn. One obvious reason for our dilemma is that we know much more about all sorts of things of a purely physical nature than we do about human beings, ourselves and other people. Our ignorance confers an immediate advantage; we can blame the sorry state of the world upon what we have just learned. But this is a fleeting and dubious advantage. Our new knowledge of physical phenomena will not compensate for our dangerous deficits in the understanding of ourselves. Nor will it save us from the consequences of such ignorance. These consequences include imminent threats to our institutions and culture, and, indeed, to our very survival. For free people, too, they include the threat of something that is even worse: survival under shameful and degrading conditions.

The human body has existed for a very long time. We think we know about all there is to be known about it. Actually, we know very little. Popularly, it is supposed that the physical mechanism works easily, smoothly, harmoniously and its organs perform their allotted functions automatically, without let or hindrance. This simply is not so. Our bodies function by a series of compromises. The issues may be so closely contested that it is not improper to speak of the battle of the body.

Metabolism is physical give and take. Satisfactory body functioning depends upon the maintenance of an even balance between the amount of katabolic or waste products produced in tissue functioning and their replacement by anabolic, i.e., repairing and upbuilding elements. If for any considerable time tissue waste exceeds repair, then inevitably symptoms of disease appear. For instance, if the thyroid metabolism is seriously upset, there may be swelling of the gland, bulging of the eyes and a racing heartbeat. Compromise has failed.

There is a principle called ambivalency (of which I have written in this book)—double weighting—"to do or not to do." Before even a thought is positively shaped and expressed, the negative weighting, opposition to it, must be overcome. Emotions have contending segments. When there is love, there is also hate. Submission includes an area of aggression. In sadism there is a component of masochism. A simple act is the result of compromise. The wish to pick up a book and glance at it seemingly is done easily and naturally, but first there must be subdued an unconscious wish *not* to pick it up and read it. And so on. The smallest and the greatest thoughts and acts, the basest and the noblest emotions are born of compromise.

Immunity against diseases, a desirable asset, occasionally is natural, inborn, if you wish, God-given. Usually it is attained either by the compromise of having had the disease, like measles in childhood, or by accepting it in miniature, as in vaccination against smallpox. If a disease appears in a people who have never had it, or at least have not had it for a very long time, it may decimate them, as measles once did in Samoa. The body chemistry had not developed defenses because there had not been enough time to come to terms with the infection. If our ancestors for countless ages had not suffered from certain diseases, probably syphilis for one, many of us would readily succumb to them. We are the beneficiaries of their many compromises with diseases. From them we have gained lessened susceptibility.

Sometimes health is maintained or life saved through a compromise, involving a concrete bargain. A part of the body must be relinquished. To be sure, it is not a difficult choice to part with a few infected teeth or a pair of germ-laden tonsils, giving them as hostages against the possible development of arthritis, heart disease or some other serious and disabling ailment. However, much harder terms may be exacted. It may be necessary to yield an arm or a leg which has been severely injured, or a stomach, the seat of disease which threatens to spread. Then there is no choice. The stake is life. The penalty for failure to compromise is death.

Again, I may give the classical example, the heart, the organ of life. More frequently than in any other organ, the heart is asked for compromises by other parts of the body. If the heart is strong and sound, the answer is simple. If the rapidly moving muscles of an athlete, perhaps a mile runner, demand more blood, the heart responds generously. It can afford to be generous. The demand is brief and then the heart can return to its usual rate and rhythm. But suppose the heart is damaged and the blood-vessel walls are thickened and their caliber narrowed so that it is harder for the blood to flow through. Then the heart would not dare give all the blood that is asked for. It must be careful, even parsimonious. It gives what it can spare, no more. Even in that effort it may have to sacrifice something, enlarge a bit. By such a compromise, life can be maintained for many years. If the heart poured out all the blood asked for, there would be a cardiac catastrophe, dilation of the heart and death.

During countless ages, organ conflict has been bred into the tissues and cells of the human body. It was mandatory to work out satisfactory adjustments. These compromises were the purchase price for evolution and survival. By virtue of these compromises, we now possess those finely synchronized mechanisms, our bodies, which, if not too ill-used, will operate satisfactorily for upwards of seventy years.

As there is a battle of the body, so too is there a struggle of the psyche.* The major engagements are hotly contested between the contending forces within the personality.

I need not repeat the description of the struggle, with the drives for power of ego, sex and herd, in the setting of the id, superego and ego. In a sense it is "Man against himself"—ancient, primitive man versus more or less civilized, cultured man. Of course, there are many defeats and casualties. Yet there are an amazing number of victories, which, translated into human behavior, make the kind of world we live in—the relationship between individual human beings—certainly not ideal, but at least a passable, going concern. And there is the promise of a much brighter future.

Psychiatry deserves some credit. Particularly in children, psychiatrists have come to recognize the significance of the maturing trend, the growth principle. By education and in other ways, psychiatrists strive to obtain for each child an environmental soil in which the growth principle may come to the fruition of a personally and socially well-rounded, mature

---

* The words body and psyche are used merely descriptively. Of course, there is no actual division of body and mind. Always, in health and in sickness, a human being functions as a total, organized unit.

personality. Much progress has been made, but not yet have we reached the level at which individual maturity is reflected, to any large degree, in world affairs. Measured by the yard-stick of our behavior toward each other en masse, our growth and progress is almost microscopic. Immature men and women are totally wanting in any sense of international social respon-sibility. Even in those of us who are more mature, the attain-ment of a relatively high level of personal and social respon-siveness and duty does not seem to add many cubits to our growth as citizens of the world. From one perspective it seems even to inhibit such growth. The needs and demands of self, family and nation seem to conflict with the needs and demands of the world beyond our frontiers.

The world is much smaller than it was even a decade ago. Time and space have been well nigh annihilated. But even for short distances, our social perspectives are limited. In the city in which I live, on a sweltering hot day, something went wrong with the water system and water was shut off completely from one section of the city. Almost every person who mentioned it to me said in effect, "I am glad I don't live in that part of the city." About one in five added as an afterthought, "In this weather it must be hard on the people who do live there."

The current social profile of man is incomplete. Much time must elapse; many additions must be made to the profile and more importantly, many parts of it must be erased, before it can be labeled *homo sapiens*.

Like individuals, nations have personalities. The id or baser stratum of a nation is not too difficult to distinguish. The ego, too, may be recognized. The superego, the nobler part, is far less readily discernible. To say the least, it is somewhat hazy. All in all, the national id usually is more primitive and moves with more assertion, urgency and power drive than the id of the average person. For one thing, there is tremendous poundage, the impact of great numbers. For another, the id of a nation has available lethal instruments of war, perhaps including the atom and hydrogen bomb and biological warfare.

Too often the national superego, its conscience, is weak and ineffectual. Almost constantly assailed and mocked by evil propaganda, its faint struggles are likely to be drowned out by tidal waves from the id.

Perhaps the chief quality of the national ego is agility. It must be ready with double-talk, expertly camouflaging double acting. Even in the face of a nation's dishonor, its ego must present to other nations a mask of fair dealing and idealism. Upon occasion, and frequent occasion, a nation's ego is shamelessly hypocritical.

One of the striking qualities of children is also agility, but it is an agility that can be directed into purposeful, socially valuable channels. The energy residing in the child's id, primitive as it may be, under the guidance of emotionally mature parents and teachers can be so released that the mediating ego can intervene favorably and the superego be made the all-powerful instrumentality for the development of an integrated and fully responsible personality.

In the early life of some children, however, there are dark and noisome places, pestilential areas of ignorance and intolerance. These unfortunate children are inoculated with the virus of hate, hate for anything "foreign," even though the "foreigners" may live only a few miles away. In the daily family life there is inculcated into young plastic personalities opposition, suspicion and violent reactions against people who are "different," different in color, race, creed—different in anything, even though it be only in the food they eat or the clothes they wear. From the ranks of these children adults are recruited, poisoned in their thinking, attitudes and behavior, the followers and sometimes the leaders of the multicolored shirted and hooded organizations. Occasionally a large-scale, dangerous dictator is produced. The smallest amount of propaganda suffices to sway such people into homicidal mobs. Incendiary speeches, waving a few flags and the beating of drums are enough to unleash their hate and make them eager to fight unnecessary and unjust wars.

No matter where any program of preventive psychiatry begins, it soon focuses intently upon childhood. Childhood is the tide time for making sound, flexible personalities in adult life. There is a tragic finality about childhood. Grown-up personal and social behavior, whether it is to be mature or immature, is contained in the early record of each child's relationship with mother, father and family. If the pattern laid down in childhood is decidedly immature, then only major upheavals will change the course of events in the life march of time, and major upheavals are rare.

Even in those who ordinarily live their lives on a mature level of thought, feeling and action, there may be behavior outcroppings that suddenly and dramatically illuminate repressed childhood experiences. I knew an exceedingly able executive whose brilliant policy had made the corporation he headed exceedingly prosperous. One day an engineer presented a proposition to his Board of Directors. To them it seemed an excellent project, but to their surprise, the president rejected it, flatly and peremptorily. He gave no reasons. Simply said "no" very emphatically. The engineer took his idea to another corporation for which it earned millions of dollars.

My friend was chagrined enough to talk it over with a psychiatrist. He could not assign a plausible reason for the lapse, so contrary to his usual sound judgment. Curiously, several times he repeated somewhat helplessly, "But that engineer had flaming red hair." In subsequent interviews, it was learned that during his boyhood for several years he had been unmer-

cifully bullied and tormented by an older boy in the neighborhood who had bright, red hair. Too proud to complain, he
endured the situation as best he could and later in life "forgot"
it, because the memory was so repugnant to his ego. Here was
the explanation of his single example of bad business judgment. It was the abrupt report of a mine of explosive material
buried in the unconscious recesses of his psyche.

Perhaps it is a coincidence, but if so, it is a highly suspicious one that there is similarity of pattern in the child lives
of three dictators, Hitler, Mussolini and Stalin. At the hands of
their fathers, they all suffered nonloving, brutal authority
and became attached, perhaps too deeply attached, to their
mothers.

In the case of the three dictators, it is well to remember that
fear, engendered and dammed back in childhood, is likely to
produce hostility and aggressiveness directed at the environment in adult life. This is a commonplace observance by psychiatrists in the life histories of psychotic and neurotic patients.
Could it be that the cold, rigid father authority of their childhoods conditioned in the dictators a hatred of all authority
other than their own? Could it be that in their ruthless behavior toward the helpless, the leading motif is revenge for
the indignities and pain inflicted upon them as children? It is
dangerous to entrust power to those who have not had a reasonably emotionally healthy childhood. The pathological compromises made in their twisted minds may mean misery and
catastrophe for millions of human beings.

What is to be the outcome? We know what we have to fear.
What may we hope for? When confronted with grave
personal danger, men may and frequently do look danger
straight in the face and scorn it. Man *can* rise above himself.
It is as if the superego, usually pitifully weak and futile, suddenly gains great strength, takes charge of the personality,

silences the id, commands the services of the ego, pulling man up by his bootstraps, lifting him to a high level of attainment and worth.

One powerful means of achieving so desirable an end is education. Give psychiatry and the other humanitarian disciplines the wherewithal to find out more about human beings, to implement what it knows and what it will learn in the future. The Government spent two billion dollars to make an atom bomb. Comparatively, only a few paltry dollars can be spared to help psychiatry write and spread the gospel of mental hygiene, and even this pittance is given grudgingly.

Education requires time. If we are to combat the world's growing discontents and threatening disasters, we need the grace of time and the will and courage to learn how to live in amity with ourselves and with others.

INDEX

A

Abscesses, 23, 127

Age,
    as predisposing factor, 16, 17
    old, 76, 78–79, 93–99; *see also*
        Senile dementia; Senile psy-
        choses

Aggressiveness, 340, 342, 345, 414,
    457

Agility, 455

Air Forces Convalescent Hospitals,
    447

Alcohol,
    allergy to, 149–150
    cause of mental disorders, 24, 41,
        129
    convulsions resulting from, 101
    decreased tolerance to, in organic
        psychoses, 83–84
    epilepsy, and use of, 110
    history of, 261
    in toxic psychoses, 40, 126, 127,
        131

    old age and, 95
    pathological drinking of, 261–
        277

Alcoholic dementia, 129

Alcoholic polyneuritis, 129

Alcoholics,
    constitutional psychopathic in-
        feriority and, 294
    family record of, 47
    Korsakoff's psychoses; *see* Kor-
        sakoff's psychoses
    mental disorders found in, 129
    number of, in United States, 5
    occupation as predisposing factor,
        19
    pathological drinking, 261–277
    treatment of, 130

Alcoholics Anonymous, 277

Alcoholism,
    cause of mental disorders, 24, 41,
        129
    delirium tremens in; *see* Delirium
        tremens

459

I